A Someday Courtesan

Memoir Stories

My Whorizontal Life Series
by Sephe Haven

Book One: My Whorizontal Life: An Escort's Tale
(The First Six Months)

Book Two: A Someday Courtesan
(A Prequel)

My Whorizontal Life Series
A Someday Courtesan
Memoir Stories

Sephe Haven

Disclaimer

This book is a memoir. The stories are as true as can be, based on my present recollections of my childhood experiences. Names and characteristics have been changed, some events have been compressed, and some dialogue has been recreated.

Paperback ISBN: 978-1-956470-33-8
eBook ISBN: 978-1-956470-34-5
Audiobook ISBN: 978-1-956470-35-2

Designed by Redwood Publishing, LLC (Orange County, CA)

Printed in the United States of America

For Arthur P

…sometimes there are miracles…

To my parents for loving me through those tumultuous teen years...

...I love you from the ground past the blue sky...

...and in memory of Mick...

CONTENTS

Intermission
Part Two: An Education

Prologue 1: Question

When I grow up, I want to be a prostitute!

Said no girl ever.

Yet. There I was. From 1989 till. Till…

Financial desperation eased, morphed.

I paid off student loans. I paid off nine years of medical bills, dental bills, insurance, credit cards. Nine years of debt that built up during my nine years in school. Paid.

Paid. Paid off.

Then, I bought.

For *Now*. For the *Future*. For *Just in Case*.

I bought:

Freedom. Choices. Time.

Money was *Safety*. Money inspired *Kindness*. Money kept life *Insect-free*. Money said *"F-U"* when nothing else could.

Money impregnated my dreams. Swollen aspirations I could now afford to desire.

So, I saved—

No.

Hoarded.

Ha-ha. *Whoreded.* The money. To make them come true.

But!

When other girls left, when I could have left, I *stayed.*

A long time. Longer than most. Over a decade. *More.*

It was not what I wanted to be when I grew up. It was not my identity. It was not how I wanted to think of myself.

Never ever wanting to answer, "What do you do?" with the word Prostitute."

No little girl does.

"The work of *Love and Pleasure*," I say. And that is true.

And I stay. Still underground. *Forbidden.*

Cloaking myself in a word: *Courtesan.*

And I stay.

Of the many women that ventured in when I did,

Only a few didn't want to escape.

We *said* we did.

We *thought* we did.

At that time, we did. For years,

Everything was about making enough to *Get Out.*

We'd say, "I'm getting out soon. Before Christmas. In a year. In two years. I have a five-year plan. As soon as I earn *this amount*, I'm done, y'all."

Here we are though. The few. *Courtesan-ing.*

Why?

As people, do we gravitate to our innate talents?

Why was this mine? Why was I better at this than most anything?

What was it about me back then

That made this

The slipper that fit?

Prologue 2: Sexpot

Sixth grade. Elementary School Graduation.

We are to accept our diplomas. But wait!

There are awards. Made with authority by our sixth-grade teachers. Orange construction paper with glued-on certificates, declaring:

"The Most!"

The Most *this*. The Most *that*. The Most *Likely to*.

We didn't know *this* was going to happen.

Miss Gish calls us one at a time to the podium to receive our award.

"Cathy Campbell."

Bumpedy-bump-bump-bah—we pretend sound the trumpet.

"The Most... Shyest!"

Cathy Campbell's face blossoms hot-pink into a cheek-cracking smile. We all clap because it's true. It's true, it's true.

"Billy McBain. The Most—*bumpedy-bump-bump-bah*—Troublemaker!" Billy holds it over his head, triumphant.

The whole sixth grade busts up laughing cause that's true, true, true.

Miss Gish says my name. I walk backward, giggling with my friends, my heart thumping. At the podium, she gives a warm teacher smile.

She holds up my certificate, and—*bumpedy-bump-bump-bah!*

The Most... *Sexpot!*

Girls clasp both hands over their open mouths. Boys' eyes go wide.

I don't think that's even an official category. I think they made it up just for me. I feel tears. It's so... I feel so...

Seen.

Because it's...

True, true, true!

They see me. They feel me. They recognize me. They care enough to know me.

It's possibly possible I thought about sex more than most girls my age.

I dress up as a Playboy Bunny. Not just every Halloween. Not just every holiday. The Easter Playboy Bunny. The weekend going-to-the-library Playboy Bunny. The Girl

Scout Cookie-seller Playboy Bunny. There was power in that uniform. Something titillating that elevated. *Flirty. Sexy. Efficient.*

Even without the uniform, even from that age. I knew *sexy* was my superpower.

What do you want to be someday?

Desired.

Was the first thing I was sure I wanted to be.

Meaningful.

Cherished.

And as Natasha, Gwen, Natalie, Delilah, Sasha, and Scarlett,

my Escort *"me's,"*

I was.

PART ONE
GROWING UP GIRL

-1-
TOUCH

my best friend Sissy and me play Doctor in my bedroom because Sissy shares a bedroom with her sisters, so there's no privacy for this game we know must be secret. We take turns. One of us is the doctor, and the other, the patient.

The doctor has a clipboard, and the patient lies face down on my yellow shag carpet with just underwear bottoms on, inches from the shut bedroom door. Body placement is important because since my door doesn't have a lock, if anyone tries to come into my room, if they open the door, it would hit a body which would cause them to say "oops" and close the door, giving the naked person enough time to hide under the bed.

The doctor asks health questions like: "Does your hair hurt? Does your skin hurt? Do your toes hurt?"

This causes an examination to be necessary.

Sissy is the patient. She lays on her tummy, and the doctor has lotion, baby powder, creams, a comb, a brush, a bird feather, and anything else that makes an interesting texture.

Baby powder sprinkles in the dip of her back along her spine.

"Do you feel that?' I whisper.

"Um hm," Sissy says.

My finger traces the powder into a paisley doodle until her back is dotted with goose bumps. I love to watch her skin behave from the different drawings and writings and textures and speeds. Sometimes it makes her laugh, sometimes quiver. Sometimes she says, "Brrrrr," but always something. I love to draw slow and then zip to unexpected places—shoulder to arm, down the back ridges, over the butt slopes to inside the knees—to, to, to. I love to hypnotize her and weave a magic spell.

From the outside, grown-ups might think we're doing something naughty because we're naked, but we're just experimenting with different feel-goods. It's like telling a story, but with touch and skin.

Our game is not about s-e-x. We like to see what secret places and feels there are to discover. Like when you hold your arm out and trace your fingernails from the inside of your palm up the underside of your arm and down again, and it feels so good you can hardly make yourself stop? That feeling but from another person, and, also, to discover what our own touch can do to someone else. Sometimes we get a babysitter or a cousin to play, making them swear not to tell.

We've been playing since we were six. Now we're both seven, and we play without underwear.

My hand trails down the rubbery slope of her butt between her legs toward the outer folds of her secret place. Barely touching. Never pressing or rubbing. Seeing if her skin will react even when I'm not touching. Watching goosebumps even when I'm just moving air above her.

Feathery fingers are leading the goosebump trail to graze the below-folds between her legs, when my hand feels something fuzzy. I open my eyes.

Without a sound, moving only my eyes, careful not to alarm Sissy that I, as the doctor, after all these years, may have found a medical issue, I take a real peek at the area that I felt between her legs. How do I tell her?

On her once smooth private part is this layer of fuzz that was not there ever before. White. The color of the hair on her head. I sit staring at the slice between her legs with the white moss growing over it. She is dying. How do I tell her?

Sissy, wondering why the touch stopped, asks, "What?"

I brace myself. Then, with a gentle voice, I say, "There's something white, like fuzzy stuff on you. On your... you know."

She sits up. Looks down at it, and says, "It's ok. All girls get it."

Which is as alarming as the discovery.

She knows because her older sisters, Mary and Margaret, had it.

"And then it becomes bushy hair, and it's what women get," she says.

I stare at her, trying to picture what she just described. She stares at me, waiting for me to comprehend.

Then we collapse into an "ewwwwww!" giggle fest.

We don't play after that. It is getting too real. Too personal. Too sexual with Sissy growing moss and all.

PLEASURE

Just after Sissy and me quit playing Doctor, I think of another game. This one with imaginary people. On the inside of my bedroom door is a full-length mirror. I place my desk chair facing the mirror. It's important I'm wearing my hip-hugger bell bottom pants with the button undone and half the zipper falling. Standing on the chair, reaching high above the mirror, I pretend to reach for something—a book in a library, something in the store—high up, causing me to stretch up onto my tiptoes, also causing me to be *"oops!"* unaware of the zipper on my pants falling and *"oops!"* to whoever is looking. I imagine a man watching, and this is how the fantasy begins.

Nothing happens between the fantasy peeker-at-my-underwear guy and me. I didn't know what happened in the first place. I know this was a "sex" feeling, but I didn't know what sex was. It's the thing grown-ups did to make babies when they were married and had their own bedroom for privacy. It had to do with breasts and the triangle. And a penis. I didn't actually know what those looked like. Aside from babies. Which I was pretty sure wasn't like grown-up ones.

Eventually, the thought of the imaginary man just seeing the top of my underwear is no longer as throbbing. I need him to see the triangle of fuzz. But I don't have a triangle yet. From my notebook, I draw a triangle on notebook paper with a blue ink Bic pen. Inside the triangle, lots of circle squigglies. Then I tuck the paper triangle into my underwear.

No. It doesn't seem like the imaginary man can see it. So, I lick it, but it won't stay. Finally, I roll a piece of scotch tape, just enough to stick on the back of the triangle so it will stay on my bare skin. I unzip my pants just a tad, tape the little triangle to my hairless private place and reach for that high up thing that distracts me.

"Oh, hello," I say, pretending to suddenly notice him, pretending to be unaware of my exposed-ness. The man says something, and I giggle, shy, writhing a little, making the jeans slip further down, revealing more of the paper triangle, setting off a warm pulse just below the triangle.

"What? Oh!" I say, feigning embarrassment, that somehow my jeans are open, and I am exposed. Tooth by tooth, I re-zip the jeans but don't button them. Then I continue the conversation, allowing the zipper to fall, tooth by tooth again.

After a few times, the juice in that scenario starts to wane. I'm not sure how to bump up the sexiness again but maybe more squigglies?

I stop the game, my jeans still hugging below the crotch. I reach for the ballpoint pen and begin to draw more squigglies and curly q's on the taped triangle. This makes the little place beneath the triangle start to throb. The lower the pen goes, the deeper the warm throbbing becomes.

I carefully climb down from the chair, my pants trapping my legs together. I lay back on the bed and continue the motion, going lower and lower to the very tip of the paper triangle. The lower the pen, the more intense the feeling. I turn the pen around to the side with the blue cap on the end and circle it lightly, off the paper and onto my flesh—the flesh between the two puffy lips.

I let my eyes close, feeling my body absorbing this new sensation. There is no mirror man. No anything but this feeling. The sensation makes a movie in my mind. I feel myself, my body, this sensation, as climbing a mountain— climbing, climbing, up and up and up and up and up, until suddenly a warm honey bursts and pours out from a space inside of me, rolling like hot, warm, thick lusciousness throughout my entire body, as if I've fallen from the height of the mountain into a heated pot of luscious honey. As I fall, I hear myself make a noise.

I pull both my upper and lower lip in tight, biting them together with my teeth. This is a sound I'm sure my parents shouldn't hear. I know it must be a private secret. I don't even tell Sissy.

I keep the pen in a reachable drawer by my bedside for easy access, never touching myself down there with my actual fingers—only the pen. I'm not sure why.

Is this something that happens in all girl's bodies if they can discover it? Is this s-e-x even if it's alone, just you and God? It seems like God made this as a gift to show us, "I love you."

– 3 –
PUNISHMENT

A bunch of us neighborhood kids are all outside playing. Johnny Scabbs has his Dracula cape on, zipping around the yards. I try to ignore him because he's such a trouble-maker. All of us kids know each other even though we're all different ages because all our houses connect either in the back yard or the sides or across the street. Plus, we all go to the same school. Hillview Elementary. Except for the Vagners and the Godwins who have to go to a school called Parochial.

Darcy Vagner and her sister Angel, who I don't usually play with too much, are laying on the grass next to me. We collected the fallen crab apples from under the crabapple tree in my front yard before Tony Scabbs could lob them at

17

us, going, "Flatsy, flatsy, you're flat, and that's that! Hahaha!" We girls hate him. He's twelve or eleven and shouldn't be picking on younger kids like us.

But now that we have the crabapples, we're playing house, making dinner for when our husbands come home. We're pulling up grass and dandelions to mix in with the crabapples when Johnny and his bat cape come swooping right between us. Instead of just keeping going, he's trying to get his breath so he can tell us something.

"Mr. Jaeger says," he says, all panting.

My ears open wide. Mr. Jaeger is Sissy's dad. Sissy didn't come out to play, and it's way past after lunch.

Johnny's huffing the words out. "All kids. Have to go. To the Jaeger house. Now!"

We stare at him. Maybe they're having a surprise party? I don't think it's a birthday because Sissy and I are both eight and already had our parties. Maybe it's a Catholic surprise? I don't know when Catholic holidays are because my family is Jewish. But I don't admit that in case of prejudice.

Johnny swirls his cape from one side to the other, whooshing us with the breeze of it.

"C'mon. Mr. Jaeger said *now*!" he says.

We sit up. But we don't move. It doesn't seem like it's a party because it seems like yelling, and Johnny looks in a panic. The other kids are coming around Johnny too. Like Johnny swirled them up in his cape.

"Mr. Jaeger's face was all red," Johnny says in his emergency voice. "And he goes, 'get all the kids over here now! Sissy is gettin' a bare belt lickin'—"

The words pour out all over us.

"Mr. Jaeger wants all the kids to watch—Sissy has to pull her pants down when she gets the belt."

My heart is thumping all the way up to my throat.

Sissy is my best friend. The back of Sissy's backyard touches the back of our backyard. The cut-through path we cross to go to each other's house is the only part without grass because we wore it out. What bad thing did she do to get a bare belt lickin'?

Everyone looks down. Johnny turns, twirls his cape up around him, and takes off through the divide between our houses toward Sissy's house. Some of the boys run after. Some walk slower but head that way.

Darcy and Angel look at each other. My mind is thinking if me and Sissy did anything bad this morning when we were playing records and paper dolls.

"Come on," Darcy says, brushing the grass off her legs as she stands. "You wanna get in trouble, too?"

I shake my head, and we start walking to my backyard on our way to Sissy's. I don't want to go, but you have to do what grown-ups say, even if they're not your own parents.

I feel scared about little girls who have to get whipped with a belt. I stop still. Darcy and Angel stop and look back at me with their hands on their foreheads to keep down the sun.

"I forgot my glasses," I say.

The willow tree behind them tosses its leafy hair to one side, then the other side, touching Angel's head.

"You better come or you'll get the belt too maybe." Darcy says.

I nod. They move away from the willow tree, shrug, and run ahead.

I stand straight still as a board until I can't see any more kids. Then I walk in tiny steps backwards to our back screen door, go quiet inside, down the hall into my room, and close the door tight.

I think about the closet, and I think about under my corner desk. But the other best hiding place is under my bed. It's just high enough, when I'm under it, to lift my head a little bit to write in my diary.

I lay flat on my shag carpet and scoot myself all the way under until my toes touch the wall. It's dark and makes me feel safe and hidden. I stay quiet to listen. I can hear the wind of my breath going in and out of my nose. My chest lifts me high until my shoulder blades touch the underside of the bed, and then drops me flatter, pressing into the rug. I don't hear anything from the Jaeger's house.

Everyone from my house must be outside visiting or playing. I don't hear my mom talking on the phone with the long spiral cord, her voice high-pitched, rising to a laugh-gack or whispering so the kids don't hear. I don't hear my brothers talking about fishing or worms then raiding the refrigerator. I don't hear the birds. I don't hear Sissy. I don't hear a belt.

My fingers separate the strands of the shag rug yellow yarn into bunches. I make eight in a patch and divide it in half like when I brush Sissy's hair and make a part to make into two ponytails. I start to cry. I don't know why. We never even get spankings in my house. My dad would never hit us or belt whip us. I can't think what Sissy did so bad she would have to have a bare belt lickin', especially so the boys could see her bare-naked bottom.

I feel scared for her like she's me. Sissy and me are almost exactly alike. Except she has blonde hair and I have dark hair that we are growing to our butts. We put it up high in ponytails so when we walk together, we can make our ponytails swish back and forth like the willow tree and hit our own selves in the face if we want.

Maybe it was because of me. What if me and Sissy were both bad and only she is getting in trouble? It's important to know what you're bad for so you don't, by accident, do it again. Maybe it was because of "Up! Up with People"?

Sissy has Catholic God, and I have Jewish God. And her God has better songs than we do. So, Sissy and I wanted to dance to the "Up! Up with People" song, which is the best Catholic song. And the record player is in Sissy's parents' bedroom. Which is a room I don't like to go in. It's the most Catholic room. Their God is really strict, so they can only have crosses in their room with no other decorations. Or crosses plus statues with ladies in long robes looking at the ground and being sad. The room is always dark, even when there is summer sun. Sometimes, when we'd run through the house, we'd see Sissy's mom sitting alone in the Catholic room with Jesus, smoking. But that's where the record player is, and we're allowed to listen to it in there.

So, we went in, and Sissy put the needle on the song and then:

"Up! Up with people! You meet 'em wherever you go! Up! Up with people! They're the best kind of folks we know! …"

And it's so full of bouncy joy, you have to start hopping up and up, and we hop onto the bed and jump up and up, singing with all our glee, then falling down to catch our breath. Sissy bounces off, puts the needle back, leaps back on the bed, and we do it again. Our ponytails hit the ceiling. We can even touch it with our fingertips. It's so much fun. When we had enough, we smooth out the bedspread so her parents wouldn't know we were on it, and we tiptoe out of the room, then run really fast through the kitchen out the back screen door to the yard so no one catches us.

I'm trying to think hard about the bed. If there was a wrinkle. Or if anyone saw us. But I can't make my head picture it.

I hear the ice cream truck outside. When it turns down our block, we hear the song over and over again because so many kids run to it from everywhere. The song has to keep playing until all the kids have their ice cream. But the song only plays once then starts to fade like it's already going down our block. Are all the kids at Sissy's waiting for the belt?

Maybe it was the Wonderbread. All my friends are Catholic or Christian. Christian is almost the same God but God-lite compared to Catholic. But they both had the best food. The number one was butter and sugar on Wonderbread. No Jewish people had that. That sandwich is like a vacation to Christian land.

After the record player, we take out the Wonderbread. Two slices only. Because Sissy would get hollered at if her mom found out she took too many slices of bread.

Sissy's God was really strict. You could be bad over the smallest things. The parents of the Catholic kids had to enforce it really hard if you broke a rule.

Sissy takes out the butter first because it's really hard from the refrigerator, and if you try to spread it too soon, it stays in a chunk and rips the bread. Then you want a different slice of bread. But you can't, so you'd have to eat it like that, all clumped. So, we go out back to distract our taste buds. We do some cartwheels and walkovers and some splits. Then the butter is mushy enough. After we spread it all the way over the bread, we pour hills of sugar on each one and then shake the extra sugar back into the sugar bowl. And a miracle! A Christian sandwich treat.

I don't think that's the bad thing she did.

Suddenly, I hear a shriek. I cover my ears and smash my nose into the carpet. My heart goes *ka-thump, ka-thump.* Another fast, high-pitched shriek. Inside my window, into me. My face squinches, hot wetness soaks my cheeks. I cover my mouth to choke my sounds. The wet of my nose runs into my mouth. I wipe it on my arm as I slide myself out from under my bed. I stay low at my windowsill, peeking out toward Sissy's house. Suddenly Johnny Scabbs, being Dracula, flies shrieking past my window. It wasn't Sissy's shrieks. It's Johnny. My eyes shift from one side of our backyard to the other. Scanning. Looking for other kids. No one but Johnny. So far.

Is it over? Is she in her room crying too? I keep peeking out my window until I hear kids playing again. Then sit on my floor and take out my Dawn dolls and make a story. I don't dare go to the Jaeger's anymore today.

I feel like if the Jaeger's God could come off the cross, He wouldn't be in so much pain and be so angry, and Mr. Jaeger wouldn't have to punish so hard.

The Jewish God wasn't as strict, but He wasn't my type either. First off, He seemed kinda immature. Even me, who is only a little girl, didn't need everyone telling me how great I was over and over again.

Even still, I always believed in God.

Mostly we people saw Him on Saturday mornings at Beth Tikvah Temple where He preferred you speak His language, which was Hebrew. He was also God for everyone else, but He split off. If you were Christian, like all my friends in my neighborhood, He had another personality you could talk to named Jesus, which was the more personal version. Like God "sort of," who you could go to see on Sunday at Church. He was Catholic God for Sissy and everyone at Parochial. He was the one on the cross. And you could only talk to Him inside buildings.

A long time ago, God showed Himself in person more. Now He is more like the Wizard of Oz who just makes you scared, and you have to travel to see him. And when you get there, you don't actually get to see him.

I prefer the God of Everywhere. The one you can talk to when you're outside or in your bed. The one that's invisible and not a man or a lady. The one that's not judgy and loves everyone no matter what. But I'm afraid to not believe in the God in the Buildings. In case I'm wrong. There's a lot I don't understand about God.

The next day, Sissy and me walk to school like always. Twirly maple seeds drizzle down. For almost the whole way to school, we don't talk. We just pick up crispy maple pod wings. Some of the maple seeds have two crispy wings, some have one. We don't mind. We save the uniquest ones in our pockets for our collections. At school we wait outside for the bell and the teachers to open the doors. We wrap our palms together and hold hands while we wait.

I ask, "Do you have to be Catholic?"

She says they have to be because that's how they were born.

I say, "Me, too."

Meaning Jewish.

The bell rings loud. Kids run screaming, laughing from the playground to get in line. Mr. Koslowski, the principal, opens the big doors. In single file, we walk in.

Nobody went to watch Sissy get a lickin'. We all went home.

No one, not even Sissy, could figure out why she was bad.

– 4 –
ACCIDENTALLY

In the backyard on a July-hot summer day, a toad, tinier than a marshmallow, hops into my palm. Instead of hopping right off, it stays with me.

I scoot to the garden hose and drip water onto his lips and watch his funny mouth with a wide tongue, open. Every time his throat gulps you can see it. His eyes are big and black and we have a staring contest. He wins most every time. My pinky dares to stroke his head with a barely touching touch. And he lets me. I touch his rubbery thigh. And he lets me.

My pinky fingertip traces the outline of his body, down his lumpy back, up again to his head and down his side, his other side. Letting my touch define his edges for him.

27

Letting him feel where he ends and the Universe begins. My touch is his mirror. Because how does he know what he looks like? Toads don't have mirrors.

I touch his throat, gentle, as if he had fur. It's not his fault he's not soft with feathers or fur that people want to touch.

He knows he is safe and it's ok to close his eyes. And he does.

I close my eyes, and I feel the same safe.

Lying on the grass, looking up at the clouds, his rubbery feet on my bare belly. I love him.

I think, maybe we 're all just invisible and take turns trying out being in different bodies to see how life looks from out of those eyes. Like how when you're high up, life looks different from when you're peeking out of a box?

Maybe you're invisible until you choose again. Then you get to be a toad or a person.

A boy or a girl.

A tree or a butterfly. Or a dog or a robin.

Everything on the inside is really an invisible person, trying on a new home for a while. Life looks different from whichever inside you're in. But the one thing that's the same is everything feels. Because everything can die, everything needs comfort and love. And the way we all feel comfort and love is with a touch that says, "Shhhh, its ok. You are safe, you are loved, and it's ok to close your eyes."

I'm a little girl, and this is what I know for sure:

1. I know my brothers and me are the children my parents wished for.
2. I know you never have to feel lonely or bored because you can be friends with everything.
3. That everything speaks the same language.
4. That plants, trees, snow, sun, wind all vibrate. Everything is made of music.
5. All creatures want love and understand each other through touch.

This is what I know for sure when me and the toad close our eyes together. Safe.

Someone calls me for lunch. My mom or my dad.

"I'm not hungry," I say.

"Come in anyway," my mom or my dad say.

"I don't want to," I say.

"Come in. Have a bite of a sandwich."

"I have a toad. What if I come out and he's gone?" I ask.

"Put him in something. You can come back out after lunch."

Then someone, my mom or my dad hands me an empty tin coffee can.

I fill it with grass and a few catchable ants and snap on the plastic lid, then charge inside. I eat the sandwich as fast as I can, staring at the back of the cereal boxes left on the table from the morning.

Which is the best cereal? If I had to choose just one? Frosted Flakes? They have Tony the Tiger. Or Flintstones?

Flintstones is the best cartoon of all cartoons. Lucky Charms. The Leprechaun is kinda stuck up and thinks he's the best. And the only part of the cereal I like is the charms, so it's out of the running.

Oh my god! My toad!

The tin can is there. Just where I left it. I open the lid.

The toad, mouth open, one hand reaching up toward the lid, one knee pulled up in mid-jump, a solid statue. Reaching to get out. Trapped, left to die, no way out.

I killed him. I meant to keep him so we could play again. I meant him to feel safe, that he could trust me.

His fear. His panic. Imagining his last moments dying of heat, starved for air. I can't breathe. What I've done won't leave me. I cry, cry, cry, all the day into the night. I wake in the middle of the night, having forgotten for a moment, then comes the image of him reaching desperate, helpless, suffocating. I can't. I can't surface, either.

Why didn't I know to slice holes in the lid? Why didn't any grown-ups tell me to put holes in the lid so I wouldn't be a murderer? I murdered another being. It's too much to take. Too much to love. Too much power over each other. It's like we're here alone and trusted with everything. Even with each other. Just here at the whim of anyone else. But we don't know yet to put holes in the lid.

– 5 –
FIRST UGLY

The tryouts are super tough to make it onto the team of only eight. We are The Commandos, the 9–11-year-old girl's Park District cheerleading squad. I am ten—right in the middle—so I can be on one more year if I make it.

We are cheerleaders, but mostly it's not about the cheering. Yes, we cheer to boys playing sports but, really, who knows the rules of basketball or wrestling or football? Cheerleading is about our sport, gymnastics, and the precision, the skill it takes to be excellent in competition.

Even though we go to state competitions, I didn't know cheerleading was an actual sport. I thought we had to cheer at the games to appease somebody—who knows who—to make an excuse to make a category for us. Just so long as we have the purpose of doing something for boys' sports, we can carry on.

I love it. Backbends and Chinese splits. American splits and walkovers. Back walkovers, cartwheels, aerials, one-handed cartwheels, "C" jumps, and drop-n-rolls from high atop three stacked people. All pointed toes and stiff hands. All to be learned and practiced, alone and together with your team. And if you practiced, you got better. All the things I want to be someday in my life, like a princess, or an actress, you have to be destined from birth to be allowed to do them. I don't know if I'm granted the destiny for my dreams yet. But cheerleading gymnastics is something I can become great at just because I try.

I wake early every morning, stretching into the splits in the dewy morning grass, pushing up into a backbend until my hands can grasp my ankles and rock and roll there. Practicing the movement to every cheer we have to do during the games. Putting myself through the gymnastic scales: stretching, back bends, jumps, flips. The more you train, the more you notice the subtleties of the movements, how one tiny fraction can make the biggest difference in the smoothness and beauty of the move. It's my first feeling of what it means to be an artist at anything.

At the boy's games, we scream until we're hoarse, thinking that since we're the loudest, we must also be the best. Then, at time out, it's our turn. We run onto the field or court and do our thirty-second cheer ending in a mount standing on one another's shoulders. Our few seconds of glory.

Because I'm the tiniest, I'm on the top of every mount. Like the star on the Christmas tree. Me, me, me. And I'm the one to flip, the bravest, all the way from the top of the mount to the ground, landing in a full, butt-bones-to-the-floor Chinese splits. Hands up, fingers tight together, elbows straight. Big smile. Peppy. Enthusiastic. Precise.

It's the second game of the new season. Something is different. The field is decorated. There's a table with corsages and a float being built. Did I miss something?

What is Homecoming?

My friend Cheryl, another cheerleader, says, "The boys all voted, and we all get escorted onto the field. Then, we find out who the boys voted for, and then they crown her Homecoming Queen."

Oh.

My.

God.

That.

Is.

So.

Exciting!

We are having a pageant just like Miss America or Miss Universe, but this is Miss Homecoming Queen! What does that mean?

And the boys voted!

33

I didn't know any of this was happening!

Secretly, I know they must have voted for me.

I don't know any of the boys, and I don't think they know any of us girls. We just get to the game, yell, and cheer and jump from the sidelines, then do our amazing gymnastics and mounts in the center field, and then we go to practice and competitions to get better. But maybe they watch us.

Aaaaand, if they watch us, I think they may have voted for me. I am the most disciplined of our cheerleading team. The most flexible. I am on the top of all the mounts. I am the tiniest and the loudest, and I try the hardest and I never stop until I lose my voice. I never do anything halfway. Every movement is precise and practiced and peppy and enthusiastic, and I am funny, and I am popular, and I have the longest hair, and the tiniest wrists, and I am the most outgoing.

I'm not better than any of them. They are all my friends. But I try the hardest. I try the longest. I do everything to the fullest of what I can do. I always do more than is expected of me. That might sound stuck up, but I'm humble too. Just not fake humble.

I don't understand people who only give a part of themselves, who just want to be normal and ordinary. It's so selfish. Being mediocre is selfish. It's like not trying. It's like not appreciating your gifts.

Did you see the crown for the Homecoming Queen? It has actual diamonds (rhinestones), and she gets to wear it! She gets to wear a crown and be in a parade with a sash and the diamond crown on. I wonder how I would look in a crown?

Oh my god.

Someday, I want to be a princess. But not a princess that just marries a prince and stands there. I want to be princess because I know how things should be in the world. There needs to be new rulers, ones that, when they see people hurting, they help instead of walking away or punishing more. That's how I would be as Princess of the World.

Our coach says, "You girls will stand on this side. The music will start and two boys will come to you."

Our eyes go wide, and our mouths open. We look at each other. Is this really happening?

Our coach says, "I'll pin your corsage. The boys will hold their arms out on either side for you to hold, then they'll walk you to the center of the field."

We are trying to suppress a threatening onslaught of giggles.

"Once you're all there," our coach says, "we will announce the Homecoming Queen."

The giggles don't explode. The weight of what's about to occur hits us. We grab and squeeze each other's clammy palms. I'm so nervous now. My stomach has the butterfly feeling.

We are lined up tallest to shortest. The boys come and take the tall girls first. I'm the smallest, so I'm going to be the last. The cheerleading coach pins on the corsage, and the boys hold their arms out like a sideways "V," and the girl slips her arm through. It's so romantic! Oh god, I'm going to die from romance! *Die!*

Cheryl goes. Next, it's meeeeeee! Here come the boys! My corsage is so lovely. It's white, and they say it's called a carnation, and it has a red "C" made of pipe cleaner in the center. I'm going to press it with wax paper and an iron and save it forever in the scrapbook of my life.

The boys, who I don't know, put their arms in a "V" for me to slip my arm through. I smile at them, my cheerleading smile. They don't smile back.

Why not?

They won't let my arm flesh touch their arm flesh. They are holding their arms in the position and making air padding in between us, acting like I have cooties or something.

My sureness at being Homecoming Queen is quavering. What if I'm not? But I deserve to be. I am the best cheer-leader on our squad. It's not just me saying that. Any girl on our team will tell you. And our coaches.

The music plays. I hold my friend's hand, and we all wait in wild tight anticipation for the announcement.

"The Homecoming Queen for The Commandos is… Trudy Johnson!"

Trudy? She's big-boned and fleshy. She has huge boobs which make her less peppy. She can't jump high or do "C" jumps. Her legs are much bigger, so she's good to be at the base of the mounts.

Trudy?

I'm trying not to cry because that would make me seem so selfish.

Trudy?

Because she has such big boobs, she slumps her shoulders forward like she's caving in on herself, and we all feel sorry for that. She has wispy blonde hair. She never talks much, and I like her. I like her because we are teammates. We are family that way.

But Trudy doesn't even try hard at things in life. One time, we saw a dying bird and Trudy said, "Oh well, it's just going to die." And it made me so mad, I yelled at her and took the bird home.

I said I was sorry to Trudy for yelling.

I don't understand that "Oh well, it's just life…" feeling. Especially not in kids. I guess in grown-ups it's too late. But kids have lots of energy and lots of hope and they shouldn't be settling. But I guess it's just my superpower. Other people have theirs.

They are bobby-pinning the crown to Trudy's wispy hair but it won't stay, so she is holding it with one hand and the big white carnation bouquet with the other as she walks into the aisle that is made up of us and the boys. And the boys are whistling and cheering. I like Trudy. We went through all of elementary school together. I just don't understand.

I ask my friend Cheryl, trying not to sound mean, trying to ask playfully, "Why did they pick Trudy?" I ask. Me and Cheryl and everyone clapping and wide smiling as Trudy takes her slow steps. The Homecoming Queen walk.

"Of course they picked Trudy," Cheryl says.

This is very startling. I thought everyone would be surprised like me.

"Really? Oh. Why?" I ask.

"Cause she's tall and blonde and has *huge* boobs," Cheryl says.

"That matters?" I ask. We keep clapping and cheering with our wide smiles.

"Yeah! That's what boys like," Cheryl says.

"I mean, I know boys are supposed to like that, but I didn't know they cared about that in real life? I mean, she can't jump," I say as Trudy passes us. Her face is the blushiest I've ever seen her have.

"Boys don't care about that," Cheryl says.

They don't? This is *astonishing* to me. What does this mean? I am none of those things that Trudy is. I'm the tiniest, completely flat-chested—maybe forever—*agh!*

I always thought I could pick who I wanted when I grew up. I got A's. I worked hard. I knew "if there was a will there was a way." I thought that boys would love me for that. They would see all that excellence, and I would be able to pick my Prince Soul Mate of True Love from among my many suitors (and never have to "settle" like my mom says some moms in our neighborhood did).

What is happening?

None of this is valuable?

"Are we pretty, me and you? Cause I thought we were?" I ask.

"Not to boys," Cheryl says, as if it doesn't matter at all to her. But Cheryl only wants to be a nurse when she grows up.

"How can we be pretty to each other and pretty to grown-ups who say so and pretty when we look in the mirror but not pretty to boys?" I ask.

"Because boys like girls who look like the ones in the magazines," Cheryl says.

"I think we look sort of like the girls in the magazines," I say. "We have eyes with shapes and eyelashes, eyebrows that curve, and lips. What's so different?"

I thought that since we were all pretty, what would put me as the most-wanted would be the devotion I put in. It felt weird that didn't matter. When it came down to "prettiness," boys thought Trudy was prettier?

"Trudy has big boobs," Cheryl says, grabbing my hand, leading us to the table with the cake.

I always felt sorry for Trudy for her boobs. Turns out they're her superpower.

- 6 -
LUCKY 13

The first day is the worst. Especially the cafeteria for lunch where there's no teacher, and I don't know anyone. The first day I have to go to the office and say I'm new and get my schedule. I don't even know where the rooms are. Not even the girls bathroom or the lunchroom, and I have to pretend I do so I don't look like a dork. My only secret hope is that I'll try out for cheerleading and, if I make it, everything will be ok.

I hate my life, and I hate my parents for making us move. For *no reason at all!* Everything in my old life was perfect. It wasn't even hard to go from elementary school into junior high, even though there would be lots of new people that me and kids from my elementary school didn't know. Because we all knew each other since kindergarten. We all had our identities that we grew since we were little. Everyone knew me and knew I was straight A's and funny and popular. The teachers liked me because I paid attention. I had lots of friends. I was the cheerleader on the top of the mounts. I had the most Girl Scout badges that went all the way up the back of my sash. Everyone knew I was a sexpot, really flirty. Lots of boys wanted to date me. That was me. Now I'm nobody. And nobody knows any of that. I'm not even pretty enough to be automatically popular.

I walk down the halls, clutching my books real tight, watching my feet on the shiny, squeaky floors. On the first day, the worst part is lunch. I open the cafeteria doors, where students are on the loose and everyone already knows each other. Not just because the school year already started but because they all went to elementary school together. Just like me and my friends at Eisenhower Junior High.

The lunch room is a dingy auditorium that has a bunch of long folding tables with metal folding chairs on two levels, some on the stage part and some where the audience would be if there was a show. The lights are off so we just get the filter of light that comes in from the long windows up by the ceiling.

I find a seat with no one sitting at any of the chairs around it and pretend not to see the other kids at the other tables noticing me. I'm afraid if we touch eyes, they'll say something, and maybe it'll be mean. And, if it is, all the other kids will join in; once a mean pattern starts about someone, it's impossible to erase, and you're stuck with that mean tease everyday of your school life unless you move. The only thing that could save you is if you suddenly got popular.

I keep my head really low to the table and eat my sandwich from inside the paper bag. I'm afraid to take it out in case it's a sandwich kids here would make fun of. I don't know what's popular here. My weird sandwich is because we're Jewish. My mom, instead of peanut butter and jelly, makes cream cheese and grape jelly on Wonderbread, then flattens it with her palm so it fits in the lunch baggie. By the time I take it out, the bread and the cream cheese are light purple, and the grape jelly is dark purple and, if anyone sees it, they will know I'm Jewish.

And maybe they'll be prejudiced. Even if they don't know, it will be something to make fun of me about. I don't know how to be. I don't know what I need to be to be safe. I don't know if the me I am—and the me I was—are any good here.

Kids' talking echoes off the walls. I can't make out full sentences. Just yelling or laughing that burst out of the loud hum of constant conversation. I put my face into my brown lunch sack. Take a bite of my sandwich. The edge of the paper bag scrapes above my upper lip. My tongue licks it checking for the metal taste of blood. What if I cut myself there? Then it would become a scab, and then it would look like I have a mustache. And I'm a girl!

42

I bend my whole face to the table and touch my finger to the spot on my upper lip. I look at my finger. I don't think it's blood. I think I'm safe. So far.

A group of girls at the stage area lunch tables, who were laughing, suddenly stand up chanting, "Fawn! Fawn! Fawn!"

The girl I guess who is Fawn, seems like she might be blushing. She seems modest. She's big-boned like Trudy from my old Commandos cheerleading team when I was in elementary. She has dyed bleach blonde hair. I can tell because she has about two inches of black roots showing. But no one seems to hold that against her prettiness. My mother would never let me bleach my hair. Anyone who had roots showing, my mother would whisper that "her slip was showing."

Fawn's face is square with all pleasing features. She has a tiny ski jump nose, a smile with dimples to make it cuter, and a chin that pushed up against her smile to make it even *cuter*-cuter. She has soft freckles on her cheeks to be *cuter-cuter-cuter*. It seems like she is the most popular. Even though she is plumpish.

"Fawn! Fawn!" they chant. Then everyone laughs and sits back in their lunch seats. They are all wearing cheerleading outfits. Suddenly I feel an icy, frozen fear, worse than the thumping fear I was feeling since I got here.

Did they already pick cheerleaders? What if I don't get to be a cheerleader again? This whole year? Or ever again? Cheerleading is who I am. It's my whole identity. If I'm not

43

a cheerleader, what am I? Just a plain old student? If I don't even have a chance to even try out to be a cheerleader, how will this whole eighth grade go? Will I just wander the halls invisible, hoping no one decides to find something bad about me to make fun of?

The girls by Fawn, the ones chanting, are all harsh pretty. Not fleshy, soft pretty. Mean pretty. The kind of pretty where you're allowed to be stuck up. Maybe they like Fawn so much because she's plump and, deep down, they don't feel like she's competition. I look at my own wrists. My hands. Compared to those girls, I look like a little kid. I'm probably one of the smallest eighth graders in the cafeteria.

In my old school, kids would wrap their pinkie and thumb around my wrist saying, "Oh my god! You're like a bird!" But they meant it in a nice way. At Girl Scout Camp, I named myself Phoebe after the bird. But, here, compared to Fawn and these girls, I just looked scrawny and not pretty enough to be automatically popular. I'm the kind of pretty you have to get to know because I have so much personality. But if you never met my personality, you wouldn't know how pretty I was.

When I look around, it seems like, except for the cheerleading uniform girls, everyone is wearing jeans with bell bottoms and sweatshirts and scruffy boots. I'm wearing dress pants and a long sleeve polyester blouse with bright flowers and school shoes. At my old school, everyone wore school dress-up clothes. When you came home from school you could change into your grubby clothes. I'm scared that, if they notice, I'll get teased for that, and they will automatically assume I'm a nerd. Which I'm not.

The scratchy noise of the speakers crackles. The kids get quiet.

The voice says, "Good afternoon, Spartans."

I think Spartans must be the school team name. At Eisenhower, we were the Eagles. What even is a Spartan?

The voice says, "A few important announcements."

The kids' voices get raucous again, ignoring the speaker's voice, making it hard to hear.

At my old school, all the kids were cool but they wouldn't ignore the teachers.

Through the roaring I hear, "Homecoming celebration will begin Friday after school on the athletic field."

The girls in the cheerleading uniforms start the Fawn chant again. Fawn does the modest blush. She must be the most popular girl. She must be the one they're nominating for Homecoming Queen. That must be why they're chanting.

The speaker says, "Monday after Homecoming, tryouts for all sports will take place for all teams. Sign up in the front office."

Homecoming. The thought makes me sad. Because I don't know anyone. I didn't like it either even though I was popular and a cheerleader at Eisenhower. It just makes you know out loud who is the most popular and who is the most pretty. Sometimes, it's better not to know.

How could they have Homecoming so soon and not even have the teams yet? I decide to go to the office to see if tryouts for teams means cheerleaders, too, or if Fawn and those girls were already picked.

***

In the office, they explain Homecoming is when the team comes home to start a new season, and the old cheerleading squad from the last year cheers them on. Then, the new season starts with the new teams and new cheerleaders. I still don't understand it, but there is a cheerleading tryout.

I'm going to practice, practice, practice until Monday. It's my only hope. I have to do a cheer that's no longer than two minutes. It has to have certain gymnastics cheerleading moves which I already know from being a cheerleader before. All I have to do is make up a cheer, maybe from ones I created before. And practice.

***

My birthday is coming up. I'm going to be thirteen. Thirteen on the thirteenth. A teenager, finally.

"That's a special birthday," my mom says, and she asks me what I want for presents. Since it's a big birthday, I get to pick something not on sale and special. I know what I want. I want one of those fish tanks with the filters, not like a goldfish bowl, but a tank with gravel, colored lights, swaying plants, and a treasure chest that the tiny fragile brightly colored fish could zip in and out of. I can stare at it, imagining myself as a mermaid, swimming in the hideaways with them.

I tell my mom I want a tropical fish tank. And pants. For school. Because I feel like if I had blue jeans like the other kids; at least that would be one less thing to be picked on for, just in case.

***

I don't go to Homecoming on Friday. I don't tell my parents about it, so they don't ask me. Fawn Hossman is crowned Homecoming Queen.

After school on Monday, the boys go to the sports tryouts for football, wrestling, track, and basketball. After they finish in the gym, the girls get to try out for cheerleading. I have time to practice out back while the boys are in the gym.

Then, it's time. All the girls get a number to pin onto our shirts. That's the order we go in. I'm number thirteen, which is the same day as my birthday and my soon-to-be age. It's a miracle. My heart stops pounding so hard because it must be a good luck sign.

The cheerleading coaches sit high in the bleachers with notepads and a stopwatch. The girls with the numbers on sit in the lower bleachers. You have to stay for the whole tryouts; you can't just leave in the middle. And you have to be quiet when everyone else is going, so even Fawn and the girls from the cafeteria who had the uniforms on are quiet right now. They all sit together, and I can see that they're nervous, too.

I sit by myself on the side by the staircase of the bleachers, which is ok, because I have to concentrate. I like to run a movie in my head of me doing all the moves that I planned to do. That makes me not so nervous when it's my turn. I keep my eyes closed and don't watch the other girls go so I don't psych myself out, but I hear when each one finishes because either the coach yells "time" or the other girls clap for her.

"Thirteen." I hear. "Thirteen," says the lady coach holding the stopwatch.

I exhale and find my spot on the floor. I'm the only one nobody knows. I can feel them. All the girls in my grade lean in, elbows on their knees, waiting to see if I'm just ok, or a failure, or whatever I am.

I think I'm good. Our Commandos cheerleading team got the first place trophy in the regionals two years in a row when I was ten and eleven. I was the top cheerleader. I made it onto the Eisenhower team for seventh grade when I was twelve. But I don't know how good the girls are here. Maybe they're so much better.

I look down at the floor with my eyes closed.

"Whenever you're ready," the coach says.

A heartbeat. *One.* Another heartbeat. *Two.* And another heartbeat. *Go. Look up. Smile.*

"Ready? Ok!" I shout. Every movement has a word. Precise, from my voice to my smile, to my arms and my fingers and the energy shooting out of my fingers. My jumps are the highest I've ever jumped. My legs are locked and my toes pointed as far as they can point on my one-handed cartwheel. I end in a bones-to-the-floor, arms to the sky, light-up-the-room-smile, Chinese splits. I am breathing hard, but I'm exuberant. I did it the best that I practiced it. The coach doesn't say "time" because I don't go over.

But the girls don't clap. Why? Because I wasn't good? Because they don't know me? I feel the exuberance leak out of me like air from a helium balloon. I return to the bleachers, my steps sounding suddenly like a giant's fee-fi-fo-fum. I sit by myself, watching the remaining girls.

At the end, the coaches stand, and the one with the stopwatch says something about us all being good and the lists being posted next Monday. A week away. When all the sports teams will be decided.

***

At dinner, my brothers are telling us about their new school, and then my mom asks me how my school was today.

And I say, "Fine."

She asks me if I went to the cheerleading tryouts.

And I say "yes" and create a center hole in the middle of my mashed potatoes. Then, I push away from the table screaming, "I hate my life! I wish I were dead!" I cannot see a way to survive this new school. Or the eighth grade.

***

For my birthday celebration, my mom made a homemade cake. She's the best baker. When I was a little girl, my mom used to bake a lot. Baking to her is like cheerleading to me. Everyone loves everything she baked. She was my Girl Scout leader, and she baked for our troop meetings. She baked to bring to holidays like Chanukah and Thanksgiving. I would stand next to her on a stool and lick the batter off the beaters. It was the way we got to be mother and daughter the most.

But, a few years ago, she decided she didn't want to be just a homemaker-stay-at-home-mom only, and she went to junior college to learn interior design. She stopped baking except for holidays, so it said a lot that she baked me a birthday cake. I know my mom loves me more than anything, and I love her too. She's my mom. But we fight a lot. All the time. It's like she doesn't want me to be me or feel what I feel or want what I want. It's like there are things I'm supposed to be and when I'm not, I'm doing it on purpose to hurt her. I'm not. I'm just in the middle of being me. But, somehow, the more I'm me, the more it hurts her.

My brothers, me, my mom, and my dad gather around the cake with fourteen candies, one extra for good luck. They sing Happy Birthday in their off-key voices. I close my eyes and make my wish, saying in my head, "Please, God, please let me make the cheerleading team. And please let me be popular at school. And make me special enough so, someday, my dreams come true."

I blow, snuffing all the candles which hopefully means my wishes will come true. Fingers crossed.

Both my parents are excited to give me their gifts. I think I know what they are, but I haven't seen a fish tank, so I'm not sure. I think they're excited because I've been so sad. Since we moved, I'd been crying for no reason and locking myself in my room after school. I don't know why I'm acting like that. When they ask me, it feels too complicated to explain.

My dad hands me a box wrapped like it was done by professional wrappers. This is the first present my dad gave me that my mom didn't wrap herself.

"Your father picked it out himself," my mom says.

"That's true, daughter," my dad says. He has a big smile.

I love my dad. So much. Both my parents love me, and it matters to them that I make something of myself someday. But my dad is the one person I know cherishes me. If I died, he would die inside.

As I unwrap the fancy bow, I think how special it is that my dad went out and bought something for me himself. He took time after work. He picked it out. I can see how much he wants me to love it. It's in a clothing box. The jeans? I would have real jeans. Like all the cool teenagers do. Like the hippies and the rock n' rollers.

51

I lift the lid and unfold the delicate tissue paper. Pants. I asked for pants. But they are beige and expensive-looking with cuffs at the bottom and a delicate, thin belt for the high waist. They weren't on sale. They are the pants of a grown-up. Of a lady. I asked for pants. But I meant jeans. Why don't they know me enough to know what I need and see the pains I don't yet have the words to explain?

I'm saying thank you. I love them. But I'm swallowing a hot lump in my throat.

"You can try them on after the gifts," my mother says. I nod. I am the most selfish girl in the world. I wanted jeans. I needed jeans. My dad went out of his way to make me happy. But I don't want them. I can't wear them. They make me feel unheard. Misunderstood.

My brothers are giddy because now is the big gift. I'm pretty sure it's the fish tank. We all head down stairs to the playroom and there it is, lit up and gurgling. For the first time since we moved, I feel like it's going to be ok. The fish tank glows blue and pink. I look inside. No flitting pretty tiny bright fluorescent fish. Only two big, fat white and orange goldfish with pop out eyes. I don't hate them but it's exactly the opposite of who I am inside.

My name has one syllable. Plain. I'm not one syllable. I'm lyrical. I'm water. I am like the willow tree and the tiny phosphorescent luminous darting fish from tropical oceans. I am full of stories, and that doesn't mean I'm a liar. I want to be an actress. That doesn't mean I'm vain or a show off. I have emotions. That doesn't mean I'm faking or being dramatic. I like playing with my Dawn dolls not because I'm immature but because, when I play, I'm writing stories. That doesn't mean I'm a loner.

Everyone is looking at me with expectant smiles. They did so much. They wanted me to be happy for my birthday. But when I look at the fish, I start to cry hard.

My dad asks, "Hey, daughter, why are you crying?"

I say, "Because I'm so happy." I run upstairs and lock my door and hate myself for how selfish and ungrateful I am. I feel like they don't really hear me or see me. I feel that way in school. It all bubbles up at once. I hate myself.

***

The lists are taped to the gym doors. Crowds gather, kids on tiptoes looking through shoulders, moving closer as the closest ranks move away. I'm scared to look. Fawn and a couple of the other girls move in, see their names, and squeal. I'm smiling so if they see me, they'll think I'm happy for them. Also, if I'm not on the list, I'll cry, so I am determined to smile if that happens.

A girl with long blonde hair and a snarl looks around, looks at me, looks back at the list. She is taller than the other girls and skinny. When she turns back to the lists, her long, straight blonde hair swishes and settles, touching the belt on her jeans. Her long nail skims down the names. I decide I'll wait until her and Fawn and the rest go, then I'll look. But I hear, "Hey." It's the blonde girl.

"Is this you?" she asks. All the girls look at me.

"I saw you at tryouts," she says. "Is this you?"

"I don't know," I say. I walk, keeping my eyes pinned to the lists. I stand on my toes so I can see the name above her red fingernail. There it is. My name.

My name.

Oh my god.

I made the team.

Lucky number thirteen.

I stand there staring at it.

"You were good," the blonde girl says.

I'm nodding, I think.

The girls squish in to read when the first practice is. The ten-minute warning bell rings for class.

"See you there," they call to each other. And to me.

To *me*.

"See you there," I say. And I go to the girls bathroom, lock a stall, and cry. So much crying lately.

I made it. My birthday wish came true.

I come home and put on the pants my dad gave me and stare at the fish that aren't my dream but seem to like being in my bedroom. I name them Sonny and Cher.

I take out my Dawn dolls and walk them in front of the tank. Most of my girlfriends stopped playing with their

Barbie and Dawn dolls. But for me, my imagination breaks free, wild, un-corralled. My Dawn dolls get the adventures I imagine I'm going to have someday. I've known them almost my whole life so far, so I just let them lead. Angie and Dale look like stars, and they talk about how excited they are to be at the Shed Aquarium. Dawn says she's meeting her date by the large goldfish tank. Gloria, with the red hair, says she wishes she could jump in because, of course, she was a mermaid in her past life. They all laugh, but they know it's true, and they all take a seat on the Milky Way bar sofa.

-7-
Virgin Slut

Now that I'm a cheerleader, I'm super popular. I feel relieved. There's eight girls on our squad. I'm the tiniest again and on the top of the mounts. Fawn and Karen are the sturdy ones. Even though Fawn is on the team, I still don't know her very much. I'm best friends with Karen and Michelle. They're both so cool.

Karen is stocky-strong and practical looking. She's on the base of the cheerleading mounts. It's her thigh I step on to climb up the human ladder and her shoulders I balance on at the top of the mount while she holds my ankles.

Michelle is the blonde girl I met at the lists. She's too thin to be on the bottom of the mounts, but too tall to be on top. She's out front, the one doing the gymnastic moves as the mount is building. Like the distraction. She is the most perfect version of the tall, blonde, All-American I've seen in person in my real life so far. She has straight white-blonde hair that she could sit on and a long, willowy body. She wears blue mascara on her white lashes and rings on several fingers, even her thumb.

We are a posse. Karen, Michelle, and I. We call ourselves "The Three Mouseketeers." All for one. The Inseparables. Together, we are impenetrable, tough, not to be messed with. The fortunate ones. Super popular. We spend every day—even weekends and some vacations—together this eighth-grade year.

We wear combat boots, hip-hugger jeans that button just above our pubic bones, crop tops, and bare midriffs. My social studies teacher hates that. For some reason, it bothers him. My bare midriff. It seems like every day I have his class, he calls me up to his desk and stamps my bare tummy with his name, Mr. Hallett. It takes most of the day, with spit and bathroom soap, to rub his name off the space above my belly button.

I feel closer with Karen because even though we are "The Three Mouseketeers," Michelle isn't as "safe feeling." Michelle could be laughing and liking someone and then, suddenly, she could lean back and start whispering something mean about that same person. I try to stay on the front side of Michelle so she can never lean back and whisper something behind me.

Karen and Michelle are the daughters of single mother divorcées. They wear the keys to their homes around their necks and can be home alone after school while their single mom is still at work. That means boys can come over and drink beers and smoke pot and cigarettes. Not at Karen's house but at Michelle's apartment.

Michelle seemed so much older during those times. She knew how to lean over boys to reach for something and then lean back, swishing her hair dramatically. She would take swigs of beer and puffs of a cigarette and make it seem like she did that all the time.

We listen to albums at Michelle's apartment. One time, when Rod Stewart came on, he sang this song that said, listen up you virgin child, spread your wings, and let him come inside. Karen and I, our faces were hot because we were pretty sure we knew it meant the "F" word. We don't know what the "F" word means exactly, but it's kind of scary, and we know boys do it to us.

Michelle dug in her purse and put this round pink case with a circle of white dot pills in it, on the table. I wasn't sure if that meant she had done "it" before or not, but she seemed so brave.

Another time, in front of everyone in the lunchroom, a tampon fell out of Michelle's purse. It seemed like she knocked it out on purpose, but then she seemed so frantic, retrieving it with her hand to her chest saying, "Phew. You guys? Oh my god! Did anyone see?"

Most of the girls in my grade already had their periods, but they still used pads because they were virgins. Michelle having a tampon was like she was ahead of the rest of us.

I am a virgin. Boring, I know. And I still don't have my period yet. Why was it taking so long?

Once a month, I fake my period. This requires me to actually do math, the only time it's useful in real life, to keep track of dates and how many dimes to stash in my white gym shoes. The tampons in the machine in the girl's bathrooms cost a dime. My ploy is, during a time out in the game that we're cheering for, I make a look of sudden surprise and then distress and whisper to Karen or Michelle, "Do you have a dime?" Or I make a big deal out of taking off a gym shoe and dropping a dime and then whispering, "I'll be right back." Then I run from the gym to the bathroom, waste a few minutes, and run back to my spot on the sidelines to resume jumping and cheering. That makes everyone know I'm a woman now.

I want to get my period so I can get my ears pierced. Michelle has pierced ears, of course. So does Karen. My dad said I could get mine pierced as soon as I was a woman because I had to be mature enough to take care of them so they didn't get infected. And I said, "How will I know when I'm a woman?" All he'd say is that I'd know when.

I think he means when I get my period.

After school, on days when there's no game and no practice, Karen, Michelle, and I hang out at a laundromat in a strip mall near my house up on Roselle Road, across from the 7-11. Michelle's mom smokes Virginia Slims Menthol, so Michelle always has a few for us to share. Sitting on the dryers and in the folding area cubbies, sipping Mountain Dews, passing the cigarette around, we talk about sex like baseball.

Michelle knows more, so she draws a baseball field diamond in black sharpie marker on the wallpaper in the folding area cubby. Four squares and the bases, connected by four lines that make the shape of a diamond. In the middle, a lump for the pitcher's mound. Next to the pitcher's mound, she writes, *"Pitcher's Mound = Holding Hands."*

On the side, away from the diamond, she draws a bench and writes, *"Bench = Hugging."* Karen and I roll our eyes because who hasn't gotten to the bench or pitcher's mound?

On the top of the diamond is a box that says, *"First base = Kissing,"* which is where most of the freaks and frocks have gotten to.

Freaks are the cool kids who smoke pot. Frocks are the jocks who do sports but are still cool and get down and smoke pot anyway. I smoke pot. Sort of. I don't like it, so I pretend. I don't inhale, and I cough a lot so you can't tell. I have strawberry-flavored rolling paper and carry a plastic baggie of some pot in my purse just so it shows I'm cool and not gonna narc on anyone.

One time, my mom found the baggie in my underwear drawer and started screaming and crying. She sat downstairs in the basement chanting, "Tell me you don't smoke mari-juana. Tell me!"

So, I said, "I don't smoke marijuana."

This calmed her down. But then she asked, "What is this? What is this, then?"

And, very calmly, I said, "Oriental incense." And that was the end of that. She gave it back to me and went upstairs to make dinner.

On the right side of the baseball diamond, it says, "*Second Base = Feeling*," which pretty much meant your boobs.

On the bottom, the square says, "*Third Base = Fingering.*"

And on the left side, it says, "*Fourth Base Homerun = Screwing*," which means going all the way.

We all take last drags off Michelle's cigarette, pass around the Dentyne gum, hop off the counters, and head home.

I love being one of the popular kids. Pretty much that's mostly all I ever want in my life now that I'm a teenager and not a kid. Especially when I've wished I could be other people; now other people wish they could be me. Being popular is a feeling inside you, knowing you can hold your nose high and keep a smile on your face as you walk down the hall. The feeling that tells you that people think you are better than them when you know you aren't. The great feeling of friends all around you. Being busy every second and getting twenty-one phone calls in a day. I found if I follow the following rules, I can't go wrong:

1. Always be fun to be with.
2. Never show you're depressed unless it's necessary.
3. Always smile or laugh.
4. Care about other people.
5. Hardly ever talk about yourself unless you're asked. Instead, ask about other people.
6. Play things cool.
7. Never be a tattletale. In other words, don't rat!
8. Wear cool clothes.
9. Be on a cool team that has popular people on it.
10. Have a good personality.
11. Have a good sense of humor.
12. Be neat, clean, + pretty.
13. Don't lie! Ever!

I feel like I shouldn't love it so much. I don't know why. Why is it so wrong to feel like everyone likes you and wishes they were you? But I feel like it's bad because it leaves people out. Like I'm better than them. Except when I think about it, there's no reason I am. Except for being popular. I don't like to think about that. It makes me scared because it feels like the only reason people like me is because I'm popular but if I wasn't, I would just be in the invisible zone. Except Karen. We are really friends. Michelle is a real friend, but I'm not sure if I wasn't a cheerleader and popular if we would be friends. I don't know. It's weird.

A couple months before graduation, Sabine Montrose's parents go to Washington or some state for Easter holiday and, even though Sabine isn't one of the popular kids, she has a party and invites everyone popular. Michelle tells everyone to be cool, and we all go.

The house gets filled inside and out. All the cool popular kids go down in the basement where it's almost pitch-black. You have to walk in scooching baby steps or risk stepping on someone's ankle who's hanging out on the floor. Kids are lining the walls in couples, making out with loud moans and slurping sounds.

Me, Michelle, and Karen came to the party together but we got separated. I end up on a loveseat with Bob Teshler, who I had a secret crush on all year, so this was so cool! We are making out. His hands are under my top, working their way up, trying to go to second. I am putting my arm across my chest beneath the bottom part of my bra to block him. He goes up, I block from above. He goes right, I turn more right. We're still kissing with our eyes closed, sort of like a blind ping-pong match. Then, his hand pushes up against my forearm that's blocking, and the Kleenex I stuffed in my bra starts to peek out of my shirt. I see it before he does. I say I have to pee and jump up and restuff in the bathroom.

When I get back, two other kids have taken over the loveseat. Pat Youngs, tall and shy and on the basketball team, is standing by himself in front of where Bob and I were.

I've never spoken to Pat this entire year. He's not in my classes, and he's so quiet that he doesn't talk after the games.

I mean, he's cute and all, but not really popular because he's so to himself.

I don't know how we get there, but Pat Youngs and I are sitting on the floor, our backs leaning against the wall. Kissing. No second base, but a lot of feeling. I'm feeling sexy, and my whole pants are soaked between my legs. He is putting his hands down my pants, and I let him because it feels so good. I can't let him get to second because of the Kleenex. So, we just skip second base and go right to third.

His finger doesn't go in, but he slides it around the wetness, and I feel like I can't stop. I put my hands in his pants. My hand feels something long and hard and very skinny, almost pencil-like in his pants. He is twelve. Or thirteen. And I am thirteen now. It's so exciting. I have crossed into sexual land. For real. This is the first time I've ever felt a boy's naked part. I've felt boys press up against me at a dance, and there is a hardness in their pants front, but I have never felt it live, *in person.*

I don't see Karen or Michelle the rest of the night. Pat walks me home. We all live in the same neighborhood in the school district. I get home with mussed up hair, the buttons on my shirt in the wrong holes, and my makeup smear-y, and I call up to my parents, saying, "I'm home," and I say, "Yes, it was a good party," and, "I'm tired," and I go to bed, giddy.

The next night, Karen, Michelle, and I have a Three Mouseketeers sleepover at Karen's house. We lay on the floor in our comfiest PJ's. Mine are my favorite. They're made of flannel with little pink birds with branches in their beaks. Flannel is so soft on your fingertips. I got them from my mom and dad for Chanukah one year. Michelle wears shiny red satin PJ's. They're her mom's, but they fit her. She looks like a model from the JCPenney catalog. Karen wears cotton ones with blue paisley and has slippers. We sit cross-legged on our sleeping bags left over from Girl Scout days. We play the Rod Stewart song over and over again, giggling and snorting with Dorito breath every time the French lady comes on at the end sounding like she's having S-E-X. And we make up words that she's saying because we can't understand what she's really saying, no matter how many times we move the needle back over it.

Michelle says, "That was such a cool party, you guys." She tells that her and Mike S. smoked so many bowls and got toasted and made out. We high five and low five, and Michelle gets the razor eye and tells about seeing Sabine not making out with anyone even though she had the party. Karen and me feel kind of bad.

"We could make her popular," Karen says.

"We could let her hang out with us. Sometimes," I say.

"Then we'd be the four Mouseketeers? I don't think so," Michelle says, taking a handful of thin mint cookies and settling into her sleeping bag. "I mean, she can hang out with us in school, like in the cafeteria. That'd be cool," Michelle says, stretching her arm out to us.

"Cool," we say, putting our hands on top of each other's then—*poof*—poofing them to the sky. All for one.

"Where did *you* disappear to?" Michelle asks me, wagging her finger.

"Yeah, we lost you," Karen says.

I lay on my tummy on my sleeping bag, my feet up, touching, waggling back and forth, teasing, and I just smile.

"Oh my god! What? Tell us!" Karen and Michelle say.

"Ok! Firrrrrrst," I say, drawing out the "r's." They both sit straight up, cross-legged, leaning forward.

"First, I was with Bob Teshler, making out," I say. Karen and Michelle both squeal. Karen stuffs a couple Doritos in her mouth and says, "Oh my god, he's so cute," as she chomps.

"But short," Michelle says.

"He kisses so good," I say. "You guys. The first time I kissed a guy, he licked my whole face. Like my whole face. Even my eyes."

"What? Ew!" Karen says, still chewing.

"I thought that was what kissing was like," I say. "And it was winter, so when I got home, my whole face was chapped, and I kept thinking, 'how do you survive kissing if you do it a lot?'"

Karen laughs.

Michelle says, "So is that all you did? Make out with Teshler the entire party?"

"Then, he tried to go to second," I say, "but I blocked him. And when I came back from the bathroom, he wasn't sitting there, and it was so dark—"

"Tell me about it," Karen says. "I practically tripped on two people."

"So, but you know Pat Youngs?" I ask.

"Basketball Pat Youngs?" Michelle asks.

I nod. "We went to third base," I say. I raise my eyebrows, and that's all I say.

It's like throwing down the winning card you secretly had in your hand. Michelle and Karen both stare at me impressed and speechless. It's like I've crossed into the cool zone where no one can reach me from the other side. Michelle holds up her hands. I high five one, Karen high fives the other.

"You guys," Michelle says, "let's go outside."

We run out the door laughing, doing cartwheels with our bare feet.

Karen shouts, "Ready? Ok!"

We look at each other and break into the cheer we know we're thinking of. I climb all the way up Karen. She clasps onto my ankles on either side of her neck. I balance with my arms in a victory "V" up to the moon. When I leap down, we all drop into the splits. Chinese for me and Michelle. American for Karen. We all have toes pointed, fingers extended, arms to the stars. We are all champions.

Then with one look, we all for one start to scream. Loud. Long. To see who can scream the loudest and the longest. And, of course, it's me.

***

Monday. At school. Something is wrong. The air feels like the heaviness I felt the first few weeks of school when I was new. Did something bad happen?

When I walk to my first class, it seems like it's about me. Kids look at me and look away fast. Kids I say hi to everyday in the halls pretend like they don't see me. It's like every bit of popularity I gained is gone. I don't know what's wrong. It's like everyone in the whole eighth grade is pissed at me.

I see Michelle and Karen walking and laughing with Sabine. Which is not regular. I wave and laugh like I know what they're laughing about. Karen looks down. Sabine smiles. Then doesn't. Michelle turns her whole face upward. Her eyes are slits with a razor-sharp look.

My body starts to rattle from inside my bones. I feel like I can't get enough air in my lungs. They walk past me. I hold onto a locker and stare. The bell for the next class rings.

In Mr. Hallett's class, instead of paying attention, I write in my notebook all the names of the people I think are my friends. I don't know why I do that. I just keep thinking of names to write. Like a "just in case" list.

Then it's the bell for lunch. In the cafeteria, there's a crowd of kids out in front of the doors, and my pajamas—the ones that I forgot from our Mouseketeer sleepover—are stuffed up like a full piñata, hanging outside the cafeteria doors. My pajamas—which are secret and have had me naked in them. My *private* pajamas, stuffed up to look like somebody is in them, hanging for the whole school to see. Across the front rests a Miss America kind of sash, with huge letters in black Sharpie marker that say: SLUT.

I get boiling hot from my very core to my skin. I don't know what to do, where to look, where to go. I won't touch them or look at them or take them down. I'll just pretend I never saw them before, that they are someone else's pajamas, not mine. I don't go into the cafeteria. I feel like I will vomit.

I go into the girl's bathroom. There are three mirrors above three sinks.

On the first mirror, in black sharpie, is my name in all capitals.

On the middle mirror: IS A.

On the last mirror: SLUT.

I close myself in a stall.

On the back side of the stall door, in black sharpie, it is repeated.

It is on the back of all three stall doors.

I leave the bathroom. Walking down the hallway toward me is Pat Youngs. I smile that "we shared something" smile. He acts like he doesn't know me, looks the other way, and walks by. I am alone. I turn and walk out the front doors even though school is not out for the day.

At the laundromat, on the back walls of the folding area cubbies next to the baseball diamond Michelle drew is the same black marker.

SLUT!

What did I do? I went to third base, but we were at a party with all the cool people, and all the cool people were in the dark feeling each other up. So were Michelle and Karen. So, what did I do?

I said I went to third. I didn't go to third. Pat did not finger me. I went to third on *him*. Is there a third base for boys or is it just for girls?

It wasn't the boys calling me a slut. It was a girl. One of my best friends. I'm so scared right now. I'm confused with Michelle. She was the one that made sex stuff seem like the coolest thing to do. Like, if you didn't do sex stuff, you were such a loser nerd. You had to put out or you weren't a cool chick.

But besides all that, it was fun. It felt natural. It felt like what our bodies were supposed to do. What was wrong about it? And then, why was I a slut and not Pat Youngs? Or Bob Teshler? And, can virgins be sluts?

***

It's one more month till graduation. I walk the halls alone. At cheerleading, we do everything we do but, outside the cheers, no one looks at me or talks to me. I feel like the air is a haze that's hard to see through. I feel tattered. I feel older. I feel like a ravaged ghost hanging in the hallways like my shameful pajamas.

I tell no one. My mother invites Michelle and Karen to a little graduation party at our house with our relatives. I can't bring myself to tell her what happened. It would break her heart even more than mine, and I don't know how to take care of her through this because I'm not sure what happened, what it meant, or even how to take care of myself.

They come, both Michelle and Karen. To our house. After graduation. I feel too vulnerable to have them in our house in my private space. An extension of my pajamas. We stay outside. They eat cake and pretend everything is sort of like it was.

Then my mom says, "C'mon. Huddle together. I want to get a picture of The Three Mouseketeers." We three look in different directions, down, to the side, all knowing right now, admitting in our heads. My mom stands with the camera in front of her face. The square flash on top of the camera has four fresh rounds ready to go. My mom's one eye is squeezed shut. I stand, looking down, trying not to show the hot tears pooling in my eyes. Karen flings one arm over my shoulder. Then Michelle.

"Say cheerleading!" my mom says.

"Cheerleading," we all say.

The flash pops.

***

My mom shows me the pictures she took at graduation. She made two more copies of each, one for Karen and one for Michelle, so we can all look back at it someday. On the bottom she writes in blue ballpoint pen, "The Three Mouseketeers. Eighth Grade Graduation."

In the picture, we three lean into each other, arms tossed over each other's shoulders with goofy eyes, smiling our cheerleader smiles that secrete the war that had just been carried out between us and the devastation it wrought.

– 8 –
VIRGIN SACRIFICE

It's time to start as a freshman in this high school where I know almost no one. Most of the kids from my junior high will be going to a school closer to them. I'm districted for a new high school. That's the good part because I can leave Karen and Michelle behind, but I'm suddenly very wary of other girls. This new school has about two thousand kids. Five hundred kids in each graduating year. That's good because no one will know my bad "Slut" reputation, and I can hide easier. But it's bad because how will I get popular? How will I get friends?

I try out for the freshman cheerleading squad, hoping it will save me like it did every time in the past. I don't make the team. I try out for gymnastics. I don't make that team, either. I don't know why. I think maybe I thought I would, and I didn't practice hard enough. I am no one and nothing, and it's probably safer to stay that way for now.

I watch myself walking the halls with my head down, my eyes tracking the square tiles of the hall floors as I find my classes. I say nothing to anyone, and if someone talks to me, instead of my voice, I hear this trilling giggle with words minced in. "Hi" always comes out with a rolling giggle like I'm talking into a high-speed fan.

Kids ask, "Why do you laugh so much all the time?" I think it's because I'm scared, but they think I just have this super giggly personality.

"I don't know!" I trill. Giggle, giggle.

I have lost me. I don't know who I am supposed to be to be ok in this school.

Everyone always says, "Just be yourself."

Yeah, but which me? There are so many parts of me. The me that was before is no longer allowed out. What's the point of being yourself if people won't like you? I only want to be liked. I want to have friends. I want to be the part of me that's likable. I don't want to be bullied or afraid to go into the girl's bathroom alone in fear of seeing my name in black marker.

There was a rumor, too, of what the older girls did in high school to girls they hated.

One time, they said, a girl no one liked—no one knew why, but no one liked her—went into the girls bathroom. There were no teachers around, and a bunch of girls came in. When she came out of the stall, they took their finger-nails and sharp pencils, and they scratched her face apart until her skin came off like it was cut by razor blades, and she was so ugly since then.

Once, they said, there was this really pretty girl with long blonde hair. All the boys liked her because of her hair so, one time, after school, when she was walking home, these girls caught her and poured tar over her head. It burned her scalp, and they had to shave all her hair off, and it wouldn't grow back the same because of the burns, and she was never pretty again. I hope nobody heard about what happened to me and my pajamas.

In my neighborhood, a few cul-de-sacs over, is a girl my age named Caroline. I don't know her that well. Her family had just moved in and she, too, would be new to this high school.

I don't get to know her. We just live close. She seems nice. She's quiet and demure. Not because she was trying. It was just her nature. I thought that was brave. Brave that she has the quiet fearlessness inside her to be still and not have to laugh or be bold or entertain or be funny or do anything really. She could just be there and not have to make anything happen. It was like she wasn't afraid people would think she was a nothing or a "dud" as my mom would say of less outgoing people. She wasn't afraid to just be *her*. The her that could just be and listen and react naturally instead of the bold, over-exaggerated way I had to be.

I was everyone's entertainment. Yes. I was naturally outgoing and dramatic and my actions and reactions were bigger than other people's. I thought they had to be. Whatever I was, it wasn't enough. Not enough to be liked. Not enough to be safe.

Caroline could be shy and quiet because that's who she was, and she was brave enough to feel it was enough. I was shy and quiet because I was terrified.

Maybe we could have been friends if we were younger when we met or grew up nearer. But right now, I'm too scared to make a friend. On the outside, we're friends. We take the bus or walk to school together. I don't know what we talk about.

One morning, she asked me to come inside and wait. How strange it was, how different her house on the inside was from ours. In our little Chicago suburb, the houses were almost all alike. Maybe five models built over and over and over for miles. The paint or shingle color differed but, basically, we all lived in the same houses. So, from the outside, it seemed we would all be pretty similar on the inside.

Our house was warm and bright and filled with love and brightly colored patterned wallpaper. My parents loved being parents. We were their world. Their identity. That morning I went inside Caroline's house was so sad. There was no one there, it seemed. The living room had faded, worn-out furniture with overused knit blankets tossed over the sofas. The tables were chipped, and there was laundry tossed everywhere. The kitchen floor looked gray and unwashed, and there was a cheap dime-store clock hanging slightly crooked in the living room making *click* sounds as the hand went around.

A woman, older, in a faded, tattered bathrobe in men's slippers shuffles through the hallway into the kitchen. She doesn't see me. I hear her speak in an unenthusiastic tone to Caroline who speaks in a quiet, warm tone back. I don't hear what they say but it's probably about stuff to do later today when she gets home from school. The mother, or whoever this woman is, seems defeated. "A loser," my mother would say. She's gruff, and her tone of voice is like bricks piling onto my friend as she grabs her things to get off to school. By the time Caroline gets to me at the door, she seems worn and tired.

As we walked to school, I told a few naughty jokes to make Caroline laugh. I wanted her to feel better, to be ok. How unfair the Universe was that I have parents who were so wonderful, who put so much effort into taking care of us, making us into productive citizens and Caroline, at such a young age, had to live in that negative, unloving atmosphere. It was our funnest walk. When we got to school, Caroline hugged me and told me she was glad she had me as a friend.

***

It happened between classes. The thing I feared the most. I was in the girl's restroom going to the bathroom when I heard the door open. I heard them at the sink. The popular girls. The popular *senior* girls. The mean girls. Girls you didn't want to "F" with. They had power. If they didn't like you, you could kiss your high school years goodbye. If they *really* didn't like you, maybe you'd get scratched or tarred. I had managed not to run into them at close range because, as a freshman, my classes were mainly in a different area of the school but, somehow, they came into this bathroom.

How was I going to get out of this stall? The bell would ring to be back in class soon. If I didn't get out, I would be marked late or absent. But what would they do to me when they saw me? What if they saw me and decided they didn't like me? I'd wait for a minute and try not to breathe. Maybe they'd leave.

I hear them talking.

"Oh, I can't stand her! Stuck up bitch!"

"...thinks she's so hot..."

"I know!"

"...sick of her. She needs a lesson."

"Did you hear that she went all the way with Doug Newbern?"

"What?" High-pitched squeals echo off the cinderblock. "Who told you?"

"...at the Forest Preserve. ...class picnic. ...fourth base."

"Fucking slut. I'm gonna kill her. I wanna kill her."

My heart is smashing against my chest. The first bell rings. I have to come out. I open the stall. They're surprised. They didn't know anyone else was in the bathroom. They stare at me, their eyes like slits. Especially the lead girl, Patti. The prettiest and the meanest. The others look at her to find out how they should react to me.

It was probably a second or two, but it seemed like a minute. I wash my hands, watching the water run over my fingers. I focus on my hands. Then, I rub the paper towel on my hands.

I smile. I'm scared Patti might say, "Why are you smiling at me? Did I say you could smile at me?" But she doesn't.

She says, "Who are you? What's your name?"

I speak my name through a maniacal giggle.

"Are you a freshman?"

I nod.

Patti squints her eyes at me. Will I pass or will this be it? I just got here. Just started. Will my whole life end here in this bathroom at the whim of Patti?

Then, I say it. I don't know how it gets out of my mouth. I don't know where it came from. I didn't pre-think it. I never thought it before. But it's out.

"I know someone who's a real slut," I say. The diversion bomb to distract enemies, create a chance to escape.

"Who?" Patti asks. All the girls face me, their ears perked up, more interested in what I have to say instead of deciding whether to pounce on me.

"This girl, Caroline. She's a freshman, too. She just moved here, and I heard she was a slut in her last school and that's why her family had to move here."

They all nod and push out the swinging bathroom door. The bell rings. I'm late but uneaten. I hate myself. Why did I do that? *How* could I do that? Maybe nothing will come of it. Maybe, since they're seniors, they won't care about us stupid freshman.

But they do.

They find out who Caroline is. They find her and yell "slut" at her as she walks to class or home.

We stop walking together. I tell Caroline I have after-school stuff and early morning stuff to do now.

She just says ok.

I see her on campus, and she's alone. At lunch, she eats alone. She walks to class alone. She walks home alone. It's hard to know if she's sad because she's so quiet and to-herself to begin with.

I hate myself. But I pretend it doesn't bother me. That it's her problem, not mine. Someone had to go down.

I laugh louder at everything. I giggle and talk at the same time, my words so goofy that it becomes my signature that freshman year. I am friends with everyone! Yet no one really. I am a social butterfly just like my mother would say to her friends: "Oh, my daughter! You know her! She's a social butterfly."

It's exhausting. I bargain with myself, "Ok, I won't force myself to smile and laugh all day long and be everyone's friend all day long. And, in return for the day off being a social butterfly, I'll make up for it by doing just that another day. When I have more energy."

And on those days, I walk quiet and sad to my classes with my eyes on the hall floor, I tell people I wasn't feeling well, or I had my period or someone in our house wasn't good. Excuses why I wasn't being my giggly, outgoing self.

I see Caroline in the halls. She smiles at me. I smile back. I realize she doesn't know. She doesn't know it was me who caused this tragedy in her life. Who made her life unbearable. Who brought this injustice upon her. She doesn't know it was me.

A few more days left of school and freshman year will be over. I have friends now. We're all going to the Forest Preserve for the end of year picnic. I'm getting my stuff to leave. Someone is at the door for me.

"It's Caroline for you," my mom calls. My heart thumps. Has she found out? Has she come to tell me off?

She's standing at our front door in a demure sweater, holding a present with a bow.

"Hey," I say.

"Hey," she replies.

"Are you going to the Forest Preserve for the picnic?" I ask.

"No," she says. "This is for you." She hands me the present.

I'm shaking. "Why? What is it for?"

"For being such a good friend to me. When school started, I didn't know anyone, and you were there every day walking to school with me. It was so nice of you."

Then, she starts crying. At first, just a few tears. And then, she sobs.

"What's wrong?" I ask, fearing it will all come out about the slut-torturing. But, instead, she says, "My dad died. We are moving. Again."

She is crying harder, and I'm sort of relieved because the present and my shame have made me want to cry. Now, I can say I'm crying because of her father's death. I can seem empathetic and sensitive when in fact I'm the biggest most selfish jerk that ever lived. I hug her. She cries into my shoulder.

"Do you want to come to my house?" she asks.

"Right now?" I ask.

"Well—"

"Or after the funeral tomorrow? It would be nice to have a friend afterward."

"I'll come tomorrow," I say.

"I'll come get you," she says.

And she does. We walk in silence to her house. The sad gray house is now crowded and mournful. Caroline and I sit on chairs by the front door. Her eyes are swollen and pink.

"I'm sorry," I say.

"It's ok," she says.

"How did he die?"

"Heart attack."

"When do you move?"

"In a few weeks."

"To where?"

"Not sure. My stepmom is deciding."

"Oh."

"I'll write you," she says.

"Ok," I say. "Caroline. I'm so sorry."

"It's ok," she says.

"I mean I'm sorry you had such a terrible year at school."

"It wasn't terrible," she says.

"It happened to me in junior high," I say. "What happened to you."

She blows her nose then holds the wadded tissue in her fist. She looks at me.

"Maybe it was my fault," I say.

"How could it be your fault? You were always my friend."

"Maybe people thought bad things of you because of something I said."

"What did you say?" she asks.

And suddenly, like coming to the end of a string, my courage runs out.

"I don't know. That I knew you. That you were new. That you were scared. Maybe they thought 'cause you were scared they should pick on you?"

"Some girls are just mean," she says, "for no reason. They just picked me. It's not your fault. It's their fault, you know?"

I knew. I know. I know I felt desperate. I never wanted to be one of them. I don't know what makes girls want to hurt other girls. It sometimes feels, as a girl, what we need, what we desire, there is only so much to go around, and the prize goes only to the few. It hurts. It's scary. I can't voice what it is I'm feeling or why it feels like scarcity, but it's this feeling that made me do it. I am ashamed. I know, even someday, I will never forgive myself. I know I can never make it up for her. I know I will never do it again. That is all I can do.

– 9 –
THE SLAP

For so many vacations, since I was little, our family drove from Chicago, stopping at hotels and motels in all the southern states on our way to Florida. Then, one year, it changed to Hot Springs, Arkansas where my parents would rent a vacation condo for the week. The condo had a big community pool and rec room with ping-pong and pinball, and my brothers could go fishing somewhere nearby.

It was the summer between my freshman and sophomore year of high school. I'm older, fourteen, and it's so uncool to go on a family vacation. Why can't I just stay home alone and hang out with Sue?

Sue, Suzy, Suze, my best friend. We met in the middle of freshman year—in the middle of my insecure giggle madness—after Caroline and I stopped walking together. Suze and I met and became best friends.

My parents refused my stay home alone offer, but maybe I'd like Sue to come on vacation with us? I'm embarrassed even asking her because how dumb would that be, going on a vacation with parents? But Sue is excited, especially about the huge pool and, she reminds me, there will probably be boys there. With Southern accents. Exotic. The answer is yes. The condo has an upstairs with three bedrooms. One for my parents, one for my brothers and one for me and Sue.

Every day of the vacation, Sue and I eat breakfast in our bikinis, our beach towels draped over the back of our chairs, ready. We already have southern Arkansas accents. Every morning, as soon as we finish breakfast, we grab our towels and run out the door without helping with the dishes or clearing the breakfast table. That's for grown-ups. That's for the parents to do. We're on vacation. They don't have an exciting life waiting for them at the pool where anything lifechanging can happen at any minute depending on who's there. We're young and wild and free.

We take Polaroids of each other dancing with our arms in the air, knees bent, swinging our hips. Titling them in ballpoint pen on the bottom of the Polaroid, "'The kid' gets down," and, "Crazy ladies, crazy times on the bayou," spelled, "Byyoo." We're rebels. Who get A's. And live at home with moms and dads.

We're the first to get to the pool. We pick the perfect chairs to see and be seen. We lay out our towels, visor our hands over our eyes to survey the sun, and angle our chairs in the exact direction for an even tan. Throughout the day, we get up, survey, and re-angle. After every hour of tanning, we take a stroll break around the pool. Because boys. This is how we test who we are, how we are. What effect we have.

It's our third vacation day. Everything is the same except for one thing: the lifeguard. The lifeguard notices us. We notice the lifeguard. And the lifeguard's friends. Boys all around sixteen, seventeen. So much older than us. Boys that are really men, with cars and facial hair.

The whole day is spent tanning near them but never looking at them. Flirting on opposite sides of the pool with them. Then, it gets cloudy, and we pack our towels and tan lotion and the lifeguard asks, "Can we take y'all to the movies tonight?"

Sue and I look at each other with huge, wide, happy, silent eyes, thinking, "Y'all? *Sigh...*" Then, we shrug, like, "Why not?"

I ask, "What time?"

The lifeguard looks at his buddy. They shrug.

"Seven?" he asks. "Meet y'all at the rec room?"

"Ok," I say for me and Suze.

"Cool," "Cool." "Cool." "Cool." we each say.

***

Sue and I are in our room in our still damp bathing suits under big white men's button-down shirts deciding what to wear, speaking in our Arkansas accents, and giggling maniacally at the possibilities of tonight because one of us, who knows who tossed it first, but one of us tossed in the possibility of "what if we lost our virginities?" to get it over with so it could stop always being a big thing. Even though we don't know what it entails, even though we know we won't do whatever it is that is, and even though we know it won't happen, it's a terrifying, delicious, "what if?" to roll around the room.

My mom calls us down for dinner. We're seated at the dining table with my dad at one end and my mom at the other. My brothers are on one side. Me and Sue are on the other. Just as my mom puts down the food, I say in my Arkansas accent, "Y'all, me n' Suze er prolly not gonna eat too much. We have ta git riddy ta gowa."

"Go where?" my mother asks.

"The lifeguard and his friend are taking us to the movies," I say, still drawling.

"At seven," Sue adds. And we smile our secret at each other.

Without looking up, my father says, "Oh, no, you're not."

I don't expect this. "We are," I say, sans accent. "Why wouldn't we?"

"Listen, daughter," my dad says, as if he's about to start a discussion. But then he says, "No."

Sue drops her face down and looks at me from the corner of her eye. This is not her family. She's uncomfortable.

"That's not an answer," I say with a cluck and an eye roll. "It's just the movies. You can meet the boys. We're meeting at the rec room." After a dramatic exhale, I ask, "Ok?"

My mother hasn't moved. My two brothers are shoveling food like it's popcorn at the movies. Sue is rolling her napkin edges in her lap. My dad looks at me.

"You are not going anywhere with those boys," he says.

"Well, that's unreasonable," I say, my voice getting louder. He ignores me so I ask, "Why can't we go?"

"Because I said so," he says.

"That's no reason," I say.

"Daughter, that's the end of the discussion." His voice is terse.

"We didn't even discuss," I say. My dad and I always discuss. That's how we are. No matter what, he and I discuss and try to come to a reasonable understanding. "Dad. We said we were meeting them at seven. We can't just not show up."

My dad doesn't answer, but the room is suddenly sharp and dangerous. The silence thuds like the room has a heartbeat. *Thud. Thud. Thud.*

"Why won't you tell me why I can't go?"
Thud. Thud.

"He said no," my middle brother says. "Just shut up about it."

"You shut up!" I yell, taking out my anger on my brother.

"You're ruining the vacation," my brother says.

"I am not. I'm just asking Dad why."

I'm getting tears in my eyes because I'm embarrassed in front of Sue, and I'm angry at my dad because you don't just say "no, that's it." I'm not five. I don't understand. I don't talk for a minute. The only sounds are my brother's silverware.

"Because you don't trust me," I say.

"You're not going, daughter."

"I thought you said you trusted me?"

"I trust *you*, daughter," my dad says. "I don't trust the boys."

"Well, they're nice boys," I say. "So. We're going."

"You are *not* going!" my dad says, yelling the word not, "and that's the end of it!" He slams his palm on the table as an exclamation point. I know what he's afraid of. The word. I know the word. I don't even really know what the word means, but I know it's what he's scared of. It flies out of my mouth.

"Why, are you afraid he's going to *FUCK* me or something?"

It all happens at once. My dad's chair falls backward as he leaps up. My mother screams and grabs my brothers, running them up the stairs. My dad reaches over the table, grabs me by the collar, pulls me up out of the chair into the air, and throws me onto the shag carpet.

My mother and my brothers are on the stairwell. I don't know where Sue is.

I'm on my back on the floor. My dad's face is over me. I've never seen him like this. Fuming. Ready to pounce. He has his hand up in the air ready to slap me.

There is only terrified fury. Nothing but now. His eyes, his hand, his strength, his rage.

"Hit me!" I scream. "Go ahead! Hit me!"

My mother shouts, "Don't, Sid!"

My youngest brother is crying.

We're frozen. Locked. Neither knowing what will happen. My body is bawling, convulsing. Eyes locked in a dare, refusing to surrender.

The room a blur.

Thud. Thud. Thud. Thud. Thud. Thud. Thud.

Then my dad puts one foot on the floor. Then the other. And he backs away from me. He moves to the stairwell, up past my mother and my brothers.

My mother yells "Go! Go!" to my brothers, hurrying them up the stairs as she follows.

I am alone on the floor, sobbing. I'm embarrassed. Ashamed. Impotent. Devastated by what I said to my dad. My dad is my hero. My dad is the one person that would die if anything happened to me. My dad is my best friend in our family. But I'm furious with him. And how am I going to face Sue after this?

I go into our room and lock the door behind me. Sue is sitting cross-legged on her twin bed. She looks at me. I roll my eyes.

"Well, that was stupid," I say, holding down the throat lump. "We should just go anyway." I go to the window, shoving it open. "Let's go."

Sue grabs her cigarette pack and stands.

Are we really going to sneak out?

Sue throws one leg out the window but then sits in the sill, one leg inside, the other outside, and lights a cigarette, blowing the smoke far away. *Phew.*

"My parents are so stupid sometimes," I say, crawling half in, half out, too. I take a drag and blow the smoke to the trees. "Now how are we gonna face the boys tomorrow?"

"We'll figure out something," Sue says.

"Just so uncool of my dad," I say.

We share the cig until it's done. Sue flicks the butt, then hops inside, snatching the can of Lysol we have hidden from under the bed and sprays everywhere. Outside. Inside. I hop in, too. We brush our teeth and gargle Listerine.

It's still in the air, what happened. We are still avoiding long eye contact. Sue starts playing with the makeup we have spread across the sink.

"I can't wait to be sophomores," I say.

"I can't wait to not be a virgin," Sue says, swiping too much blush on her cheek.

"Then everyone can just stop worrying about it," I say as I paint dark circles around my entire eyes, making myself look like Alice Cooper. Black eyes with lines that point up and point down. Sue finds it incredible how much I can look like Alice Cooper. I have a strong nose like his, huge eyes that are intense like his, and tease my hair to be wild like his.

"Can you imagine someday it's not going to matter?" Sue asks. Our eyebrows raise. We can't.

"We should do it together," she says.

"Oh my god, oh my god, oh my god!" I say.

"Double date!" We both yell at the same time, then, we snatch up our hairbrushes and sing "No More Mister Nice Guy" into the bristles. I pose as Alice, and Sue takes Polaroids of me.

There's a knock. We freeze, and our eyes go wide.

"Daughter, I want to talk to you," my dad says.

Sue moves to her twin bed, grabs the *Seventeen* magazine, and pages through. I unlock the door and sit on my bed. My dad sits next to me.

Sue tries to become invisible inside the magazine as I sit there looking like Alice Cooper.

My dad says, "Listen, daughter. Don't you ever talk to me like that again."

I stare at my legs. "I won't," I say.

"I'm not going to have it," he says.

"I won't," I say, with more emphasis.

"It's not you I don't trust. It's boys. Men."

"I can handle them," I say.

"No, you can't," he says. "You don't know men."

"I do," I insist.

"Men are wolves," he says.

I almost laugh. I furl my eyebrows inward and look at Sue.

"I know lots of boys who are all really nice," I say. "So not all are wolves."

"Daughter, all men are wolves."

How can that be true? I am blossoming into a woman. My future is going to have men— lots of men, I hope—to date, to love, to marry. Men are going to be one of the biggest parts of my life. How can I accept that all men are bad? That all men are wolves? My dad is wrong. He's just being overprotective because he loves me so much.

"You're not," I say.

"I *was* a wolf," he says.

I shake my head. Sue has her nose in the crease of the magazine.

"Now it's my job to protect you," he says, putting his arm around my shoulders and pulling me in for a squeeze hug. I let myself fall into him. My dad. My prince. My hero.

I have to believe all men aren't bad. All men aren't wolves. Men will like me for me. Not just sex. Maybe there are a few wolves, but I can spot them. I have to step into the world thinking that men are good or else how will I ever become a woman in the world?

The mascara is running black streams down my cheeks.

My dad leans back and takes me in.

"What kind of shmutz is that you got on your face, daughter?

"Alice Cooper," I say.

"It's not very ladylike," he says.

"Alice Cooper isn't a lady," I say.

"I can see that," he says.

I roll my eyes. Sue smashes her smile into the glossy pages.

"I'm looking out for you, daughter. You're gonna have to take my word. Unless they love you," my dad says. "Even some who love you."

– 10 –
Tomato Soup

Sophomore year is over. No virginities were lost between me and Suze. But she got her driver's permit and a Mustang. And I have pubic hair. *Finally!* I'll be fifteen after school starts again in the fall, so I don't have my driver's permit yet, but this is a win because I want to be a woman. *Right now.* I want to participate in the adult world so I can start making my dreams come true. I want to cross from "I wish" to "I can make it happen." I have a big future planned, and I can't make any of it happen if I'm sidelined as a kid.

School just let out for summer. I don't even have a bathing suit yet. Suze lets me borrow one of hers. In her bathroom, I take off my clothes. All of them. Growing up in Chicago, I didn't see my own body in full for the long winter. It was so cold, I'd put my nightclothes on as I took off my day clothes while standing with my stocking feet on the metal vents of the blowing floor heater.

I put on the bikini bottoms then the bikini top, bunch up my clothes and jam them into my purse. My hand goes for the door handle when I see myself in the full-length mirror on the back of the bathroom door. Sue's bathroom has a full-length mirror. I never noticed before. Our house has only mirrors over the sink that I can only see my upper half in. I haven't seen myself with all my clothes off all at once in nine months.

The body in the mirror is not the ironing board with two raisins of last summer. The body of nine months ago when school began. The body in the mirror is the swimsuit model from the JCPenney catalog. The body in the mirror is the centerfold in my uncle's secret *Playboy Magazine* collection. The body in the mirror belongs to a woman.

"Does it fit?" Sue yells through the door.

"Yes," I say.

I can't believe this body is mine.

"Do you want Kool-Aid or a Pop?" Sue yells.

"Do you have any Popsicles?" I yell back.

"Probably," she calls.

"I'm almost changed," I say.

It's like I made a wish and, *abracadabra*, nine months later, it's the exact body I wished for.

God gave me a good one.

And I know I'm going to need it for a successful run toward my dreams in the grown-up world.

Men ruled the world. We knew that. Men got to be in charge of things. Men could act in all sorts of ways and be forgiven. Men got to have jobs women couldn't imagine. And if they could imagine them, they wouldn't want them because men don't like women who are better than them. Or smarter than them. Or make more money than them. You have to play it down as a woman. Because men could open or close the doors in the grown-up world.

Men could say which parts of a woman's body were important. To be a virgin for a woman was a prize, so she had to guard it. If she lost it in the right ways, like to someone who loved her, that was ok. But if she lost it in the wrong way, it was her fault, and she would be punished. It seemed like this shouldn't be a rule. They didn't say that for boys. Boys could have virginities or not and there was no big deal around it. It was confusing but it was a rule and you just knew it.

Men were "heads of the household." Whatever they say, goes. It was important that men were happy. Even if it meant the woman had to suffer a little. It was the trade women made to get to be with a good man. Because if he was a good man, he could give you a really good life. So, it was very important to be as perfect as you could be.

If you learned to please a man, you could attract the most men. You'd have bigger chance to pick a good one and

98

get a good life, hopefully with your dreams coming true. All women know this. No one had to tell you. And there were tons of magazines and books that kinda told you anyway.

At the store, there were tons of books and magazines just for women about three really important things:

1. How to figure out babies' needs; what they mean when they cry this way or that because they can't tell you what they need.

2. How to figure out men's needs so you can guess what they mean, what they want, and you can be chosen by them. Or so you can avoid the ones that you think like you but are just "using you" and are not "committers."

And, of course, three. How to be beautiful.

There are no magazines for men about figuring out women, so either we're not as hard to figure out or they don't have to because they're the bosses anyway.

Men were the key to the world. And what I noticed was that men had one weakness, one thing that could make a grown-up man act silly. Anything to do with sex and/or beautiful women with nice shapes. Women with figures that were called hourglass. Women like that were so dangerous that other women bothered to hate them.

I close my eyes, clasp my hands, and say, "Thank you, God, so much!"

"Are you almost ready?" Sue yells through the door.

"I'm coming now," I say.

In terms of swimming pools, we can go to the Park District in our neighborhood, but they're filled with hundreds of screaming little kids who pee in the pools 100 percent guaranteed.

We can go to someone's backyard above-ground pool, but summer just started, and nobody's having pool parties yet.

Or, there's an apartment complex up by Higgins Road across from the strip mall next to the laundromat and the 7-11, and it has a nice cement pool with chairs for sunbathing, like in Arkansas, and, most importantly, cute guys. The perfect place to flirt and see if these new bodies have the power to paralyze boys and melt men.

The only thing is, since we don't live there, we have to sneak in. And if they catch us, we're not sure what the punishment is. But the risk is worth the reward. If anyone asks us, we're gonna say we're in town for the summer visiting our cousins who live in apartment 102. We don't even know if there's such thing as an apartment 102, but this is what we're going to say if anyone questions us.

We go to the pool three days in a row. We get there in the morning around 10 a.m. Sometimes we leave for lunch, sometimes just stay straight through till 3 p.m. when it's no longer prime tanning time.

And there are lots of guys there—older guys, like, eighteen and older—with their own apartments and probably their own cars, which adds a hint of danger to the excitement. Even though we're too shy to talk to them, we notice them notice us. We notice how when we walk by, all conversation stops as they take us in. We can make grown men lose their train of thought. We can make mouths hang open. We are kryptonite in bikinis.

On the fourth day, we meet him.

His name is Dave. His V-shaped torso has no hair except a fine trail of soft brown-peach fuzz pointing down into to his tight red Speedo trunks. Around his neck, he wears a thin brown macramé choker with a sea shell at the front that sits in the hollow of his throat as if pointing out there is vulnerability in all that masculinity. Oh god! You can just tell he's one of the cool people in the world.

We are waist high in the shallow end.

He's twenty-one, he says, when I ask.

I thought maybe eighteen, which is still really old, but he's not in high school, he's already a person in the world.

"What's your job?" I ask.

He says he's in a band. They go down to places like Fort Lauderdale, which is in Florida. It's where all the cool college kids go for spring break. His band plays at spring break parties every year.

"Wow, that's so cool," Sue says.

He says he'll be right back, and we watch him shake out his hair as he walks toward the bathroom.

We stare at each other and squeeze each other's hands till it hurts.

"He's so handsome!" I say.

"I think he likes you," Sue says. "I have to go home at lunch, but you should stay and talk to him."

"Oh my god! By myself?" I say. "Maybe he'll ask me to be his girlfriend?"

And we squeeze hands in delicious hope.

I would love to have a boyfriend as cute and as cool as Dave and so much older in the real world.

After Sue leaves, it's just me and Dave.

We stand next to each other, in the shallow end of the pool, our elbows on the cement edge, flirting, looking forward, squinting in the white-hot sun. Occasionally, our upper arms graze together as the cold water rises and falls around our waists. It's the perfect-est day of the summer so far.

"Why'd your friend leave?" Dave asks.

"She had something she had to do with her mom around lunchtime," I say.

"Oh, yeah. Lunch. Are you hungry?" he asks. "Wanna come up to my apartment? I'll make us something."

"Ok!" I say. We spring out of the pool, wrap ourselves in our towels, and I pit-pat behind him to his apartment.

My mind is on spin cycle. I'm going to a boy's apartment. No, I'm going to a *grown-up man's* apartment to have lunch. He's going to make me lunch. He probably goes to the grocery store and shops and then brings it home. Just like my mom and dad do. He has a job and money and buys groceries and pays for his apartment and lives on his own. And I am stepping into the grown-up world as his equal.

The apartment feels dark after the bright white sun all morning.

His living room is cold from air conditioning—he has an air conditioner! He must make a lot of money. I have to remember to tell Sue that he has an air conditioner!

He leads me into the tiny kitchen—just a stove, a counter with a toaster, a refrigerator, cabinets, and a small table with two metal chairs.

"How 'bout soup?" he asks.

"I like soup," I say, and I imagine myself eating soup with Dave in the metal chairs every afternoon.

I admire the way the curve of his wrist twists as he rolls the metal lid off the Campbell's can.

He's so capable.

He empties a can of Campbell's Tomato Soup in a pot.

He can cook.

We stand, listen to the gas flame kick in, not knowing what to say now that we're away from the pool.

I look around, pretending to look at things, but I just don't know what to say to someone so grown-up.

While we wait for it to boil, he puts his hands on my hip bones.

"I really like you," he says.

I blush. I'm so happy. He might end up being my new boyfriend. Can you imagine me with a grown-up boyfriend?

Sue will be so surprised and happy for me. My life will change just like that. Just like that, I will be in the adult world. And he will know things I can do to start making my dreams come true.

One of his hands reaches under my damp, tangled hair, cupping the back of my neck, pulling me into his body. His skin is tight and smooth and smells of freshness and chlorine.

He pulls my hips to his.

Against my stomach, I feel something round and solid. I've never felt anything like it. I don't know what it is. It feels like a big round rock the size of a fist in the front of his bathing suit. That's so weird. Why would he put a rock in there? I know boys have penises, but I didn't know penises changed shape. I didn't know they got hard. I've only seen pictures of penises in anatomy books where it's not so big and seems soft and it lays down and points to the ground. Or Pat's that felt like a number 2 pencil. This didn't feel like a long-shaped thing. This feels like a round rock.

"Do you have a rock in your pants?" I ask.

He pulls back. "Yeah!" He's laughing. "For you!"

I laugh too but only because he's laughing.

I still don't know what the rock is, but it's so hard that it hurts me as he pulls my belly into it.

"Let's go in here."

He leads me into the bedroom. It's plain. It has a tall dresser, a double bed with white bedsheets and white pillows—no headboard—a nightstand with an alarm clock and, in a frame, a picture of a young woman.

We sit on the bed, and he starts to kiss my neck.

"Who's that?" I ask about the girl in the picture.

"Oh, that's Tammy," he says, still kissing my neck.

His hands on my waist start making their way up toward my breasts.

I cross my arms on my ribs, blocking his path.

"Is Tammy your sister?" I ask.

"She's my girlfriend. She lives here," he says, nuzzling the back of my neck.

Oh.

Confusing.

Why would he want to be my boyfriend if he already has a girlfriend?

"Do you think she'd be mad about me?"

"We have an open relationship," he says, which I don't know what that means. "I like you so much. You're so beautiful. You make me weak. I just have to kiss you," he says.

I make him weak. He just has to kiss me. How can I deny him? I'm not a monster. I had no idea I had such power! I am fourteen going on fifteen.

I mean, I knew men reacted to the hourglass and naked women and prettiness, but I had no idea that I was the keeper of this unique one-of-a-kind, God-given flame that could reduce a grown man, with an actual girlfriend, to weakness and begging. This is some serious power. This is like one of those fairy tales where the ordinary girl is just living her life and it's revealed to her she is actually special; she is actually a princess.

He tries to untie my bikini top. I lean in, leading him away so his hands have to move instead to my back and my bottoms. I don't want him to feel my breasts because they're not fully grown in yet. Even though I have boobs, the nipples are still raised mushroom nipples, and I feel embarrassed of them so, instead, I let him feel down below where the pubic hair is.

He lays me back on the bed and struggles to remove my still damp bikini bottoms over my legs. Once they're off, he puts his mouth on my pubic hair, then between my legs, which is not something I read about in the dirty books my girlfriends and I used to smuggle under our beds and read to each other through giggles and titillation.

I don't know what I'm supposed to feel. It's not like when I'm kissing boys, and that builds up into a sexy feeling. This is just him diving right there. I don't feel much pleasure from the physical touch but a great deal of pleasure from the adoration.

As his mouth touches me, I make sounds like the ones in quotations from the secret dirty books. Sounds like "oooooh…" and "oh, yeah, baby, just like that, mmmmm!"

All of a sudden, in an urgent hurry, he yanks down his Speedo, stepping out with one foot, then the other, back and forth until they're off. I see now what that hard round rock in his trunks was, only it's not round nor a rock. It's long and straight like an arrow of flesh, and it's pointing at me.

All my confusion about what was happening in the sex scenes in those magazines and books, all the mysteries of "how" and "what" are answered just seeing his erect penis, naked and yearning for me.

Yet I still don't know what is to be done with it. I don't even know it has someplace in me it could go. All my sexual pleasure to this point in my life had been self-pleasure on the outer part of my body. Or making out like with Pat Youngs. Nothing on the inside. I knew there must be a place inside where the blood came from and where babies came out of, but I'd never seen it or touched it. When I had my period, I wore pads. Everything around sex was so vague or tangled.

I'm still giggling and being flirtatious and although the "Tammy" thing bothers me, it feels like he likes me so much, and this is all part of our courtship flirtation.

He climbs on top of me, his hands up on either side of my head. His arms are extended and stiff at the elbow. He kisses my lips. I think that's what he's above me for—for kissing. He takes a hand down to his hard penis. I feel him push it against me between my legs. It hurts. It hurts. It hurts too much.

"Ow, no it hurts. That hurts," I say, thinking we'll stop and do something else that feels good.

He is pushing it, but I know it won't fit. Something will tear. This can't be the right way. I'm not wanting this. This doesn't feel sexy. He pushes again.

"Stop! No, stop! It hurts! I don't like it!"

A flame of pain I've never felt before tears up into my lungs. I brace my feet up against his chest to push him off.

"Stop!"

He can't stop now, he says, and he pushes all the way in. I feel like a giant steel sharp-ended pole is stabbing me up through my body into my lungs, into my throat, until my eyes turn white with pain. I can't breathe. I'm being strangled in the pain.

Suddenly, quickly, frantically, he pulls it out and white goo hits my tummy and chest and chin, and he's dead on top of me. He's heavy, but I can feel the thumping of his heart pounding hard against my chest. Not dead. He is so grateful. He's kissing me, and he is saying how beautiful I am. How I'm so tight and, oh my god, he could fall in love with me. He rolls off my body onto the bed. Quiet, tender for a moment. I feel tears roll down into my hair from both sides of my face.

"Oh shit! Oh fuck!" He's up and scrambling. "Why didn't you tell me you were a virgin? Fuck!"

I don't know how to answer. I can't answer. I didn't know we were going to do this. I didn't know there'd be blood. I thought he'd think it was good he was my first. I am still in pain. In shock. It's too much to have an answer for.

I flail off the bed as he strips off the sheets.

He runs to the bathroom. He grabs a wet washcloth and tosses it to me.

"See if you can scrub off the blood!" he says. "Oh fuck! It's on the mattress! Fuck!"

He grabs the pile of sheets and runs out of the room, leaving me to scrub my virgin blood from the mattress which I try my very best to do. I don't want to get him in trouble with "Tammy of the bedside picture."

Then from the kitchen, I hear, "Fuck! Fuck!"

I peek into the kitchen. The Campbell's Tomato Soup has boiled over the pot onto the stove and onto the floor. I watch as he takes the sheets and wipes the floor and stove top commingling the red soup with the red blood. I watch as he crumples the sheet with my virgin blood on it and throws it in the garbage.

He doesn't kiss me goodbye. He's too frantic trying to figure out what to do about the mattress. I can tell he's never going to be my boyfriend. And Sue and I probably can't go back to that pool anymore.

I walk home down the hot suburban sidewalk, with my crochet shorts over Sue's teeny bikini, listening to the sound of my Candies flip flops smacking my heels.

I am the same as I was an hour ago but completely different.

I spread my arms out for the sun and the summer breeze to caress.

I am a woman now.

I am a woman now.

I am a woman now, *and the world is going to be mine.*

– 11 –
POOL PARTY

That same summer, before our junior year, just after we can't go back to the pool of Dave and the Tomato Soup, Sue and I stroll into the backyard pool party of one of the kids in our class. All the boys are up. Moving toward us. As if we're brand new. The atmosphere is electric. We've shed our winter layers. This must be what caterpillars feel finally leaving their cocoons. All this exposed skin. As if we're all seeing each other for the first time. That's how Jett and I notice each other after two years of already knowing each other.

Tall and blond with dimples on both cheeks and the soft good looks of a teen idol, Jett could be a blond David Cassidy. Jett had no enemies. Guys liked him. Girls liked him. He wasn't neurotic. He didn't demand attention. He

111

was understated. In the cool crowd. He's a Libra. Charming. Friends with everyone. He had an after-school job. Bought his own light-blue Monte Carlo and a motorcycle that he worked on himself. He played bass and sang. In between classes, he hung out in the smoking area.

He didn't have a girlfriend, and I didn't have a boyfriend when we met again at the pool party. So, we hang out and flirt in the pool. We stand by a picnic table and smoke, him sitting on the edge of the table, his long legs stretched straight out in front and crossed at the ankle, and me standing next to him, him moving his upper arm so it touches mine in a way that's casual, a "it just so happens our arms are touching" sort of way.

We're in the pool, him standing with his back to the cement wall, and me, floating up in front of him until our hands are on each other's forearms so I don't float away. Until I float closer. Until our pelvises are touching. His, hard. Mine, heated. Until his thigh is separating my thighs as I float and bob and drift into him, an inch in, an inch out. So discreet no one at the party, in or out of the pool knows we're almost dry/pool-wet humping.

As the party clears out, Sue, Jett, and I towel off and slip-on shorts. Jett goes his way. Sue and I hop in her Mustang.

Sue gives me the raised eyebrows as she lights her cig, pressing it alive with the car lighter.

"I don't know," I say, laughing. Because I don't. It was fun. It was flirty. I felt powerful with my new JCPenney model body. He's nice. He's cute. We're on the same level in terms of popularity. Neither of us are in the "innest" crowd, but we're not nerds or dorks. We aren't jocks or freaks who came to school high. People like Jett. People like me. We match in a lot of ways.

That night, he calls. I sit under my corner desk for privacy. We talk for hours about nothing: school gossip, who likes who, what electives we're taking when school starts, our jobs. By the end, we don't have anything to say, but we don't want to hang up. Then he asks, "Do you want to go out with me?"

That means, do I want to be his steady girlfriend? And I say, "Yes, I guess so."

We're a couple, a "we" in our junior year of high school. When people say my name, they say his, too.

In between the bell for classes, we meet at his locker or mine to make out, and then walk to our next classes, his hand in my jeans back pocket and mine in his. Is there anything sexier than the barrier of clothes that we feel each other's body parts through? I've never seen him naked and yet feeling him through his jeans, his shirt, I feel like I know exactly what his body looks like. Some days, making out at our lockers or against his car or in the smoking area, feeling his cock harden in his jeans, in just those five minutes, my jeans are soaked.

The cool guys carry a condom in their back pocket and in their wallets. The circle makes an indentation in their jeans or a permanent outline in the leather of their wallets. One day in the hall, I twiddle with the one in Jett's back pocket as we kiss. Neither of us say anything out loud. He waits for me after school, and we drive to his house in the Monte Carlo. His parents don't get home from work till at least five, so we have from about three-thirty.

It's after-school time. The time kids run around, play sports, go to practice, eat snacks, watch TV. At Jett's house, despite it being bright afternoon, we want to do whatever it is that grown-up couples who live together do. He goes to his parents' liquor cabinet and makes us screwdrivers. A bitter, hard taste ruins the orange juice, but I pretend "yum," and we toast and sip, certain that's what adults do.

We go to his room. His twin bed. He takes out the condom and rolls it on. Ahhhh, so that's how those work. We go slow. At first, it hurts, so he takes his time. He turns his nightstand clock to face us, and we keep an eye on the time, making sure we're dressed and sitting at the kitchen table doing homework when his parents get home.

We give each other pet names that only we know: Bo and Toto. We go to the Junior Prom together. We go to the Valentine's Day dance together. Wherever there is to go, we go together, a couple. Always holding hands, interlacing fingers. Always his arm around me. Always leaning our bodies into each other's.

In the winter, Jett makes a fire in the fireplace and lays back on a pillow while I move on top of him. He holds my breasts and tells me how beautiful I look in the firelight. Even though it's bright mid-afternoon. I never have the honeypot with him—I actually don't know how to do that with a man—but it's still so romantic. We're sure this is what grown-ups do. Cocktails. Making love by fireplaces. We are a mature couple. This is the age my parents met. Kids got married after high school. There are songs, little ditty's about Bo and Toto, two American kids doing the best that they can.

– 12 –
FOREIGN EXCHANGE

Jett takes German. He tells me he wants to do the foreign exchange program our school's German department is participating in. First the German kids will come here in April, then the Americans will go there in August.

"I'm signing up," he says, tossing his books in his locker then shutting it.

What? Could anything scream dorky more than that? I am so not into anything "school." But Jett has never done anything dorky. Jett is the epitome of cool. He wants me to go.

I'm standing behind him, my cheek resting on his back and my arms around his waist clasped at his navel.

"I'll put your name on, too," he says, taking my hands and pulling me to face him.

"I'm totally not going," I say.

"We'll be in a foreign country together," he says, inter-lacing his fingers with mine as we walk down the hall.

"Yes, but with the school. It's so for nerds and dorks," I say.

He stops. I stop.

"I have protests," I say.

He drapes both his arms over both my shoulders. He drops his head and stares me in the eyes.

"For one, I take French. I'm not even in the German department."

"Anyone can go," he says.

"Two, everyone in your class speaks some German. I understand no German."

"Doesn't matter," he says.

"It matters in Germany," I say.

"All German kids speak English," he says.

We are standing in the middle of the hallway. Kids have to pass us on either side like a divided swimming stream of sardines.

"Um, it's $500," I say. "My parents'll say no. They don't have $500 for me to go to Germany. Guaranteed. Are your parents gonna pay?"

"I got it covered from work," he says, holding my hand as we join the stream toward classes.

We stop at the door to his German classroom. He leans down and we kiss, warm and delicious like we do before and after every class we walk to together.

117

"Jett," I say as he's walking into class. "If my parents say no, are you going to go without me?"

"You're gonna go," he says.

"You know we're Jewish, right? And it's Germany. Right?"

"You're going," he says, and he disappears into the room.

The whole thing feels so nerdy, but I tell my parents. I tell them about having to have a German student stay at our house for several weeks. I tell them about me going there. To Germany. I tell them it's $500. I know my dad's gonna say, "no way, kid."

Instead, my dad says, "All right, daughter. Your mother and I will discuss."

What?

And then it's settled. I will go. And someone will come stay. We are participating in the foreign exchange program. My parents are paying. What is happening?

***

It's a cold April toward the end of our junior year when they arrive. Fifteen teenagers and their teacher, Heir Schmidt. I've been matched with a girl from a farm just outside her city. Marie-Louise. We've exchanged a postcard or two before her arrival. She's a good illustrator, drawing a cute Snoopy on his dog house in pencil cartoons in the corner of her cards. It's her favorite American cartoon, she tells me.

We meet in the high school parking lot as they come off the bus from the airport, fifteen German kids finding their fifteen American hosts. Marie finds me before I spot her. Marie is tall and angular, with a shy smile of uneven teeth. Her hair is a just-below-her-ears practical brunette bob with bangs. She wears a modest button-down collar shirt over dark blue jeans with cuffs, a look all the female German students seem to have. She removes her wide circle, gold wire frame glasses, huffs on them, wipes them with the tail of her shirt, and replaces them on her make up-less face.

She looks like a person. They all look like people. Why does this surprise me? What was I imagining? I never imagined foreign countries. Or people from them. For a second, I feel disoriented. As if my world, my high school and mall job world in Chicago, America was the world and everywhere and everyone else was flat-dimensional, unreal, pictures, like I saw them in history books.

My parents hug her, and my dad says, "*Willkommen. Wie geht es*, Marie?" He's tickled to be practicing his German. My dad has been studying German since he was in high school. I have no idea why. He never says. But he walks around the house singing German folk songs. "Valerie! Valerahhh! Valerahahaha! A knapsack on my back."

I think he was looking forward to this more than me.

Marie sleeps in my brother's room, next to mine. My brothers take the basement. We both try, Marie and I. We're nice to each other. Polite. Marie is nice. *So nice.* Sweet smile. Introverted. Simple desires. She's plain. She's ordinary. A studious good girl. What you see is what you get. A virgin.

119

I am blue mascara and Farrah Fawcett hair, platform shoes, tight t-shirts with 70s feminist empowerment sayings across my large breasts. "Never underestimate the power of a woman." I am loud, funny, needy, desirous, sexual, extroverted. A sexpot. We make bumpy efforts to find things in common.

Besides coming with us to classes, there are places we're supposed to go to with the group. Radio shows. Plays. Dinners. And then there's just hanging out, showing them around. My parents take her. My parents entertain her. My parents hang out with her. Most of it, I skip.

***

It's after dinner when I come in the front door from work. My parents, my brothers, and Marie are all sitting in the living room, all staring at me. Marie shyly smiles and looks down.

"Hey, *tóchter*," my dad says in German. "*Komm und setz und sprechen.*" I'm pretty sure that means "daughter, come and sit and talk." I roll my eyes and sigh. Like I really want to hang out with my family and just sit around. I don't want to do ordinary life stuff. I'm already doing this stupid school group stuff. I hate mundane, everyday, boring, normal, humdrum life. But I sit. I pick up our dog, Lovey, and put her in my lap.

"We missed ya, *tóchter*. We went and had some delicious Lou Malanoti's pizza. I'm tellin' ya, I can still taste it." He smacks his lips. He's funny that way.

"Was very good," Marie says. "We don't have anything like this in Germany."

"That's good, then," I say, trying.

"We went for ice cream," my mom says.

"Dad got us double scoops," my brother says.

"Oh, good," I say. Lovey has the softest ears, especially when you stretch them up and feel the underside.

"Hey, daughter," my dad says, "Where ya been?"

"Work," I say. They know.

Marie gets up. "Well, good night," she says. "Thank you for the peeeza."

Everyone laughs. They like her accent.

"*Du bist müde?*" my dad asks, and Marie laughs. It's like they have a secret clubhouse language.

"*Ya. Ich muss schlafen,*" Marie says. Which I think means she's going to sleep.

"*Guten nacht,*" my dad says. And then, "gooten knock," my brothers say, and my mom sounds ridiculous saying whatever it is with an American accent.

"Good night," I say, petting Lovey.

When her door shuts, my brothers go downstairs, and it's just me and my parents staring at me.

"What?" I ask.

"Daughter, what's going on?" my dad asks.

"What do you mean?" I ask.

My mom does a back of her throat groan that means she has a lot to say but isn't going to say it.

"Here you have this nice Marie staying with you—all the way from Germany—and you're missing in action. What are you doin', kid?"

"I have to work," I say. "What? Am I supposed to stop my whole life just because she's here? She's got her whole group. She doesn't even miss me."

My mom raises an eyebrow, gets up.

"I'm going to change," she says, leaving the room.

"You'd better hope when you stay with her in Germany, she treats you better."

"We're not the same," I say. "You wouldn't understand."

"Try me," he says.

"She's fine. You get to practice your German, anyway."

"I'm disappointed in you, daughter," he says. "I don't know what's got into you, but I don't like it."

"Fine. I'll take her somewhere," I say.

"Why don't you take her to Old Chicago? That's a fun place," my mom says, coming back in, zipping up her robe.

"Old Chicago?" I moan. "It's stupid."

Old Chicago is an amusement park built indoors in a mall because of the weather in Chicago. With actual rides like roller coasters. But it's for kids. Not people like me.

"You can take her on Sunday since you don't work that day," my mom says.

And that's that.

Sunday morning, Marie has breakfast with my family. I don't eat breakfast. Marie brushes her teeth then sits on the couch waiting for me. She wears flat shoes with laces and jeans. She doesn't do makeup. She only combs her hair. With an actual short grandpa comb. Like four passes. That's it. Done. I have blow dryers and curling irons, foundation and eye shadow, and I have to decide which shoes to wear to ride rides but also walk a lot. And my shoes have to be platforms. It's a couple-hour procedure to look perfect enough to go out.

Finally ready, we climb in the car with my mom driving, Marie in the passenger seat and me quietly staring out the window from the back seat. We set a time to meet my mom back up front to be picked up and, for the first time since she arrived, Marie and I are alone together. No group, no school, no family. Even if she spoke perfect English and I spoke perfect German, it feels like we are two separate species. Like she's a horse and I'm a fish.

At first, it's awkward. "What do you want to do? To try?" "Whatever you want," she says. Of course. Over and over. So, I pick. Roller Coaster. We climb in. They put the bar down. We wait for other riders to load. It's kinda weird being on a roller coaster where there's a floor instead of outside ground, and the floor is the same linoleum as the floor in school. Where there's candy wrappers and crushed cardboard chocolate milk containers littered below like in a school cafeteria. I look at Marie. Her face is bright with anticipation. I've never seen her smile that way. I look behind us. A wad of pink gum is stuck to the front of the car behind.

123

Suddenly the ride jerks, and off we go. I mean, it's not a super high, super scary roller coaster because it's indoors, but we scream. Our hair is whipped backward and, several times, we look at each other, wide-eyed with fear and glee. And when the coaster stops, we climb out, breathless and laughing.

We go to the bathroom to go, and also for me to fix my makeup. I hand her my lip gloss, nudging her. She shakes her head but then puts it on, both of us suddenly delighted.

"Shoon?" I ask. I think shoon means pretty.

"*Schón*," she says.

It gives her a sparkle. She's like a black and white photograph with a bright splash of pink. It's hard not to keep looking.

I feel a layer between us fall away. One curtain closer.

We get tintype photos. They dress us in the Old West clothes. The photos come out sepia on tin. Shades of beige and brown. They paint a little splash of color on both our lips, just like Marie with the lip gloss. We buy two so we each get one to remember us by. We ride all the rest of the rides, and we eat too much junk food. We smile at boys, and I tease Marie about the ones that looked at her, and she blushes. I point to her lips and wink. We ride the roller coaster one last time. We meet my mom with stories and sit together at dinner. At bedtime, she says good night. I say *guten nacht*. We close our doors.

Monday. We go to school together. *Schúle*, in German. A bunch of the foreign exchange group is hanging outside.

Marie and I head toward them. A group of cool kids are walking past toward the smoking area. Guthrie and Riley whistle, call my name, and wave me on, calling, "Smoke?" I wide-eye them, tilting my head to Marie, indicating. They both give a quizzical look, like, "you're with her?" I shake my head. I don't want people to think we're *friends-friends*.

"I'm gonna grab a cig," I say to Marie, who doesn't smoke.

She says, "*Ya*, ok." She smiles and melts in with her group. I leave her.

I go to my classes. I go to work. The week goes by. It's as if Old Chicago never happened. It wasn't complicated. Old Chicago was like a foreign country. Equal terms. Away from our regular lives, but once I got back to my real life, life went back to the way it was.

I hear my dad's voice in my head, "I'm disappointed in you, daughter." Easy for him. His life doesn't depend on staying popular. Easy for him, he's just an old dad and doesn't need people to like him. It doesn't matter what people think of him. He's already married, and his life is half over.

At the end of the week, I come home to a note, written on a scrap torn from her journal in her elegant European script, in perfect English:

Hello, it's one o'clock now, we leave for the radio programme and return at five o'clock (I'm not sure) I'll call your mother to pick me up if I can't go with another person

Bye, Marie

It seems like a plain note but underneath the words, a mirror to my awfulness. My abandonment of her. She's telling me she knows she couldn't count on me to pick her up. I wouldn't care to remember the activity. That she knows I don't care. I'm MIA. Her note is an indictment of how hurtful my actions have been. Her having to find a ride to a stranger's house where she is staying in a foreign country. Hitching a ride from someone in the group. Calling my parents. No one could have told her to expect that she would travel to a foreign country and be ignored.

She's right. I didn't even know there was a radio program we were supposed to go to. Where was I instead? I don't even know. I don't know how to bridge what I feel, how to reach beyond myself.

At the next group get-together, I go. Marie is with her friends. I'm sitting next to one of the German students. She leans over, nudges me with her elbow and gives a secret look, like "Blah, blah, blah, the teachers talk so much." Irreverent. Conspiratorial. I look at her. She winks. She's casual. Slouchy. Tongue-in-cheek humor. Pushing buttons. A tomboy with a shag haircut. We are instant compadres. Gudrun Horstmann.

I'm shallow, sentimental, romantic. Gudrun is earthy, easygoing, grounded. She teases me out of my self-absorption.

"You and Marie?" she whispers, and then wavers her hand back and forth.

"Did Marie say something was wrong?" I whisper back.

"No," she says.

Marie is smiling, standing with the group. I don't think Marie said anything. She's too noble. It must be noticeable that I'm not participating. They must think I'm a jerk. I must seem like that. But if they saw my insides, they would see I'm like a tiny caged bird desperate to be freed.

"I couldn't get off work," I say.

Gudrun nods, elbows on her knees, looking down at her feet.

"I like Marie. She's one of the nicest girls ever," I say.

"Ever?" Gudrun asks. She's making fun of me. I knock her arm with my elbow. Gudrun side-eyes me. I side-eye her back. Whatever this is I feel with Gudrun, it feels sister-like. Pals. Easy. Meant to be.

At the farewell party, Gudrun says, "Maybe you can stay with me when you come to Germany."

"Would they let us trade?" I say.

Gudrun shrugs but raises a hopeful eyebrow.

We exchange addresses.

They're boarding their bus. Jett finds me, stands behind me, and wraps his arms around my waist as the American group waves goodbye. We have till August.

-13-
GERMANY

It hits me. I'm going to Germany. I'm going to a foreign country. Where I don't speak the language and everything will be, foreign. I wonder what will be the same, if anything. Someday I want to be considered worldly, exotic. "Oh, she's been all over the world. She speaks five different languages. She can meld into any culture. She's fascinating." I want to fascinate. Suddenly, I want to learn German. A little. *Ein bisschen*.

They gave us a what-to-pack list from school and told us what the weather is like in Germany in August. I feel like I stick to the list, but my suitcase is so heavy my dad almost can't lift it in the trunk. Possibly because of the *many* pairs of platform shoes.

On the plane, my first ever airplane ride, the teacher tells us to try to sleep so we don't get jet lag. We don't know what jet lag is, so no one pays attention. This is too exciting. An hour before we are to land, the stewardesses come around with breakfast and offer us coffee. Why do grown-ups like it so much?

We stare out the oval windows at the morning sun pouring down on the rolling mountains and green hills with orange-roofed cottages tucked and sprawling in the valleys. Our first glance of Germany. I don't expect it to look like that. I don't know what I'm expecting. I've only seen it in pictures, in black and white or fragments of pictures in our history books. Germany. Where all the Jews were murdered. I can't help but think that. It seems unreal. It seems like such a long time ago. Before I was born. Why do I make this connection just now?

I don't think of my Jewish background as part of my identity, it's just something like a small birthmark I sometimes feel safer hiding. My grandparents talk about it. My grandma used to ask me why I dated all the blond boys. No Jewish boys. I'm wearing the Jewish star necklace she gave me. I think probably the German people who are alive now aren't prejudiced anymore to Jewish people. None of the German kids were prejudiced against me. And I wore my Jewish star all that time too.

The landscape below changes to city. We buckle our seat belts. I lean my head back, suddenly tired. Jett squeezes my hand. Then, just before noon, on August 4th, we land in Cologne, Germany.

"I thought Cologne was French. In France," I say. Everyone laughs. I was serious.

They steer us to the passport line. Jett and I hold hands. The men in uniform do not smile. We get our passports stamped. My first foreign stamp.

As we're funneled to the luggage, there are German signs everywhere: Gepäckausgabe. That's where we're going, so I think it means luggage. The kids who've been studying German are getting excited; they're using everything they've learned. I'm carrying a Berlitz translation dictionary from Deutsch-English. It's thrilling not knowing anything, seeing life with eyes of not knowing. Like a child again. Like a chance to be reborn.

My suitcase is the heaviest. Jett helps me carry it. Other boys in our group take turns. Even a few girls. It becomes a joke of how I smuggled a dead body.

We pile on the waiting bus that will take us to the *öberschule* which, I think, is the German word for high school, where everyone will meet with our host families. On the bus, I sit by the window holding hands with Jett, practicing phrases from the translation book.

"*Mein liébling,*" I say, and I kiss his stubbly cheek. "My sweetheart."

"*Mein liébling,*" he says, kissing my head.

"*Mein liébling,*" I say, memorizing it as I place my temple against the cool glass window.

The roommate switch was agreed to, and I'm pairing with Gudrun. Gudrun lives in a town a short distance away from Soest called Lippstadt. Her parents, who want me to call them Mama and Papa, speak almost no English. Gudrun will be the translator. She says it's really her generation that was taught English in school since the very first grades. Gudrun's parents, Mama and Papa, seem the age of my grandparents. I wonder if they mind if I'm Jewish. They don't seem to notice even though I'm wearing my star. If they are the age of my grandparents, were they around when there were Nazis and Hitler? It seems so long ago, not here, in technicolor Germany in real life. My grandparents remember it, except they were in America, a world away.

Mama and Papa seem so happy to have me. They ask through Gudrun if I have a job in America. Because they don't know me, no one but our group, who are not with us, knows me, I can be whoever I want. I can reinvent myself. I say, "Yes! I'm a model."

They nod and smile. I'm not sure they understand so I say, "Yes. I'm an American model."

I know I'm not, but *they* don't know. I thought they would be so happy to have an actual model living with them. Do they have models in Germany, or are American models the models for the world? They don't seem awed.

Papa tries to lift my suitcase into his trunk and makes surprise grunts. Gudrun and I sit in the back. She watches my face as I take in Germany. The streets are much older than our planned suburban enclaves with sidewalks and lawns and curbs. These streets, spotless with narrow sidewalks, also spotless, come right to the houses. No front lawns. The homes are beyond old, like the ones in fairy tale books. We go over a little bridge and pull up in front of an enormous building. It's white with brown wooden crossbeams visible on the outside. Like Shakespeare's cottage. Old England. Two stories, three if the triangular roof has rooms. Facing the street, there are six forest-green shutters on the top floor, five on the first floor, and a heavy dark wooden front door. There are two shutters, some open, some closed, on the sides of the building. The sidewalk in front is very narrow. On the sides, there is a little more room, but there aren't any potted plants or flowers.

"Are we stopping at a museum?" I ask Gudrun. "Would it be ok if we sightsee later? I think I have jet lag."

She laughs, says something in German to her parents who laugh and turn around in their seats and speak to me in German, forgetting I don't understand.

"We're home," Gudrun says. "This is our house. *Wir sind zu hause*."

A white and black hand painted tile with the number 6 is screwed into one of the outer wooden beams. Lippestrase

6. Lippe street. Number 6. All the houses on the street look similar, but this is the largest. The rest are cottages or one story with the same tall triangle roofs.

Gudrun is laughing at my awe.

"*Wir sind zu hause*," I say.

Inside her home, there are dark wooden walls, but not paneling like my house. This is real heavy dark wood. She says her house is over a hundred years old. It's a family home. Generations. It's like an enchanted fable book. There are real wood burning fireplaces, tall as me, in almost every downstairs room.

We all climb the stairs to the second floor to "my room." A full wall of windows looks out to a backyard of lawn and trees, bushes and flowers. And a one-hundred-year-old faded wood gazebo. The room itself has a wooden bed that is as high as my tummy and, when I climb on, I sink in as if I've laid inside a wooden crate. The bedding is all feathers, both the mattress and the covers. By the windows, in the middle of the room, is a clawfoot bathtub with a shower nozzle and hose attached to the side. Against the wall is an ornate wooden wardrobe with drawers, all empty for me. Mama seems overjoyed that I'm speechless. Both Mama and Papa start talking, and I'm looking back and forth between them and at Gudrun waiting for the translation.

"Ya, ya," Gudrun says to her parents. "So, ya, this was my brother's room. He died. Years ago. Cancer," she says.

"I'm sorry," I say. I feel terrible now. I wonder if they suddenly hate that someone—me—is now going to be in their child's bed. "I'm so sorry."

"They're glad to have you in his room. They're happy you are here."

I say, "Dunka shoon, Mama, Papa."

They are so happy that I'm trying to speak German that it starts another ravel of both of them speaking German, praising that I'm speaking German, punctuated by the words *"Danke schön,"* imitating my effort.

My parents told me to call when I arrived, and I didn't. Gudrun takes me downstairs to the room the one phone is in.

"So, if it's 4:30 here..." Gudrun says, looking at her watch, doing math between her head and her watch. "So, maybe it's too early there?"

"Is it yesterday there?" I'm confused.

"I think it's today, but very early."

"I should call anyway." I know not to talk long. Long distance from Germany is very expensive.

Gudrun dials. I hold the receiver. With every scroll of a number, I hear the backward reverberation in the earpiece. Then, the oddest-sounding ring tone. More like a *tink, tink* tapping than the long ring we imitated as kids with our tongue trilling at the roof of our mouths.

My mom picks up. "Hellooooo?" she says, drawing out the "o." And in the phone, it echoes, and I hear it again.

134

"Hi, Mom," I say, and it again echoes, repeating me back to me. "I'm here. With Gudrun and her family. They have a beautiful house, and it's really nice." I hear all this back and Gudrun and my eyes stay locked.

"I'm so glad, honey," she says. "Sidney!" she calls. "She made it to Germany!" Then, she says to me, "Do you know what they did to our people there?"

"Yes, Mom," I say, hoping Gudrun didn't hear.

"Hey, daughter. You're in Deutschland!" My dad has taken the phone.

"I am, Dad."

"Well how about that," he says. Gudrun writes something on a scrap of paper and slides it in front of me. I question her with my eyes.

"It's really nice here so far," I say.

"Are you learning the Deutsch yet?" he asks.

On the paper, Gudrun has written three words in German. She points and nods urging me to say them. She mouths them, and I try to pronounce them.

"*Ich liebe dich*," I say.

"*Ich liebe dich*," my dad repeats, astonished and thrilled. "I'm gonna look that up. How about that. Learning Deutsch so fast."

Gudrun writes on the piece of paper and I say, reading it, "It means 'I love you,'" I say. "*Ich liebe dich*." It's echoed back to me as if from a distance. I feel like I just learned the most important thing to say in German. In any language.

135

"This has got to be expensive, daughter," my dad says. "I'm gonna let you go."

"Ok," I say, knowing he's right but disappointed that he's thinking of the expense in this moment. "*Ich liebe dich*. Tell mom, '*ich liebe dich*,'" I say.

"Love you, daughter," he says, and the line buzzes.

I hang up.

I nod at Gudrun, smile, and flash a thumbs up.

They all decide I should nap before the evening meal to cure my jet lag. They leave me tucked in like a baby bird in a fluff of feathers. I take out my spiral journal and write:

Discovery! People in Germany smile just like we do! Can you believe it?

And I fall heavy into sleep.

***

My spiral notebook becomes a collection of exclamation points filled with "same, but different" and experiences I never had or even imagined.

Gudrun and I walk the streets of her town. We enter a pub, dark, especially compared to the bright daylight outside. Gudrun has said nothing about needing an ID.

"Are you hungry?" the bartender asks in English and then checks, seeing if he said it right. I nod. He said it right.

Gudrun whispers in my ear and I say, "*Ich bin* hungrig."

Gudrun and the bartender discuss.

He places two cardboard squares in front of us. On the squares it says: Warsteiner Pilsner.

"Can I keep this?" I ask about the square. "To remember this by."

"Every place has these," Gudrun says.

The bartender takes a new coaster and stamps it with the name and address of this bar. I'm delighted.

"Danke shon, danke shon!" I say. I write the date on it and "Gudrun and I, first pub."

***

Every day is a discovery. Not only of German and Germany but of myself. How I was before. Before what? Before needing to be liked, needing to be popular. When did that come upon me? At the new junior high. When we moved. I needed it to be safe. Then it became my identity. I don't know if it'll be a weighted jacket I'll put back on when we get home, but here, now, I feel light, free. Wings and a heart. The me I used to be when the world was discoveries.

Half of us from the group are brought together. They take us to the Netherlands, which I discover is also known as Holland. Where Anne Frank lived. I think of that once when I realize we're in Holland.

The rest of the day, even though it's August, through freezing rain, they let us loose in and out of shops. We're magnetized to the record stores. They have top forty charts.

That means kids in Holland listen to music like we do. I wonder if they understand the words the way we do.

The number one song is "You're the One That I Want" by Travolta and Newton-John. I don't know if they have their own movies here or if all their movies are from America, but if I was a movie star, people in Holland and Germany would know me. Most of the songs on the chart are from America. There's only one I think is German or Holland Netherlands: Ik Heb M'N Wagen Volgeladen by Henk Wijngaard. I look it up in my translator, and it's something like "I have loaded my car" or "there's bird poop on my car." That's enough to crack us up half the day.

I take pictures of Holland streets. A brick windmill. I take pictures of kids in my group. Of a pink rose opening to its fullest that is special because I'm seeing it in a foreign country, Holland. I've been living in a sealed container, and the sealed lid is peeling off. I feel like the pink rose.

***

Mama, Papa, Gudrun and I are going to Munster today. It's about an hour's ride from Lippstadt. There's a new sort of doll stuffed animal that's taken Germany by storm. A Schloomph. It's all blue like an elf or a gnome and has a big white curling hat like a wizard. Everyone in Germany wants one. Most of the stores are sold out. Gudrun says it's most important I take one back to America. There's a department store in Munster Gudrun called and they say they have one left.

We pile in and Papa drives.

When we arrive, Gudrun and I jump out and arrange a time to meet her parents later in the day. For now, Gudrun and I are on our own free to explore Munster. First stop is the department store. She asks a sales clerk in German and I'm pretty sure she's saying that she called and they said there were some and the store just opened so they couldn't be sold by now. That or where's the bathroom. I'm always thinking she's saying something complicated when sometimes she's just asking about the bathroom.

The lady points. Gudrun runs, waving me to follow. We search, we search, until—

"Agh!" Gudrun screams.

On a high shelf in the bedding department is one last Schloomph. She jumps, knocks it down, puts it in my arms, and we hug it together. I offer to buy it, but she won't let me. It's a gift, she keeps saying. It's like getting a puppy. We walk the streets of Munster taking turns holding the Schloomph like a baby and taking pictures of each other kissing it. Compared to the small towns in Germany, Munster is a true city. And we feel like a sophisticated twosome wandering the streets.

***

There's a vase of roses on the dining room table. Mama keeps pointing me toward them. They're from Jett. Why is Jett sending me flowers?

The card says, in German: *Verandere dich nicht, Baby. Ich liebe dich.*

"Don't change, Baby. I love you."

I guess Jett's been getting into his German, too. The flowers feel less like flowers of love and more like flowers of insecurity. Maybe because I haven't seen him? Have I changed toward him? I feel the same. I love him. We've just been in separate groups. Do I feel different? Not toward him. But my persona, the one that couldn't be close to Marie, is shedding. Molting. Like a bird, I don't even feel it leaving me.

***

Upstairs in my room, I stare out the windows onto the backyard gardens below. The grass is mowed. There are pine trees as tall as my window and flowers surrounding a stone wall that separate this backyard from the neighbor's. The neighbor's yard, too, has some sort of gazebo or very old hand-built wooden structure. Several children are playing in the yard. Holding hands, spinning, then flying away from each other, falling on the grass. It looks like they're laughing, although, I can't hear them.

I think of Anne Frank. I think she was in a regular Holland house with her room facing a backyard. I think. I read in the book that she had to be careful not to look out the window during the day so she wasn't seen by the neighbors or the children in the backyards. For a moment, I pretend I'm Anne looking out the window, never knowing if we will survive to go outside again. And the children below don't hate Jews unless someone tells them to.

I think about my grandparents. How old was Anne Frank? I think it said she was my age, sixteen, when they captured her and her family. What if I was here in Germany hiding for my life, watching life go on, watching the sun shine, and watching little children laugh in the backyard? It seems so hard to imagine that this happened here. Or in Holland. That the stores and the pubs and the restaurants that I've been in were not safe for people like me and my family. Just walking on these same streets was dangerous. People like me were just shot on these same streets. How long ago? I think Anne Frank was captured when it was 1943 or 1944? That's only thirty or thirty-five years ago. My parents are older than that. What does that mean?

I leave the window, go to the bed and let myself be absorbed into the feather-y comforter. I'm not good at math. But wouldn't that mean that Mama and Papa were around then? I don't know how old they are but probably fifty? Even if they're forty-five, that would mean they were my age when Hitler was real. Not in history books. That would mean they saw their neighbors taken away and killed. That would mean that Gudrun's grandparents were adults then and were either for or against the Nazis. Since I've been here, everyone has treated me with kindness. I wonder, when Hitler was around, if they felt sad and angry and scared. Did they pretend they hated Jews to survive? Or did they just have to look the other way even though they didn't agree? Is that why everyone I meet asks me how I find Germany? Do I like it? Were they asking because I'm Jewish?

It's incredible to imagine that if I was born here just forty years ago, I would probably be dead. Like Anne Frank. If Jett and I were married, I would be taken away and he wouldn't. Or would he be taken for being married to a Jew? If we had kids, would they live because he wasn't Jewish or die because I was? It's impossible to believe this is the same place those things happened. Before I came here, this history stayed in the books on the pages in the black and white pictures. Now, I can't help thinking about it every place we go.

***

At the end of our trip, Papa goes to lift my suitcase into his trunk and says, "*Schiese!*" (Shit!) Then, he covers his mouth, not having meant to swear.

The goodbyes this time are tearful. Most of us may never see each other again. How do you thank people so embracing in their generosity? I see Marie hugging her American roommate. I'm grateful this is her happy ending despite me being in the middle of her story.

Jett and I hold hands as we board the bus, whispering how much we've missed each other. We did and we didn't. Both of us have been absorbed into this experience. I wonder if he feels changed like I do. Now that we're body to body again, this is what I missed. But being with no one that knew me as I was, I could shed that me. Everything was new. I understood nothing. There is such freedom in that not knowing. Not knowing anything. Letting everything be new. Especially me.

On the flight home, we sleep. Jett and I have the armrest up so we lay crossed on each other. Our parents pick us up and, for now, we go our separate ways. I come home to flowers and a long card from Sue. She has the floweriest handwriting of anyone. She's going to go to art school when we graduate.

***

Before the new school year begins, we foreign exchange students are asked to come to the school. The newspaper wants to interview us about our trip. The teacher asks that I bring the Schloomph.

Several days later, the article comes out.

"Ever see a Schlumpf? (They spell it wrong). This exchange student is holding one she got as a gift in Germany. Fourteen students from our Berg High School toured Berg, Germany this summer, where the founders of our Berg came from."

The text runs below a large half-page picture of me with the Schloomph. I'm seated with my back against the chair in a white t-shirt with red letters that say "Coca Cola." I'm holding my Schloomph in my lap, facing me like a baby, a toddler. In the picture, I look older, sophisticated. My eyes are calm and full with thought.

Sue showed me the paper when it came out. She opened it to the picture and, before I realized it was me, I thought, *look at her eyes, there's so much emotion, she's so self-possessed.* Then I realized.

It was me.

– 14 –
HOLD MY HAND

September. We're back. We're seniors. We're one of the high school power couples. Confident. Hot. A solid couple. Everyone knows us. We've been to a foreign country. Jett's going to be a front man in a rock band. I'm going to be an actress. Freshman and sophomores look at us with eyes of awe. Respect. Envy.

We returned from Germany in late August. Senior year started just after. The kids we went to Germany with have a pool party before the weather turns. In the pool, Jett and I find a space in the corner to float and tease. To melt our gravity-less bodies together. His cock is hard, sliding up against my bikini. No one can see what's happening under the water. Above the water, my arms circle his neck and we whisper. I lay my head on his shoulder. It looks like we're cuddling. But under the water, he pulls his cock out of his bathing suit. The tip teases at the barely-there crotch of my bikini bottom until I feel the tip slide between my lips.

We never made love without a condom. It was a source of macho pride to be able to use your condoms. Guys liked to brag how many condoms they'd been through, complain—*ha-ha*—about the cost. I whisper in Jett's ear, "Condom?"

He whispers, "Pulling out."

"In the pool?" I whisper.

"Chlorine kills sperm," he says.

And I relax into the slow up and down thinking that's probably true. Our faces are buried in each other's necks. I feel the pulse of him and the warmth of his extra wetness fill me.

***

How do you know if you're pregnant? My period doesn't come. That's one sign. I only talk about it with Sue. Other girls might spread rumors. If I'm not, and a rumor started, I would be called a slut and a whore. And once that starts...

"Do you have cramps?" Sue asks.

"No," I say

She makes a face. That's bad. We run down the list.

Breasts sore? Mmmm. Sort of, but my nipples hurt. A lot. That's bad.

Peeing all the time? Yes.

You feel too normal at a time when you should be having your period? Yes.

That's all bad.

The only way to know for sure is to go to a doctor. I don't know a doctor. The only doctor is my parents' doctor, and they can't know. If my parents find out I was having sex, I would be grounded for life. If they found out I was pregnant, they would kill me.

The school nurse. Would that be safe? It was the only choice. I pee in a cup. And wait. Over a week. I don't say anything to Jett. I pretend like everything is normal. Then I'm called to the nurse's office. It's a yes. I'm pregnant.

The only abortion clinic close to us is in Rockford, about an hour's drive. Sue and I call the clinic on the high school's hallway payphone. An abortion is $250. Two-*hundred* and fifty dollars. Half the price of a round trip to Germany for three weeks and back.

"Just make an appointment," Sue says. "Jett will pay half."

I make the appointment. I call Jett after he gets home from work.

I'm ok until my fingers move the holes of the dial with his phone number. Then, I can't stop crying. His mother answers.

"Hi. Is Jett there?" I ask, holding my breath so she can't hear me crying.

"Just a minute," she says. Then she calls, "Jett! Pick up!"

"Toto," he says his nickname for me, sweet, as if my voice just ran it's fingers up his neck.

I'm holding my breath, deciding when to speak so I don't choke into sobs.

"Are you ok?" he asks after the silence.

Again, like waiting for the perfect moment to jump on the merry-go-round, my silence rocks back and forth.

"Toto?" he asks.

"I'm pregnant," I say in a burst.

Now he's silent.

"Are you sure?" he asks.

That's what he asks?

"Yes," I say.

Neither of us say anything.

"I think it was from our last time, in the pool," I say.

I don't even hear him breathing.

"So, there's an abortion clinic in Rockford," I say. "Sue and I called. It's $250."

No sound from his end.

"I have an appointment for next week."

Nothing.

My face is soaked. Soft sobs. I'm out of words. It's his turn; I have no more words. *It's his turn.* But there's silence.

"I have to go," he says.

What?

"Ok," I say, furious. "I just need your $125."

"I don't have $125," he says, his words hissing out through closed teeth.

"Well, neither do I," I say, "so I guess I'll just have it, and you can pay child support, 'cause, yes, I wanted to be a mother someday, but now is fine. Right?"

All I hear is the dial tone.

Dial tone?

He hung up on me? My Jett? My boyfriend of over a year? My future fiancé?

At school, I see him at his locker. I walk up, and he slams the locker and walks away as if I'm not there. My problem. Not his. Who is this *boy?* This *child?*

"Fuck him," Sue says. "I have $125 saved from my job."

I cry. Sue was promoted from fry girl at the Long John Silver's to manager. She always left smelling like grease and cod, with slippery skin and wet looking hair, running home to a long shower after her shifts. She's giving me her so hard-earned money? And Jett can come up with nothing?

"I'm gonna call his mom and tell her I need $125," I say.

But I don't. Because I'm scared. And what if his mom told my mom?

In the hallways where we walked hand in hand, he's strutting, cheerful, saying, "Hey, how's it going?" to everyone and ignoring me as if I'm invisible.

People notice we're not together. Because we always were. People notice I'm crying. I'm sad. Alone. Or only with Sue. People notice how charismatic he's being, outgoing. The boss.

I can't wait to get it over with, to never speak to him again. It's incredible how we said how much we loved each other just a few days ago, and now I hate him more than anyone on the planet.

They say it's a painless ten-minute procedure, that you will need a few days taking it easy after, but I can still go to school the next day.

Appointment morning arrives. Sue and I call in sick to school and drive up to Rockford, Illinois in her Mustang singing Stevie Nicks songs with no idea what's ahead.

We sit in the waiting room of a small private building together, not talking. Suddenly, I need to focus on actually breathing in and breathing out. They come over to where I'm sitting and take the clipboard and papers they'd had me fill out. Then, a nurse takes blood.

And we wait. We try to talk, but the conversation ends after a few sentences.

"I hate Jett," I say, tears pooling.

"I hate him, too," Sue says, putting her arm around me, letting me weep.

"I thought he loved me," I say. "We went to Germany together," I say. "We were a couple," I say.

The nurse returns and confirms I'm pregnant, and she gives me a pill because my blood is negative something. We have to wait for the pill to work.

"I can't believe he's ignoring me. I should have told his mom," I say.

"You should have," Sue says. "He could have paid. He makes better money than we do."

I roll my eyes. She rolls her eyes. We both snort.

They come get me. The nurse holds my hand. I look back at Sue. Now, I'm scared. Now, my heart is thumping. She has me change into a hospital gown and special white socks. She has me lay my clothes in a bag.

Now, I'm not seeing, yet I'm noticing odd details: Oh, that's a small wicker garbage pail. I'll remember that. Oh, that's a nice clean sink with flower smelling soap. I'll remember that. I know that this is a moment in my life I will never forget. I'm collecting memory markers along the way.

The room has a patient table. At the bottom are metal things with spaces in the center for your feet.

I put my heels in. My legs are spread. We didn't picture any of this. There was nothing to picture. We didn't know anything. No one talks about this. The only thing we knew was the word, abortion. In case of emergency. This was an emergency. Only five years ago, if this happened, you had to go to someone who used a coat hanger or a button hook or something that could kill you. We didn't know anything.

The nurse holds my hand the entire time, from the moment I lay down through now. I turn my head to look at her. She smiles a warm but closed-mouth smile. She is looking at me like I am a child. I am *sixteen*. She looks at me like a mother or a nice babysitter looked at me when I was little.

"I'm the hand holder," she says.

"Ok," I say, not understanding how important a hand holder is.

The doctor comes in. He's not a big man. He has glasses and graying hair with the start of a bald spot. He wears a white coat. Each of his palms rests gently on my socked toes. There are speckles of blood on his coat. He, too, smiles a sad, closed-mouth smile. Kind. They are kind.

He repeats what they say, "This will be a relatively painless ten-minute procedure. I'll explain each step as we go. Ready?"

I nod awkwardly in my horizontal position.

He inserts something cold and metal that pinches against the walls of my insides because it's shaped to push out on the sides. He says he's going to open it up, and I hear the sound of metal on metal turning and feel a pressure. Nothing has happened that should hurt, but, already, I feel tears falling out the sides of my eyes, rolling into my hair. I am so sad. What a terrible moment this is. I want to be a mother. Someday. I don't want my body to be excavated. I wanted Jett and I to be real. I didn't know one thing like this, a thing we should decide and take care of together, could scare unflappable Jett so much that I would no longer exist. That he could walk down the same hallways and ignore me and make himself extra charismatic at the same time.

"I'm going to numb the cervix," he says. "You're going to feel a little pinch."

The little pinch makes me cry out, surprising myself with the immediacy of my uncouth, impolite, uncontrolled reaction. I squeeze the hand holder's hand, grateful for her palm in mine.

"You're going to hear a loud noise," he says. "I need you to breathe. Focus on relaxing. Keep your bum on the table right where it is. Ok?"

I nod.

The machine is as loud as a construction site. Suddenly, I feel it. I scream before I can stop myself. I am no longer in control of me. I am in the red screech of pain. I am sobbing, I am hysterical. My sobs are punctuated by more screams. Squeezing her hand. *Crushing* her hand. I feel her other hand on my brow. I feel her hand go to my pelvis and lay upon it, coaxing it to relax. I cannot relax. My insides are being torn out like hundreds of sharp toothed mice vicious in their hunger are eating me alive from the inside.

I am in my body, but I am *out* of my body. I hear myself cry out. I feel every morsel of pain. No! No, this is not a painless procedure. I don't think they numbed my cervix. Why don't they tell you how much this will hurt? This isn't ten minutes.

The machine dies down, quiets, then stops. The doctor takes out the metal thing. I'm cramping hard; it's hard to breathe through them. The doctor again places his well-meaning hands on my feet.

"You're going to be ok," he says, and I watch him leave the room. There's more blood speckled on his white coat.

The hand holder says, "I'm going to let go now." I squeeze my eyes, and I squeeze her hands. I won't, I *can't* let go. If I let go, I'll plummet like a broken-winged bird falling from a wire. She's patient as she untangles her fingers, one finger at a time, from mine.

She instructs me to stay. She'll be back to help me. I'm freezing. My teeth are chattering, and my body is quaking in chills. She covers me with a blanket. By the time she returns, I've started to fall asleep from the stress, the exhaustion. How long has it been? Just a few minutes, she says. I wonder if they tell time different from me.

She helps me up. My body shudders again with icy chills. She has me put on a large sanitary napkin and then my underwear. She helps me get dressed. I wore a dress. They told me to. A dress or light, comfortable clothing. She carries my things in one arm and has her other arm on me, guiding me into another room near the back. La-Z-Boy chairs are separated around the room. She places me in one. I don't want it laid back. I need to sit up straight. I feel nauseous. Vomitous. I feel too dizzy to do anything but sit up straight and stare at the window sill on the opposite wall. She brings me a plate of three cookies and a small cup of orange juice.

"You need to drink it," she says, and stands waiting for me to empty the juice. "And a bite of the cookie," she says.

And I take a nibble. "I can't let you leave until you eat," she says. "Your blood sugar is too low."

I nod but don't touch them.

"I'm going to bring in your friend," I hear her say, but I'm drifting into a sadness and away from the now.

At some point Sue has come in, and is sitting next to me in a folding chair. Her eyes are on me with helplessness or pity. I can't tell. Her eyes have pools of tears too. She takes a Kleenex out of her purse and dabs the wetness, saving her mascara from running.

We just stay. Finally, I'm able to close my eyes without being overcome by dizziness and nausea. Just as I relax my head back in the La-Z-Boy, the checkout nurse returns. It's time to get me up. I don't want to get up. I'm not ready. I know I'm not ready. I know for certain I absolutely cannot ride in a car right now. Motion. No. Motion. I can't ride in a car for an hour. I can't sneak into my house like this, into my room. I'm not ready.

But up we go. Sue and the nurse help me scootch forward, *forward*. Inch by inch. And then I'm standing. Sue has my purse, my bag. They give me birth control pills. She gives me one right away. Not for birth control but to regulate my period again. Sue puts them in my purse. With one arm held by the nurse and the other by Sue, they walk me to the car, place me in the passenger seat, and shut the door.

Usually, Suze would light a cigarette. She likes to have a fresh one when she starts the drive to anywhere. But she doesn't. Usually, she blasts the radio. But she doesn't. We drive in silence. Every stop light, Sue looks over at me with anxious eyes. I hold my belly, my fingers rolling over it in light, soothing circles as I stare out the windshield, tears dropping here and there out of either eye. I let them roll. I don't wipe them away. They are a running stream for now. There's nothing I can do to stop them so why make the effort?

We get into our neighborhood. We have to drive past our high school. It's 2 o'clock. Everyone gets out in an hour. Sue drives slow. Jett's car is parked on the street instead of the school parking lot. This means he has to run to work right after and can't be late chancing the back up in the student parking lot.

"We should slash his tires," I say. "I want to slash his tires," I say.

Sue has stopped the car. We stare at the Monte Carlo across the street.

"Should I slash his tires?" I ask. "Maybe key his car?"

"His precious Monte Carlo," Sue says. "He deserves it."

Neither of us could do such a thing, but the rage is pinballing, ricocheting hard off every corner of me.

He got off with nothing. He could pretend it didn't exist. His body went through nothing. He lost zero dollars. He felt no emotional trauma. He even broke up our relationship just like that.

"Let's get you home before your parents get home from work," Sue says. She's right.

She walks me in my room and gets me undressed into my flannel nightgown even though it's not winter. I'm still having moments of sudden chills.

The instructions were no tampons and no sex for a couple weeks, was it? And sleep today. There will be bleeding for a few days. Spotting for the month possibly. Sue leaves. I fall asleep for that day, that night, the entire next day and night. I know my mom came in, and I said I wasn't feeling good. I was grumpy. I told her to let me sleep.

A few days later, I was back at school. There were whispers about it. The incident. Me. Jett. Was it true? Sue and I said nothing. Jett probably said nothing since he was ignoring me.

A few weeks later, there is a school assembly to honor the seniors. Jett's band is going to play. Jett's band? Jett never had a band when we were together. I guess, while I was pregnant, having an abortion, and missing school, Jett must have teamed up with a band.

The principal announces their group and they come on singing cover songs. Jett looks so handsome wearing white jeans and a white t-shirt, holding the mic as if he was already a rock star. In all the time we were together he never sang. Up there in the lights, he's transformed into a rock star. He's on his way. He's done with me. We don't speak again through most of the rest of the school year.

That's ok. My next boyfriend will be a man, not a boy like Jett. After Germany, I know it's a bigger world than this

ordinary town. I don't have to be defined by high school and
who I am now. I intend to be worldly. To speak languages.
To know people from other countries. To become an actress.
To feel everything.

Someday, my life is going to be extraordinary.

– 15 –
FIRST SIGHT

This is my fifth job since I started working when I was fourteen. Back then, I had to fib about my age and make up a social security number to work because legal working age is sixteen. But I wanted my own money. If I had my own money, no one could tell me what I want for my life is wrong and what I hope for and dream of, I can't have. But now I'm legal. I'm sixteen.

I'm a hostess and coat check girl at a sophisticated steak restaurant not far from home called The Cork and Cleaver, which we dub, "Pork the Beaver." It's the best job I've ever had.

Our skirt and blouse uniforms make all the women look pretty. The food is delicious. My whole job is not only to show guests to their tables but to be the first to usher them into a night of pleasure. What's better than that? Plus, I do coat checks and, in Chicago, most of the year, it's coat weather. A dollar a coat. I'm rich!

It is a dead night at the restaurant. I'm in the coat-room making out the hostess schedules for the week when the heavy wooden front door opens. With a big, Mid-Western smile, I turn to greet the incoming customer, and I freeze mid-turn.

It is *Him*.

In body. In flesh.

I have never met him before.

But I recognize him in an instant.

He has been living inside me all my life.

He stops, too.

For one infinite second, the world is on pause.

White-blond hair.

Feathered-back hip 1970s a la David Cassidy.

Snow-white eyebrows.

Fragile, translucent eyelashes fanning out around blue eyes that twinkle like melting ice.

Fiery-red mustache that attempts to hide full lips that spread into an infectious, indomitable smile.

Elegant nose turned up slightly at the tip.

Five feet, eleven inches tall, 180 pounds.

Round, almost circular, hard biceps.

A V-shaped torso.

Pectorals outlined and visible under a thick white sweater.

Hands like fluttering wings. Graceful, conscious, lined with bulging veins, perhaps from good circulation?

A tight rear-end.

I register these, his physical features,

As the Universe holds its breath.

No. I have never met him before,

And it is none of these features that I recognize.

It is his *Spirit*, his *Energy*, I am held captive by.

I know him.

All that has been living inside me materializes into flesh and form as *Him*.

Our bond is wordless, an unbreakable connection.

Eyes to eyes.

We comprehend.

We recall.

We recollect.

The Planet exhales.

Instead of going to the bar, he sits on the sofa across from my hostess stand and requests a glass of Chablis, his blue melting-ice eyes never leaving mine. I place the order. The waitress hands him the glass and the cocktail napkin. I recall little of what we actually say.

The words are unimportant.

They are only the conduit.

His Spirit leaps and pirouettes.

161

His conversation is lively, vivacious.

He reminds me of those silver sticks used on the Fourth of July. The ones that look like incense, and, when they are lit, they shoot sparks everywhere. Even as he is only sitting, there is a "be-bop" in his body. He sings when he talks and shares his sentences with songs when he can't think of the right word to express what he's feeling. He doesn't talk about cars or sports, getting high, or getting laid.

I don't have to listen to him with the lower part of my mind.

Behind his eyes are stories he has lived and suffered and read and thought and wished and hoped and been disappointed in. Beyond all that emanates a life force that conquers all.

He seeks the Life in Life.

He revels in Life's Stories.

As I bask in the effortlessness of the darting, dancing, flirting, cascading, embracing of our energies, I realize,

I am a hopeless, helpless, optimistic, indulgent, unstoppable, sentimental, lost Romantic. He is all that and more.

He's not a boy. He is a man.

The first I am meeting. Romantically.

For hours, we talk and flirt and laugh, only interrupted a few times by incoming patrons who I quickly show to a table. Each time on my way back to the hostess stand, I pray he hasn't left. He remains there the entirety of the evening.

The restaurant closes. He offers me a ride home, but I have my car.

We go to the parking lot and sit in his little Datsun. Cozy blasting the heat against the icy Chicago winds, never breaking our conversation. He slides a George Benson cassette in the player, and sings, full, unabashedly, looking into my eyes, holding my eyes throughout the song, his voice rising and falling about what a difference that true love has made in his life.

Delighted, giggling, I watch him groove in his seat, arms up, shoulders twisting, graceful hands snapping to the beat. I divide into two selves: the Me that is there, mouth open in joyful astonishment, and the Other Me, observing us both, memorizing the night, memorizing him. He's so playful, so quick to move into fantasy, able to do in front of me what I can only do alone. He's so free. The smile widening my lips is palpable, peaceful, and permanent.

I close my eyes and send a silent "thank you" to the Universe and my guardian angel for bringing this man here to me. There is someone out there, a kindred spirit in a male body.

He exists.

Even if I never see him again, this one night confirms it all.

But I will see him again.

I know. I feel it.

Our paths have finally crossed.

It will be through the mirror of his eyes,

That I will finally meet not only myself but the possibilities of me. "Becoming."

I may continue to remain unknown to my parents, unknown to my friends, but I will no longer remain unknown to myself. I will no longer be alone. His name is Mick, and he will change the course of my Spirit and my Life forever. I feel this. I feel this in the bubble of his car, in the bubble that is the energy of us.

He sings through to the last note of the song.

Our eyes sparkle.

Our bodies hesitate.

He reaches into the ashtray, removing the roach of a joint. He lights it, and fire blazes then becomes smoke. He takes a hit and offers it to me. I take a hit even though I don't smoke pot; it makes me feel tired, stupid, paranoid, and ravenous. With him, I just feel safe and joyful.

I am exactly where I am supposed to be. As if I finally caught up with the Universe's plan for me. Yes. Meant to be.

Our faces move closer.

His kiss is full and tender and patient.

His lips drip liquid heat.

Then, suddenly, the Enchantment dissolves as his hand slips under my skirt, into my panties.

Panties that are wet.

No, *no*. I want him to stay magical.

I want this to be about our spirits connecting.

I don't want this to fade into "just sex."

I let him slip his finger inside me, moving it in and out.

I moan not out of real pleasure, but because I think I should. I don't want the night to be going this fast in this direction, but I'm afraid if I don't let him touch me, he will think I am too young, being coy, or he will be bored and not want to see me again.

His fingers stroke. In and out. In and out.

Spreading my juices onto my thighs.

He slips in a second finger. In and out. In and out.

Moaning.

Conscious of how I look.

Pretending.

What did I have to offer a man that he would be interesting enough to stay with me for? I am sixteen. Boys seemed to care about looks and sex before anything else. Men and boys pay attention to me because of my sexuality. Like Jett or the waiters at "Pork the Beaver" who flirt with me.

He takes his fingers out from between my legs, placing them fully in his mouth. I gasp. Then giggle. Outrageous. He's tasting it?

He takes my head in his hands and imprisons my eyes with his. "You are so incredibly beautiful. You are a lovely lady, one of the loveliest I have ever kissed."

My mouth is open, but no words come out. *Lovely? The loveliest? Me? A "lady"?* I am a girl. A *"chick."*

His hands are still on my cheeks. "Can I see you again?"

I nod, feeling my head move up and down, speechless.

The Magic returns.

I am not in a car in a parking lot.

Together, alone, just him and me, we are floating away somewhere in the ether.

"Tomorrow night?"

I nod up and down again, my head still in his hands.

"Should I pick you up?"

My parents would never allow this. He's at least twenty-five. Sneaking around would be required. I could say I had to work, come here, drop my car, and then meet him.

I shake my head side to side.

"No?"

"You could pick me up here," I say.

Another kiss. Long, slow, burning, melting.

He walks me over to my car, the only other car left in the lot, watches me get in, start the engine, and pull the lever to Drive.

He taps on the window.

I turn my head to see him placing his lips on the glass.

I place mine on his from my side of the glass.

We drive off in the same direction, his car behind mine.

The first traffic light is about two minutes down the road. The light turns red. I stop and look in the rearview mirror. He's climbing out of his car—in the middle of traffic and late at night—on the highway! What is he doing? Wearing no coat, he runs to my driver's side and makes a circling motion with his arm. I unroll my window. A blast of icy air hits my face. His gloveless hand pulls my chin upward. He kisses me, and I feel the heat.

"Lovely!" he sings to the moon. "Never, never change!" he sings, jogging back to his car just in time for the light to turn green.

Three more red lights.

Three more kisses.

Then, through the rearview mirror, I watch as he turns off, heading in a different direction.

I don't remember the rest of the drive home that night.

I don't remember washing my face or climbing into bed.

Something in the Universe, in *my* Universe, has shifted. I know my life is about to change. Forever from the ground past the blue skies.

– 16 –
FALLING

The alarm sounds and with it, the radio.

It's morning.

Eric Clapton sings of being at a crossroads, looking for an answer, but his intuition tells him he already knows.

I think of Mick.

He has come to the restaurant every few nights for the past, well, month. Two? It's ethereal. Nothing from calendars and earth. He stays my entire shift by the hostess stand. After closing, in his car, in the parking lot. We drive to places we can't be seen. Places we can make out in his car. We sing, talk, and kiss, encased in the warm bubble of otherworldly romance. My heart is his, straining and tearing in the stretch between love meant to be and the lies we tell to be together. Will we ever be a real couple? How crushed will I be if he evaporates? If I was nothing yet my entire heart loved, raw and pulsing faith? Eric sings to just let go, to allow things to flower on their own. Is this a sign?

My mother has left me a note by the phone in my room: "Jett called. Wants you to call him back."

I don't.

In school, Jett finds me at my locker, sheepish.

"Can I talk to you?" he asks.

This is the first time since Germany, since the abortion, that he's come to me. We walk outside to the smoking area. He places two cigarettes in his mouth, cupping the flame with his hands against the wind. He passes one to me. His tall frame leans against the brick wall, and his long legs cross at the ankles. I stare at him, remembering what it was like to run my fingers through his soft blond hair. He extends one long arm and takes my hand in his. I let him. His eyes are on his cigarette, afraid to look directly into mine. "I miss ya, Toto." His nickname for me. It feels strange hearing it again. I haven't heard it since I told him I was pregnant. "Do you miss me?" he asks, his eyes venturing a look up to mine. I still love Jett. I think. Maybe I just want him to love me and be sorry for what he did. Or maybe it's just the comfort of familiarity, desire for the closeness we shared before the abortion. To take possession again of the dreams and hopes that I'd built around him.

"Yes."

I don't know what else to say. There is too much.

He pushes his body upright and embraces me. I let my arms encircle his waist. My head comes to the level of his lower chest. I mold myself, pressing my body into his familiar shape, the familiar warmth, listening to his heart.

He holds me out at arm's length, looking down at me intently. "Wanna hang out tonight after dinner?"

I know he means we should get back together. I know if we hang out, we're Bo and Toto again. It would be so nice, it would close so many wounds, it would be such a relief to be back as a couple again. I am about to accept when I remember.

"I can't," I say.

He looks confused. "What are you doing? Gotta work?"

I ponder the idea of lying, but then I think better of it. Lying wouldn't be a good way to start this relationship again if indeed we were going to get back together.

"I have a date," I say.

He sucks a hard drag from his cigarette then snaps it to the ground, grinding it into the pavement with his boot. He breathes hot air into his palms, then shoves them deep into the pockets of his jeans. He stares out toward the parking lot at nothing in particular then turns and looks at me.

"Ok, forget the whole thing then."

"Jett?" I reach to take his hand out of his pocket, but he jams it in firm. "I accepted before this. I didn't know you were going to come back."

He kicks the butt around with his foot.

"I just met him. It's probably nothing. Anyway, it's you I love, it's you I've always loved."

I say that and think I mean it, but I also want him to love me again and feel bad for all that happened. No matter how much I've healed from what happened, it feels like the wound won't completely close until I hear how sorry he is.

"Then how can you go out with another guy?" he asks.

I give him a look that encompasses all that we've purposely left unsaid. "You weren't around anymore. But you're here now. Ok?"

"Someone from our class?"

He means our senior class in high school.

"No. Just a guy I met at "Pork the Beaver," I say.

We laugh at the name.

"I'm gonna make you forget him," he says.

The bell rings for our next class.

It doesn't make up for his abandonment, but I feel a sort of closure. Like I'm not disposable after all.

He nods and walks away backward watching me, kisses his forefinger, then points it at me.

"Love ya, Toto," he says.

My heart expands, rupturing into a hot pink flower.

***

"Hold the line!" Mick sings the name of the song he's been singing as he drives. One hand is on the wheel, his head is raised up, eyes half open. He's smiling.

"Who is this?" I ask, because I'm too shy to join in and sing.

"Toto," he sings the word.

"What?" I ask.

"Toto," he sings. "Love isn't always on time!" as if he's reassuring himself.

I let the song finish.

He looks over at me and smiles.

"Why did you call me that?" I ask.

"What?"

"Why did you call me 'Toto'?"

"It's the name of the group—Toto. You asked," he says, reaching across, putting his palm under my hair on my neck.

I store it in the "meant to be" column in my head.

But I'm not sure which column it belonged to: Mick or Jett.

***

I have never dined in a restaurant before that didn't have tables that were easy to wipe by a frantic waitress with a wet rag.

I have never dined in a restaurant before that had menus that weren't plastic.

172

I have never dined in a restaurant before with white tablecloths and candles.

We are led to a comfy booth. Instead of taking the seat facing me, he scoots in next to me. He blankets the tablecloth over our thighs, slipping his hand underneath the cloth-hang, resting his palm on my thigh.

He orders two Chablis. I hold my breath, burying my face in the menu and only exhale when the waiter leaves, not "carding" me.

My first real wine—nothing like Mogen David. I feel so grown-up.

I feel ready to feel grown-up.

Under the tablecloth, my fingers blindly trace the lifted veins on his hands.

Candlelight melts ice-blue eyes.

"Do you believe in Soul Mates?" I ask.

"I do," he says.

"Do you believe they are destined for each other? That the Universe brings them together?" I ask.

"Do you?" he asks.

"I hope so. I like to believe in destiny, in fate. In meant to be," I say.

"Why?" he asks.

"I guess it makes Life more dramatic. It makes Life have meaning," I say.

"I don't believe in Fate," he says.

"You don't?" I ask.

"I believe there are a lot of Twin Souls out there, and, somehow, in the midst of the Chaos we call Life, some paths cross."

"I don't like that version," I say.

"You don't think it's romantic enough? I think it's more romantic," he says.

"How?" I ask.

"Because it gives us the chance to show what we are made of. It's out there. It's up to us to recognize it when it happens and to fight like hell to keep it. It teaches gratefulness."

"Huh," I say, not really grasping what he means. "That's another thing about you, you know? Like, you're always saying 'Thank you' to everybody for anything."

"And?"

"So, it's…weird. Like you're always so grateful for everything," I say.

"So, you think I'm weird?" He takes my face gently in his warm fingers and pulls my mouth to his.

When we separate I continue, "You're not weird. It's weird."

"Kiss wasn't enough to distract you, eh?" he asks.

"Very distracting. But really. I mean, like, 'cool' people don't say 'thank you.' At least not all the 'cool' people I know. So, it's weird to me 'cause you're the 'coolest' person I know."

A wicked smile blooms on his face. "Thank you," he says.

I punch his arm. "See? See how you are?" I ask.

"Try it sometime," he says.

"Oh, right. I'm so sure. Everyone will think I'm a geek," I say, picturing how Jett would stare at me if I started acting like a stiff old grown-up, all polite, thanking everyone. Yes. Please. Thank you. La di dah.

"How old are you?" he asks.

My eyes fall to my plate. I take a bread roll and break it open.

"How old are you?" he asks again.

"Why? How old are you?" I ask.

"Twenty-eight," he says.

Wow. He is a *Man*.

"How old do you think I am?" I ask.

"Twenty-one?" he guesses.

"Nope. Eighteen," I lie.

He stops eating and stares at me, for the first time, without a smile on his face.

"Is that ok?" I ask, afraid to hear the answer, afraid of everything collapsing right here, right now, just when we were floating away again in our bubble.

"Do you go to school?" he asks.

My heart thumps, and I wonder if he can hear it.

I nod casually.

"College?"

"I go to Berg," I say.

"What's that?" he asks.

I take a bite of the bread roll and chew.

"The high school," I say, swallowing.

The waiter sets two more glasses of Chablis in front of us.

"Thank you," I say. The words surprise me as they come out of my mouth. I look at Mick, a bit astonished.

He takes both my hands in his and bows his forehead to touch them. He looks up at me. "God help me if I fall in love with you," he says.

"Do you believe in love at first sight?" I ask him.

"I do," he says. "Do you?" The effervescent smile returns to his face.

"I do," I say, and I mean it.

That strange magic, that palpable connection, that "knowing" I feel in my gut, must be what happens in true love, in love at first sight.

"You are a Soul Mate. Our paths have crossed. Now it's up to us," he says, intertwining my fingers with his. "You are so lovely, my lady. Are you my lady?" Everything he says sounds like a poem or a song.

"I hope so," I say.

Jett's visage, like a balloon popping, explodes and becomes invisible as air.

***

Through the mirror of Mick, I am no longer a high school girl easily dumped, forgotten, or disposed of. I am beautiful. I am promising. I am talented and radiant, and I will amaze the world with my luminosity one day.

Loving Mick is effortless.

There is no choice. It is meant to be.

Sneaking around to do it is becoming another matter. Mick is older than me which is ok but maybe not to my parents. So, for now, we sneak, staying out way later then my restaurant shifts, making up shifts, lying as to why. I don't think I was ever good at lying. Lucky for me, my parents are easy.

Their curiosity about me is a narrow box of questions— as long as my answers stay within the box, they don't need to know anything more. They love me, but they're like ostriches when it comes to wanting to know, *really* know me. This is one time their "not-wanting-to-know" is a blessing. I just give safe answers.

"Where are you going?"

"To a barbecue party from one of the kids at school."

"To work."

"To a sweet-sixteen party."

A variety of choices.

I am my mother's social butterfly.

***

In his Datsun, with Mick smoking a joint and me an Eve extra-long, skinny cigarette, we drive downtown to the Chicago Marathon, Mick's Canon 35mm hanging from his neck.

"Why do you always have your camera?"

"Life only happens once. I like to be a part of what's going on. To be able to look back at it."

We are spectators in the crowd, The runners pass by in groups. In a break, as the runners thin out for a moment, I see the crowd across the street.

My parents.

My parents are directly across the road from us.

I pinch Mick's arm.

We dodge and scramble and duck through the crowd, pushing our way back to his car. Safely inside, we exhale and laugh.

Mick starts the engine.

"Where are we going?"

"Some place gorgeous."

I snuggle into my seat and ask no more questions. I love surprises. I love when he amazes me.

He tucks into a parking place.

I read the sign.

"The Botanical Gardens?" I'm disappointed. This is the kind of place my parents would go to.

How uncool.

But I'm with Mick, and Mick is the "coolest" so I wait.

Because every day, every moment, every outing with him, I come home with a headache from all the newness he pours into my inexperienced life.

***

"These are orchids."

"Duh, Mick. I know. I can read the sign."

"Look at them. What do you feel when you look at them?"

"What do I feel? They're pretty? They look plastic? They look like a vagina?"

"Imagine you were an orchid. Come on. Close your eyes and do it."

"Noooo. I can't. It's too embarrassing."

"I thought you said you wanted to be an actress."

"I do. But not an actress of orchids."

"Do you want to be an actress, or do you just want to be famous?"

I know he thinks being famous is superficial.

"I want to be a great actress," I say.

"Great actresses have potent imaginations."

This feels too vulnerable.

"Close your eyes. Imagine you are an orchid."

I close my eyes. I feel hot and self-conscious.

I listen to my inhale. My exhale.

My mind drifts open, and I'm no longer here.

I feel his lips on mine, and I open my eyes.

"What do you know about orchids?" he asks.

"They are loners. They are survivors. They're chameleons," I say, and I feel I am speaking of me. "They're teases. Sexpots."

He places his camera to his eye and begins to click not the orchids, but me.

"What are you doing?" I am blushing.

"No. Don't look away. Keep telling me."

"Why?" I ask. I am giggling. I am sixteen and giggling.

"I'll tell you later," he says.

I sigh. "They're very specific about what they need, but they know how to flourish where other flowers might perish."

When I finish, he removes the camera from around his neck. His eyes are looking at me with that loving twinkle I love to be the object of.

"You're beautiful," he says. I can feel he means it.

"So, tell me. Why?" I ask.

"You'll know when you see the pictures."

"No!" I push him onto his back. "Tell me."

He is silent. I curl up next to him. We lay together on the cold hard grass, fully in public but alone in our bubble, letting the afternoon sun warm our faces.

As the sun heads lower toward the horizon, we brush ourselves off and, in silence, hand in hand, return to the car.

"You have the hands of an artist," he says, examining my fingers.

"You do, too," I say.

"Your hands are like bird's wings. They move like birds in flight." He kisses my hands one at a time, pressing his lips flat on my palms. "Your fingers are long and gentle. Mesmerizing. Like flowing seaweed. My lovely lady."

I am a teenager.

I read. I write.

But I am bereft of words to answer such poetic compliments.

"When you imagined yourself an orchid..." he says, breaking the silence, "...when you spoke of what you understood, everything about you changed. You looked different. You'll see when I get the pictures developed."

Again, I have no words to compete with his. All that comes is, "Why?"

"Why?" he repeats.

"Yes. Why do I look different?" I ask.

"Your heart was in empathy, your mind was busy processing what you felt, so you let go of your self-consciousness."

I love him.

I love who I am when I am with him.

Through the Mirror of his perception of me,

I am all the unborn possibilities buried deep inside that I could someday become.

In his company, I dare not know anything I think I know or I am certain to miss what I truly need to learn.

He is my Master. My Mentor. My Lover. My Savior. My greatest Fan. My conduit to Becoming.

"Would you ever change your name?" I ask. I'm always imagining new names for myself. Imagining the possibilities of who I could be under a different moniker.

"I might," he says.

"If you did, what would you want it to be?" I ask.

"Maybe, Mick Monet?"

"Oh, that sounds so French. I want to go to France. I love everything French. I want to live in Europe somewhere. By the sea. Or in a bustling European city like Paris where all the great writers convene. I know it's my real home."

His eyes drift, somewhere else, far away.

Occasionally, the smile would dissolve from his face, and I'd see him go somewhere distant, to a thought that sobered him.

"I'll call you that. Mick Monet. Micki Monet? I think you are really cool. The coolest."

He doesn't answer me.

We climb into the car and blast the heat. For my benefit. Not his. He's always warm.

"What were you thinking about just now?" I ask.

"When?"

"Now, when you stopped smiling. Did I say something?"

He looks at me, ready to say something, but hesitates. Then, the effervescent smile returns and he says, "Do you know that even your underarms," he traces his finger into the hollow ticklish part of my armpit, "are sexy and so elegant?"

"You know, Mick? Micki Monet. I think you could be a writer someday if you wanted to be."

He laughs an adult laugh, a knowing laugh, a laugh I don't yet have inside me.

– 17 –
COUPLING

For our six-month anniversary, he gets me a membership to his gym.

The Chicago Health and Racket Club. It becomes our home. We meet there at the juice bar, work out together, eat there, have friends as a couple there. At the club, we're free to be together, have a social life with other people. I can't share my own friends with him. They're too young.

Mick's two best friends happen to be members as well. Michael, who is married to someone named Patty, and Rick, a younger Humphrey Bogart look-alike. Italian. Suave in a Mafioso wanna-be kinda way. Who knows? Maybe he is Mafia.

Mick and Michael work together in construction. They've been best friends since childhood. Most of the people we hang with there are his age.

The women whisper behind my back. An under-current of something, something I can't put my finger on, something *we* are, Mick and I, is disapproved of by these women. It doesn't continue long enough for me to pin it down. I become part of their group, these twenty-eight-year-olds.

***

Halloween.

I want to go as a Playboy Bunny. Mick says we should go as Little Bo Peep. If I'm Bo Peep, is he the Wolf?

Nope. Mick dresses as Little Bo Peep in a feminine cotton paisley pattern dress with ruffles, a blonde short curly wig, and a shepherd's crook.

I'm the sheep. Singular. I'm dressed in a white woolly sheep costume from head to toe with tiny sheep ears, and only my face and blackened nose tip are visible.

We attend a party given by friends from the health club.

Michael and Rick are there as well as all the twenty-eight-year-old girls dressed as sexy nurses and cops. They are so pretty, those girls, but Mick never flirts with them.

"Don't you like any of the girls from the club?" I nudge him with a playful elbow.

"Not my type," he says.

"But they're older and more your age than I am," I say.

"They're old and cynical now. When a woman gets

cynical, it steals her beauty," he says. "Try not to let life make you bitter. Nothing makes you ugly faster than a crusty heart."

I don't know what he means, but I vow to never let myself be angry and harden over.

***

We spend a lot of time in cars and public places, Mick and I. My house with my parents is not an option. We only go to his home once. There's no privacy there, he tells me.

It's late. After midnight. We tiptoe inside, our voices hushed. His roommate is upstairs sleeping, Mick explains. We lay together in the dark on his living room carpet, touching and kissing. He brings out a tube of peppermint flavor oil.

Softly, he lifts up my blouse and bra. With a drop on his pinkie, he massages the oil into my nipples. His lips fall upon me, and I lie there, open-eyed, watching him suckle it off.

I'm not feeling what I know I'm supposed to be feeling, but I'm thinking maybe he'll be able to teach me things I don't know about sex. I pay attention.

We kiss without sound and make silent love on the floor. He pulls out when he comes, shooting his love on my tummy. He always pulls out, so I never worry about getting pregnant.

Again.

***

It becomes obvious to my parents something is going on. My late nights with Mick get later and later. I pull in the driveway at 1 a.m.

2 a.m.

3 a.m.

4 a.m.

The battles with my parents become more devastating.

5 a.m. I pull into the driveway. I inch the car door closed into itself. My waiting father flings open the front door.

"Get in here, dammit."

He grabs me by my arm, yanking me through the threshold and slamming the door behind me. This is not like my dad. My mother is at the top of the stairs, half on the floor, holding her body up by the railing. She is crying, complete with choking sobs and wailing. Her chest is red, and her face is swollen.

"You're trying to kill me!" she cries. "Is that what you're trying to do?" She is sobbing. Her face is wet.

"No, Mom!" I say.

"I didn't know if you were dead," she screams.

"Get upstairs. Into the living room," my dad orders. "Sit down."

He pushes me backward into a chair.

"You're a selfish girl!" my mother wails. "I can't sleep! I can't eat!"

Her words keep coming over my father's, over mine.

Her voice becomes the background hum during our argument.

"She's trying to kill me." My mother wails and sobs.

"I'm telling you, daughter. I won't have it. As long as you're living under my roof, you'll live by my rules!" My father's face is red and distorted with anger.

"She wants to kill me. She doesn't care. What did we do to deserve this? What did we do?"

"Mom, nothing. I'm sorry. I just didn't know how late it was," I say, pleading.

"You do this every night. Now, dammit, I want to know what's going on!" my dad yells.

"Nothing's going on—"

"You couldn't find a payphone to let us know? You're a selfish, selfish girl!" my mom yells.

"I am not! And fine! Then maybe I won't live under your roof!" I say, yelling back at both of them, countering their attack.

I try to stand up, but my dad hollers, "Don't you move!"

Down the hall, the door to my brothers' room opens. I see their little faces, distressed, one on top of the other, peeking out from the crack of the slightly open door.

"What are we supposed to do? Tell me that! Tell me!" My father is standing above me, demanding an answer.

There is a long silence. We stare, defiant of each other. My mother is coughing like a cat with a hairball stuck in the back of its throat—very dramatic.

I don't know whether to speak or keep silent. My heart is racing. I never meant for this to happen.

I just want to be in love with the man I love and have it be ok.

I just want to see him.

I just want to grow up.

I don't want this.

"I'm sorry," I say.

"Sorry's not good enough. I won't have this happen again; do you understand me? Have I made myself clear?" my dad asks.

"Yes," I say.

I can't leave well enough alone.

I don't want it to be like this.

I love my parents.

I want a relationship with them.

I hate having to live my life one way with them and live an entirely different secret life away from them.

All my emotional badgering, as my mother calls it, is my desire to make our relationship better, our communication stronger. Yes, I've been breaking the rules and sneaking around and lying, but they leave no space for the truth. They forbid, without realizing it, they forbid me to be me.

Mick delights in who I am, sees me for more than I appear.

"Dad?" I ask.

There is no other choice. I have to take the risk.

"I'm listening," he says.

Deep breath.

"I met someone. About six months ago. We've been dating. And I love him."

My father's chin tightens.

I am shaking, but I continue.

"He's the best man I ever knew," I say.

"Man?" my father asks.

Ignoring him, I go on.

"We stay out late because we have no place to go."

"Why haven't we met him?"

"I didn't think you'd let me date him. Because. He's older than me. He's not from my school."

"How old is he?" my mother asks.

"He's twenty-three," I lie.

"You're right," my father says. "He's too old for you."

A stupid, humiliating tear drips out of my eye and rolls down my cheek. I hate being vulnerable in front of my parents.

"Well, maybe I'm more mature than you think," I say. "I'm sorry I lied. I didn't know what else to do."

"I'm not unreasonable," my dad says.

He's right. He's not.

He's strict.

He sees only what he thinks he knows.

He's stubborn,

But he's not unreasonable once he has a chance not to be.

"I want to meet him," he says.

"You promise to be nice to him?" I ask.

"What kind of question is that?" my dad asks.

"Just promise me."

"I won't promise anything."

"God, Dad, you're so stubborn."

"How are we going to solve these late nights?" he asks. "Midnight, daughter. That's the time."

"But I get off work at eleven," I protest.

"One a.m. on a work night, the rest of the time, midnight. *Verstehen sie*, daughter?

"I understand. But it's like you think I'm Cinderella or something," I say. "Maybe, after you meet him and you're nice to him, we could come here sometimes and hang out? Then we could stay together longer?"

"That's a good idea. Your mother and I would be more comfortable if we knew where you were. Otherwise, midnight, daughter. That's the time. Midnight."

– 18 –
GRADUATION

"It's May. It's May. The lovely month of May..." we sing together to the Camelot tape.

"And my prom is coming up..." I sing.

Mick stops. He presses the off button on the cassette player.

"And graduation is in June," I finish, looking at my lap.

He puts the car in park, and I see his eyes get distant, traveling to that faraway place he goes to.

"My mother really wants me to attend all the parties and go to my prom. It means so much to her."

"What do you want?"

"I couldn't care less. I haven't been into my school's social thing since I met you. I don't care."

"Ah ha."

"For my mom, high school was the best days of her life. She went from high school to marriage, so it was all she knew. All she values. So, she wants that for me. She's unable to imagine that the things that had meant so much to her when she was young mean nothing to me."

"Ah ha."

"I wanted to please her, so I agreed to go to the parties, at least. Would you want to go with me? I know it's stupid and dumb and everyone there is just boring teenagers, but maybe we could just go to make her happy?"

He lights a joint.

I light a cigarette and wait. I decide the parties would be good enough. So far, the past few weeks, we've hit our evening curfews, but Mick still hasn't met my parents. How could I go to the actual prom? With Mick? He is too old for that sort of thing. I can't even ask him.

For the moment, he makes no reply. We hold hands walking into the movie theater. A Woody Allen Film Festival.

Woody Allen. Mick's favorite.

We hold hands, caress arms, and slide palms up thighs as we watch. We laugh.

Bananas, Sleeper, and *Annie Hall* play on the screen. During the break before the last picture, Allen's latest and newly released film, *Manhattan,* we head outside for some air.

He lights a roach. I, a cigarette.

He gives me the "I hate when you smoke those things" look.

I give him the same look back, indicating the pot.

We both eyebrow raise and smile.

Taking an inhale of smoke for courage, I tell Mick about the fight with my parents. Would he mind meeting them? Maybe hanging out at our house sometimes? I mention again the upcoming prom and graduation events.

"Let's talk about it after the movie," he says, but the ever-present smile is not on his face.

Manhattan begins. It's in black and white. That's surprising.

I am there. In that city. That mysterious city called New York. For a moment, I forget our conversation.

The story begins. Unfolds.

It is about an older man who falls in love with a teenage girl.

Mick watches the movie, and I watch Mick.

Woody Allen, the older man, questions himself about how crazy it is to be dating her, even though he has never felt the kind of joy he experiences with her with anyone else.

He breaks off the relationship and realizes almost too late that even though the age thing may be a problem for the rest of the world, it is not with him. She is the one pure thing in his life.

He runs across Manhattan and gets to her apartment building, huffing and puffing, just as she is walking out with her bags to get in a cab for the airport.

He asks where she is going.

She says she has been accepted to a famous acting school in London.

He tells her that he loves her. That he wants her to stay.

She says she can't. It's too late. She tells him that she loves him, too, and she assures him they can be together when she gets home. In two years.

He is cynical. He says that he knows by then it'll be too late, that she will be different.

She smiles and, in her eyes, you see that she loves him purely, and she simply says, "Have a little faith."

The movie ends.

Mick is quiet. It's so unlike him.

We walk to the car not even holding hands.

Inside the car, we sit in silence.

"What's wrong? Is it the movie? Did it remind you of us?"

"Michael thinks I should break up with you," he says.

I'm blindsided. I hate Michael right now. This wasn't what I expected to hear. Ever.

"He thinks our age difference is a problem, I guess."

"Do you?"

"Sometimes."

"Are you going to?"

"What?"

"Break up with me?"

My body begins to vibrate, to shake uncontrollably. I can't believe we're actually giving voice to these words.

"I get scared sometimes," he says.

"Why?"

"Oh my god. My lady. You're so young, and you have all your dreams in front of you. You have to go to college—"

"But I can go around here. I don't have to go away. I can stay here. I don't want to leave you, Mick. And when I become a great actress, I can act for a while in the theaters in Chicago. Maybe we could move there together and get an apartment in the city? Maybe, when I go to school, I can move out of my house and move in with you. You could tell your roommate to move out?"

We look straight ahead. No music plays. I hear him breathing. No words come. Cars leave the parking lot. My fingers open and close the clasp of my purse.

"I want to take you to your prom," he says.

"What?"

"I want to take you to your prom."

"You don't have to. I don't care that much about it, really."

"I want to. And I want to go with you to the graduation parties."

"Really. I don't care. Forget about it."

"I've been selfish. I've taken you away from your life," he says.

"No. You've given me the life I was meant for. I never cared about that stuff."

"When is your next graduation party?"

"There's one tomorrow afternoon. It's just a barbecue. I wasn't even going to go if you wanted to do something else?"

"I'll go with you and, after the party, we can go to your house, and I'll meet your parents."

***

Graduation parties are happening. I've skipped them so far, but Mick said I shouldn't miss them. That he'd join me. This one is in the backyard of one of the girls from our Germany group. Mick said he would meet me there.

I hadn't been around any of my peers in a social way much of the year. Not since the abortion. Since Mick. The party suddenly seems silly to me. Kids drinking beer out of plastic cups, acting like they're so grown-up to finally drink in front of their parents. It seems like a lifetime ago that I felt that way, a lifetime ago that I had my first Chablis with Mick at that restaurant.

I stand on the lawn and scope out the party. Lots of classmates I no longer know. No Sue and no Mick yet. The stereo is playing the Carpenter's "Only Yesterday." Under my breath, I sing along as I pour myself a Styrofoam cup full to the top of cheap wine.

A voice tickles my ear.

"Hey, Toto. What've ya been up to?"

I don't have to look.

"Jett," I say.

"Are you still dating that old guy?"

"Um hm. How about you? You still dating a young girl?"

"Very funny. I'm kicking back as a bachelor."

"You make a good bachelor."

"Hey! What's that mean?" He wraps his hands around my throat and pretends to choke me.

I giggle and tease, "Nothing. You must be having fun."

I don't miss him.

I have feelings for him, yes, ambiguous and confused.

"You look good," he says, winking and patting my rear.

"So do you. You always look handsome." I wink back.

His eyes leave mine and move up and behind me.

I follow his gaze, looking back over my shoulder.

"Mick!" I say, thrilled he's finally arrived.

On his face there is a smile, but it isn't on fire the way it usually is. My mind races for an answer. He must have heard me and misinterpreted.

I reach for his hand. He allows me to take it, but there is no reciprocation in his grasp.

"Mick, this is Jett. Jett, Mick Monet."

A "guy" handshake follows; each holds his own territory.

"Can I talk to you for a minute?" Mick asks.

"Nice to see you again," I say to Jett.

Jett nods.

Mick and I walk to the side of the house away from the crowd in the backyard.

"Who was that?" he asks.

I have never seen him jealous before. I gave him no reason to be. Nor have I seen him angry before. It's terrifying and delicious at the same time.

"He was my boyfriend before I met you. Why? Are you jealous?" I wink, teasing him.

He has no expression, only hard eyes.

"I heard what you said to him."

"What? That he's handsome? He is," I say, still playful, teasing.

"This is beneath you," Mick says.

"What is?" I ask.

He has hard eyes again, and his head shakes side to side in disapproval, disbelief, disappointment.

I don't know how to respond. I was acting out a skit I was used to acting out with men before Mick came along. The "I've-got-the-power-and-you're-jealous" game. But this was such an old, familiar game boys and girls in high school played, that I couldn't imagine what Mick's problem was.

I never played games with Mick. He treated me like a lady, like I was an ethereal irreplaceable spirit, and I always rose to that. I hadn't been trying to play one just now with Jett.

Even if I had been, it was harmless. Mick could play, too, couldn't he?

"He was my boyfriend," I say. "I loved him. But now I'm with you, and I have every right to tell him he looks handsome if I want. Stop telling me how to act."

Our first argument.

My adrenaline is pumping.

I'm scared.

I'm excited.

I'm waiting.

Poised for the battle.

But no battle comes.

He doesn't fight back or throw a macho fit like I expect, *almost look forward*, to. He shoots me a disappointed look, tosses his cup in the trash, and walks toward his car.

I'm stunned. My feet grow roots into the earth. I look back to the party and catch Jett watching from over his cup out of the corner of his eye.

I see Mick get in his car.

I look to Jett, and I see him sauntering in my direction.

I hear Mick's engine hum.

Then, I see Sue walking into the backyard from the other side of the house, looking around.

Looking for me.

"Suze!" I shout.

She finds me and waves.

Jett looks back at her.

"Wait for me! I'll be right back!" I yell.

She gives me a thumbs up.

I sprint across the lawn to the street, wait for a passing car to go by, then I cross to Mick's car, letting myself into the passenger side.

My side.

"I'm sorry," I say. "Please don't be mad at me, Mick. Please. I'm so sorry."

No answer. No eye contact.

He presses rewind on the tape player. The tape screeches backward. He presses play. He fishes a roach out of his ashtray. The flame burns and crackles, and he sucks the smoke in with a noisy inhale. The song plays. I know better than to speak during it.

The Doobie Brothers sing: What a fool believes…"

"Mick, you are not a fool," I say when the song finishes.

"I've never loved anyone more than I love you."

"What about Jett?" he asks.

"I don't know if it was love. *We* said so, but *we* were a couple. We just had so many hard things happen. I don't know how I feel about him," I say.

"What does he mean to you?"

"Promise me. Promise you won't think bad of me?"

I am still ashamed about the abortion. It's the 70's. *Roe v. Wade* just passed. There's such a stigma. I am fearful Mick will hate me for it.

"Tell me," he says.

I do. We sit in the car. I tell him about Jett and the abortion. I tell him how I felt the first moment he walked in the door at The Cork and Cleaver. I tell him about my dreams and Germany and how it changed me. I tell him my little life story up to this moment sitting in the car.

"I think I was scared," I say, discovering my feelings as I speak them. "I was scared because I love you so much, and maybe I'm afraid God won't let me keep you. Maybe I'm too happy. Maybe you'll leave me. I think I just wanted to cover my bases, make sure Jett was still 'gettable' in case you ever left me. I'm so sorry, Mick."

He doesn't say anything through my entire monologue.

"Do you hate me now?" I ask.

"I don't hate you. You just don't know who you are, what power you have."

I know this is a compliment, but I don't know exactly what he means. Or what it means to the outcome of this situation.

"You are a very special lady. Look at me."

I do. Deep into his eyes.

"No matter what you've done or will do in your life, you have the purest heart I have ever known. You have so much love to give, it almost drowns you if you don't give it away. There may be many men in your life to come—"

"No, Mick, I only want you. Don't say that." Why is he saying that? The trembling in my bones begins again.

"Listen to me. It's important for you to hear. You may have many men in your life—"

"Are you breaking up with me?" Tears flood my eyes. At any moment, my bones are going to explode out of my body. I can't bear to hear him talk this way.

"I'm not breaking up with you. I love you. But I'm older than you, so I want you to listen to me."

I force myself to stay quiet, wiping the tears from my cheeks with the hem of my skirt.

"Now, don't do that," he says, smiling again. "You'll just distract me."

He takes my hem and puts it back over my thighs. I look at him and go for my hem, teasing. He puts his hand on top of mine, and we engage in a "hem" struggle until we're both laughing and ourselves again.

"I want you to hear me."

"I am." I sit up straight, behaving myself as I did when my dad talked.

"You have the potential to be a great artist someday if you want to be. You have the most interesting imagination, your mind soars. I'm in love with this brain of yours. I think you will be a very, very good writer someday."

"I want to be an actress," I say.

"You want the truth?" he asks.

I nod. I'm terrified at what he is going to say. His words, his opinions, mean more to me than anything in the world.

"I don't know if you have the kind of discipline it takes to be an actress."

"I have discipline," I say.

"It's different. You have the discipline to *act*. To *learn* to act. To be great at acting."

"Ok. Thank you," I say, a bit miffed, but more scared still.

"But the discipline to be in that business? I don't think it's in you. You're too sensitive to be in that business," he says.

"I'm not that sensitive at all," I say.

And we both look at me. Me, from the inside, him, from the outside.

"Don't say that. Please don't say that." I sit on my hands so he won't see them shaking.

"It's a different kind of discipline than being a writer. You love stories. I want you to promise me something."

"What?" I ask.

"Promise me that you will never lose faith in yourself."

"I won't," I promise, not really knowing what he's driving at, still a little hurt by the actress comment.

"The world needs what your imagination has to offer. You have to think of it as a gift. It doesn't matter how much you need to give it; they need it, too. Don't forget that. You are a lady. You are not a petty, shallow, little girl. I don't care how old you are. I see you. I know you. Don't sink to it. There will be plenty of temptations. Don't sink to it."

"I didn't slash his tires," I say with a crooked smile and twinkling eyes.

He ignores this. He waits for me to reply, to assure him I understand his words. But it's so dramatic, and I think I'm missing the bigger gist. I'm trying to grasp it, but it's eluding me. I don't have the life experience to put his words in context. I feel like a dog barking at only the familiar words and inflections I understand.

I feel so naïve.

I feel *seventeen*.

Sue knocks on the window and waves. I had forgotten about the party.

"Hey, gimme a cig, and thanks a lot for deserting me, lil' bitch!"

She is smiling her rowdy grin.

"Fuck you, Suze!" I say.

I blow her a kiss and toss her a cigarette.

Mick opens his door and gets out to say hello.

I introduce them for the first time. My best friend and my Soul Mate. I've told each of them so much about the other. Mick is embarrassingly polite, the way grown-ups are.

"Pleasure to meet you. Heard so many great things about you," he says. smiling his beaming all-teeth smile.

"From her? Ha!" Sue whacks my arm. "Totally cool to meet you, too."

We all stand, Sue and I smoking, with Mick watching us as if he's seeing a side of me that's new to him.

"Hey, don't we have to go meet the parents?" Mick asks.

"Oooh!" Suze raises her eyebrows. "So, Mick," she says, belting him on the arm, "are you taking her to the prom?"

"I am," he says, eyes twinkling.

Her mouth opens. She's shocked. She gives me a thumbs up.

"Wow, I'm impressed. Ok, see you there, then. Maybe we can all hang out afterward."

I look at Mick. He is charming and sweet and agrees right away.

Sue starts to walk away, tugging under her t-shirt at the back of her bra. Suddenly, she turns around.

"Did you read the board today at school?" she asks.

"I didn't go to school today," I say.

"I know." She winks. "Guess who's nominated for Prom Queen?"

"Sue! Really!" I scream. "I'm so happy for you!"

"Not me!" she says, whacking my arm.

"Who? Fawn? She's nominated for everything."

"Not Fawn. Oh, no wait. Yeah, Fawn, of course. Duh. But also… you."

Mick grasps it before I do and puts his arm around me, squeezing my shoulder.

It won't sink in.

Had I really changed that much?

I hardly remember this school year.

It must be Mick and the way he makes me feel. Outside, in the mirror, I see the same face, but, inside, I feel like a different person.

***

I bring Mick into the living room where he and my parents shake hands. For the entire time I've been with Mick, I've been scared to introduce them. But here we are. The big "Meet the Parents." I stand aside, beaming at him, proud of this man I have brought home. I am anticipating the impressive conversation ahead. Instead, the air in the room changes. I sense it before any words are exchanged.

"Your mother and I want to talk to Mick alone," my dad says.

"Why? About what?" I ask, trying to sound light, unconcerned.

"Go outside," my dad says.

Mick nods, indicating that he will be ok.

I'm furious. They're going to ruin this for me.

Slamming the front door, I sit on the ground at the end of the driveway. Why did I ever think to bring him here?

Stupid. *Stupid. Stupid!*

Ten minutes later, an enraged Mick comes storming out, strides past me without a word, gets in his car, and slams the door shut.

"What's wrong? What happened?" I leap up, following him. God, I hate them, sometimes. "What did they say?" I beg him.

He looks at me, his eyes a scowl. He gets out of his car, re-slams the door, and leans against the side of the car, his arms crossed over his chest. Through clenched teeth, he says to me, "You told me you were eighteen."

My body turns inside out.

"How old are you?" he demands.

I hesitate. I want to stick to my lie. Too late. It's obvious my parents have revealed it.

"Seventeen," I say.

"How old were you when I met you?"

"Sixteen," I say.

"You lied to me!" The words hissing between his teeth. "You lied to me."

"I know," I say, trying to breathe and make word sounds. "I was afraid you wouldn't like me if I was too young. What difference does it make now?"

My father storms down the driveway to where we are.

"Do you know how old he is?" my dad asks.

"Twenty-five?" I say this knowing that he told me he was twenty-eight, but figured he, at least, kept the lie up.

"He's twenty-eight, and you are sixteen."

"Seventeen," I say.

"We could have him arrested for statutory rape. What the hell is he doing with a seventeen-year-old?"

"He loves me! Why is it so hard for you to believe that I would be interesting to an adult, to an older man? Not every man is a wolf. Why do you have to go and ruin things! I hate you! *I hate you!*"

I fall to the ground in my fury, not trying to be dramatic but being dramatic anyway.

My father and Mick stare at one another. My father understands forbidding this would only make things worse.

I hear him say, "Treat her well. Or else. That's all I have to say." He turns and goes into the house, slamming the door behind him.

I watch him go and see the faces of my brothers pressing against the screen of their bedroom window.

***

With Mick as my escort, I attend the prom. Instead of a traditional prom dress, we picked a mauve-pink elegant evening gown of several sheer layers, so light, that when a gentle wind fluttered the edges, it looked like wings in flight. My hair was rolled into a French knot with a little tiara at the top like Audrey Hepburn in *Breakfast at Tiffany's*.

Mick wore a white tuxedo with a light-blue tie that matched his eyes. We'd never seen each other so dressed up. For a moment, I felt like we were getting married.

With his proud, effervescent smile, his feather-light fingers on my elbow, and my arm tucked under his, he promenaded me, in my pink gown, elegant and flowing, around the dance floor for the Prom Queen ceremony. I don't win, but I don't care. Jett is there, but I hardly notice him. My mother is relieved. I attended my Senior Prom.

***

With Mick tolerated at my house, we spend our evenings watching movies in the living room. Once my parents go off to sleep, their bedroom door shut, we lie fully clothed on the sofa, covered entirely by the most enormous blanket we can find. When we're certain they've fallen asleep, hushed, we remove our lower garments only, stashing them behind the sofa. I guess we figure if they come in the room, we'll appear fully dressed and will have seemed to have fallen asleep that way, tucked under the blanket. Then without a sound, we make love.

During the day, I go to school, and Mick goes to his construction job. Some nights I go to work, but we talk on the phone or see each other late. Always, we meet up at the health club from four to six in the late afternoons. The several nights a week that I don't work, and at least one full weekend day, we spend together.

So many times we have made love, Mick and I. In cars, on the sofa with a blanket covering us, on his living room floor, in doorways, in parks. Of the many times we've made love, we've never been fully undressed together.

On my parent's wedding anniversary, they take a trip out of town for the night. For the first time, Mick and I lay naked together. On my twin bed. It's almost too rich, too luxurious.

I lay him on his stomach. I want to start from his back and work my way around. My tongue goes low. I lick him at the top of his buttocks, in the little "V" at the top. The sight of his skin shivering and goosebumps jumping out of his flesh delights me. His skin is looser than the boys I have been with before. I count all his freckles, reveling in my study of the body of this man I am so deeply in love with.

I try to memorize every texture, every crease, every freckle, and white-blond hair on his body. Every turn and twist of his bones, his muscles, and his smell. His scent. His scent seeps into my nostrils, into my bones. My hands, my mouth, and my eyes could recreate him without looking. I finally know my Soul Mate, soul and body.

– 19 –
TRUTH

Several nights later, we're watching the movie *The Deer Hunter*. It's a long film. A saga. It's heart-wrenching. Terrifying. There are images I'll never forget about a war I never knew. Vietnam.

Mick is devastated by the film, by the relationship of Mike and Nicky, the two best friends since childhood in the picture. They grow up together in small-town America. They go to the Vietnam War together. Mike gets out, but Nicky goes back. Nicky is so scarred by his experience as a prisoner of war that he returns to Vietnam, to the prison camps to gamble at Russian roulette. Mike returns to Vietnam to rescue him. But it's too late. In Mike's character, I know Mick is seeing himself. And he's seeing Michael, his best friend since childhood, as Nicky. That's what I think. But I don't know why.

211

Mick sits in the car, shaken by the film, his head leaning back on his seat. His eyes are closed. Tears are rolling down fast, one after another, soaking his cheeks, disappearing into his mustache.

I am immobile in the passenger seat, facing him.

"What made you this upset?" I ask, gentle, careful.

It's a tragic film, but he is beyond disturbed. I know Mick's Spirit, his Soul, but I'm becoming aware I know so little of his life. His past.

He turns off the radio, but when he starts to speak, there are no words. He swallows a lump in his throat.

He turns the radio back on.

I switch it off.

I want to know him.

This part of him. The part of him that drifts far away.

I want to know where he goes.

I need to know.

Now.

Eyes still shut, his palms smear the tears away from his cheeks, his neck, his chest. I notice his hands again as I did the night I met him—the most graceful hands I'd ever seen on a man. It was as if each finger had a curve all its own, as if each finger had something unique to say.

He opens his eyes. They're red, his white eyelashes wet with little droplets of moisture. He glances at me. He looks straight ahead out the windshield.

"Lovely, lovely," he says. "I've been lying to you."

My heart stops.

"I didn't think I would fall in love with you, so I didn't think it would matter," he says it soft. No smile comes to his face to burn the tension out of the car.

Lying? Does he mean he really never loved me? That all this has been a ruse, maybe thought up by him and Michael? Maybe this was funny, to trick a young girl into thinking you loved her and have it all turn out to be a practical joke. Maybe this was the reason for all the looks I felt and the whisperings.

Everyone was in on it.

They all knew.

I should have known it was too good to be true.

I wasn't special and lovely. I'm just a teenager caught up in a prank.

Is it all going to end like this?

I will die.

My world will end.

My Spirit will evaporate.

Boiling tears smear my vision.

"What do you mean?" My words float out like an errant feather.

He puts his head back and closes his eyes again. Two more tears run down either cheek. He grabs me hard, hugs my body tight to his, the stick shift of the car separating us from the hips downward.

I let him squeeze me. I feel his body shaking with sobs.

I start to cry, too.

"Dear God," I pray in my head, "please don't take him away from me!"

He releases me and takes a deep breath.

I can't breathe at all.

"Just tell me, Mick. Just say it. If you don't want to be with me, just say it, whatever it is."

"Lovely. My lady," he says, his eyes searching mine. He plays no music to speak for him. He holds my eyes in his.

"I'm married," he says.

There's a white blur in my head.

No thoughts, only static. Like a bad radio station.

I don't know what this means, where it fits into our world.

How could he be married? Married men are taken. He's *mine*.

"Are you divorcing? Do you love your wife?"

"We're good friends. We went to Kent State together. I met her at the riots."

"What riots?" I'm not old enough to know much about Vietnam.

"There were riots at Kent State, where I went to college, protesting the war."

"You mean the Vietnam War, like the one we just saw in the movie?"

He nods.

"I met Wendy there."

"Her name is Wendy? Your wife?"

214

A wife.

A *wife*.

He has *a wife*.

And it's not me.

But he loves *me*.

There is no place for this information in my seventeen-year-old brain.

"She got pregnant, and we got married because of it."

My mind is humming like a computer, trying to process these new pieces.

"You have a child?"

The world is getting darker around the edges. Like a piece of paper lit at the corners, the edges turn to ash with the flame creeping closer to the center. As it is, my world with Mick is burning in on itself.

"My daughter's name is Lissy. She's twelve."

His daughter is closer to my age than I am to his. She and I are only five years apart.

"I love Wendy. In a different way than I love you. She's my friend and my partner, but you are my True Love. You are my Soul Mate. I never thought I would have one. When I got married, I thought, 'this is it.'"

He laughs an ironic guffaw then sings, "Love isn't always on time." The smile fades.

I am aware of the tears as they fall down my face, but I can make no sound, no movement. I stare out through the windshield at the full moon.

215

It's a yellow moon.

Soured by the news, maybe.

"We thought about getting divorced, but then we thought to try and make one last effort."

"What happened?" I ask, staring at the squished bug on the window.

"I have two twin boys, one and a half years old now. Rickey and Shaun."

"You have three children?"

This wasn't in any of my plans, of my fantasies for my True Love and me. This is not the way it's supposed to go.

"Do you live with her?"

"Yes."

"So, it wasn't your roommate who was sleeping upstairs?"

"No."

He reaches to take my hand in his. I let him. Our hands squish the tears we have tried to wipe away, our palms wet together.

"What about me?" I can barely say the words, "Are you breaking up with me?"

"I know I should," he says.

The words grab my throat, and I combust, racked with a cry so deep it doesn't sound human.

"But I can't," he says. "You are my lady. You are the one I have been waiting for. That I gave up on ever finding."

"Oh, God, Mick."

"Will you stay with me?"

I am laughing and crying all at once.

"You make me feel so special. You make me feel..." my words eek out, halted by chokes and hiccups. "You—*hick*—make me feel—*hick*—known. It's like—*hick*—you see through all this—*hick*—surface stuff that nobody else ever—*hick*—sees through and—*hick*—you see my spirit—"

The last "hick" makes me laugh suddenly.

"I don't know how I could ever—*hick*—live without you now—"

He reaches to the back seat for his cassette box, rummages through it, and pulls out a tape. I wait, "hicking" next to him in otherwise relative silence. I'm emotionally drained, but relieved, overjoyed. And confused.

He puts the cassette in the player. He sets it on the track he wants to hear, turns the volume up, and looks at me intently. The music begins. He sings the entire song, holding my hand, staring at me, never taking his eyes from me.

I hear the first lyric of The Commodores, "Three Times a Lady." The first line is about coming to the end of their time together.

I am alarmed again. "What do you mean 'the end'?"He shakes his head and "shooshes" me with his eyes. The familiar translucent, shimmering bubble surrounds us as we listen. No one exists but him and me. As he sings, all that he ever inspired me to be becomes Truth.

The year we've been together, we've lived so intensely that it seems like half a lifetime. I am no longer the unsure girl I was. Through the mirror of Mick, I am transformed into a Goddess. I am three times a lady. And nothing can keep us apart.

Only death.

Nothing will separate us. Not his marriage. Not my parents.

Nothing.

– 20 –
& CONSEQUENCES

Saturdays. Mick has his boys, and it becomes a Saturday ritual that I take my youngest brother with Mick and the twins on an adventure.

We go to ball games, to adventure parks, anywhere we can think of.

Wendy, his wife, goes out of town for a week, and I meet his daughter, Lissy.

That's how Wendy found out about me. I don't know what he was thinking when he arranged that meeting. I don't know whether he wanted us to be caught together, but we were. I don't know how long she knew or if she ever confronted him about it. But eventually I would find out that she knew.

And she knew well.

We get in a fight about something at the health club. I try and try, but I can't remember how it started or what we were arguing about. We never fight, but emotion has overcome reason.

I drive the five minutes to The Cork and Cleaver. I park my car in the lot and head to the payphone. I call Jett. I'm scared Mick and I are going to break up. I don't understand that couples fight, and it's ok. It's part of the deal. This feels like I'm tipping off the edge of the world. I want to see if Jett still likes me. If I have a "backup."

As I'm chatting with Jett, Mick comes up behind me at the phone booth. I don't hear him. I don't realize he's behind me. He must have driven over, thinking this is where I'd go and saw my car. Realizing who I'm talking to, he walks out.

I slam the phone down and run out, following him, but he doesn't wait. His car is gone from the lot. Distraught, I climb in my car and light the joint that Mick had left there. I smoke the entire thing while listening to "The Piano Man" by Billy Joel. With my forehead pressed into the steering wheel, I weep without pause for all the lost souls in Billy Joel's bar.

The song lasts forever. Hours and hours, my deluded brain cells inform me. I am crazy high and spend the next hour under the torturous bright lights at the 7-11 candy counter, trying to decide how to buy a candy bar without the 7-11 man knowing I'm buying it because I'm high. And, munchies. I have no idea why it matters. I manage to purchase a Charleston Chew.

I eat it in bed when I get home, imagining it's an extended family of paisley patterns partying on my tongue.

Mick doesn't call to say goodnight like he usually does. He doesn't call to say good morning the next day like he usually does. He doesn't call when I get home from school in the afternoon, and he doesn't call at The Cork and Cleaver that night when I am at work.

Terror.

Disbelief.

Is he really throwing us away?

Is this really "the end"?

Rage.

Fury.

"Well, if he wants to play this game," I tell myself, "I'll show him. I'll just go back to Jett, and then he'll see."

I sit outside in my car getting high again. "Free Bird" by Lynyrd Skynyrd plays on the radio. Alone in the 7-11 parking lot I sing, defiant, loud, and rebellious.

"I'm a free bird, yeah!"

I'm trying to convince myself I am going to enjoy this new freedom.

Fuck him.

- 21 -
WHISPER, PLEASE

It is 7 a.m. My parents have left for work.

I don't know how I got home.

I don't remember getting into bed.

I hear the phone as if from a great distance.

I think it is in my dream.

I wake and realize it is indeed the phone.

It's Mick, I'm sure. I'll show him. I'll be silent and make him apologize. I answer the phone.

"Hey, kiddo. It's Michael."

I am quiet.

Why would Michael be calling me?

"Hey, kiddo, um, Mick's been in an accident."

A cold fear seizes my limbs. I have no voice.

"He was on a scaffold at the new construction site. We were putting in sprinkler systems for the grocery store. He was singing and groovin' while he was up there. You know how he is. He lost his balance and fell. He tried to grab hold of the bars on the way down, but the scaffold tipped. A cement block fell and caught him under the chin on his way down. Broke his neck. He's in intensive care."

I hear myself inhale sharply.

"Is he going to be all right?" I hear myself ask.

"I don't know," Michael's voice cracks.

"Where is he? Can I go see him?"

"I'll try to find a way. I'll get the doctor to call you. I'll explain the situation to him. He's in intensive care. They don't allow anyone but family."

"Did you get to see him? Is he conscious?"

"I saw him." I hear him choke and breathe in hard through his nose. "Wendy said it was ok for them to let me see him. I'll try to find a way to get you in, ok?"

"Ok. Will you call me and let me know what's going on?"

"I promise," he says.

The line goes dead.

I lay in my bed in the dark, wearing Mick's Ektelon racket ball gym shorts and his extra-large t-shirt, cradling his gym shoes and racket, and clutching all the photos I have of him and I. For a day. Two days. Three days? I'm fading in and out of a blinding-thick gray fog that's smothering my mind, listening only for the phone to ring. I leave my room only to go to the bathroom.

Down the hall, I see the back of two heads sitting still on the living room loveseat. My Grandma Ethel and Grandpa Henry, my mom's parents. I guess my parents asked them to come while my parents were at work. Suicide watch, maybe? I wasn't even aware they had come over.

I didn't go into the living room, just back to my room to dissolve. Sometime during those vague days, the phone rings. My limp body springs to answer it as if jolted by lightning.

Michael.

It could be arranged.

Go to the back door of the hospital, and he will meet me.

I can go for a short visit.

The time is arranged for later that day.

The doctor is next to him and will talk with me.

Michael's voice is kind.

I plead with him for certainty, for answers that will make everything go back to the way it was.

His voice is gentle but without much hope.

I call Sue. She arrives a short time later and gets me up.

Still wearing the peculiar outfit of Mick's enormous gym clothes, I walk out of my bedroom with Sue by my side, carrying photos of Mick and I as well as his gym shoes.

My grandparents tell me my parents don't want me to leave the house. I say, I'm ok, Sue's with me, I just need some air. I want to go to the store with Sue. We will be back in an hour.

They let me leave.

We circle the parking lot until we find the door with Michael standing by it. With no words, no sounds, he embraces me. I collapse in his arms. I register both him and Sue looking at me with eyes of pity.

Michael knocks on the back door. A guard opens it. He asks to see ID. I have none.

"What relation are you to the patient?" the guard asks.

Before Michael can intercede, I'm weeping, explaining, feverish and without pause, "I'm his fiancée. These are his shoes. This is his shirt. These are his shorts. He loved to play racket ball. He sang all the time. See? These are pictures of him and me—here's him singing by the car. Here's him singing after we actually played in Buckingham Fountain— we weren't allowed to and got kicked out but Mick didn't care—it made him sing. And here's me and him—

The guard becomes a human being. He bends the rules and directs us upstairs to the Intensive Care Ward, a white, sterile, bustling space with glassed-in cubicles, filled with bodies hooked up to machines.

White sheets, silver railings, humming machines, and hushed voices.

We walk to a glassed-in room.

There is a body covered to the chin in a white sheet.

Michael opens the door to the room.

I step in. I look back at him.

He closes the door behind me.

I look forward to the bed.

Who is it?

I take a step closer, the pictures in my hands rattle against each other.

It's a blond-haired man, unconscious and silent, with tubes coming out of his nose, his mouth, and his arms. Tubes run like branches from everywhere to a machine next to the bed. He lies, small under a white, tight, precisely tucked sheet. He appears so short, so tiny.

Could this be my Mick?

I stand close to him, the metal railing of the bed pressing hard into my ribcage. Every bone in my body begins to tremble as if loosened from my skeleton.

"Oh, God, Mick," I whisper, my face scrunching up on itself, my mouth open, lips pulled tight into a mournful frown. "Oh, God, Mick! You have to get better. Pleeaasse, Mick," I say. "I need you so much. Please don't leave me. Please don't leave us. I need you. Michael needs you. Rick needs you. Your family needs you—and your children. Oh, God, Mick, you are too special to go. Please get better. Even if you end up in a wheelchair, I'll never leave you. I love you so much."

I hear my voice strain in its whispers and pleads.

There's a television on above his bed. *The Price is Right.* Bob Barker is condescending to the next contestant. It suddenly makes me furious.

226

Mick hates TV. Especially game shows.

"God, Mick, I'm sorry about all this. I'm sorry for our fight. I don't even know why we were fighting. I have never loved anyone as much as I love you. Look, see? I brought our pictures."

I hold them up by his closed eyelids.

"Remember this? You were so funny as Little Bo Peep. And this? At my dad's surprise birthday party. See, I'm wearing the pants you bought for me. Mick?"

My legs buckle, the pictures scattering on his chest on top of the sheet.

"I can't go on living without you. Please."

I let myself cry, my tears falling on his still face.

My stomach is a hard black rock, my limbs watery and weak.

When my moans melt into heaving sighs, I look at his face. As if under a microscope, each feature is isolated.

Here are the white, fragile eyelashes I loved to watch guard his sparking eyes.

And here, the soft, fine eyebrows.

The turned-up nose.

The full lips dotted with sun freckles.

The chin with the Barbie-doll butt cleft in it.

The bristly red mustache.

I place my lips full and wet on his cheek, closing my eyes to feel the texture of his skin.

His scent, the scent of my Lover, the scent of my Soul Mate, enters my nostrils. It courses through my body, penetrating my Soul.

Michael touches my shoulder. Time to go. He leads me out of the room.

Not taking my eyes off the fragile man in the bed, I hear myself repeating over and over, "Tell them to turn off the TV. Tell them to turn it off. He hates television. Why do they have it on? Tell them to turn off the TV."

Michael whispers, telling me it's good for patients in comas to hear voices all the time.

"He's in a coma?" I cannot comprehend this. "*This* is what a coma is?"

I had heard about comas on doctor programs on TV. *On TV.* In unreality.

Now, suddenly, it is the most important word in my life.

I head back home to the gray fog surrounding my twin bed.

Two nights later, in the middle of the night, I'm tossing and turning in the heat of Chicago summer. I wake for no reason. I had pushed the sheet off myself.

It happens suddenly.

My bedroom walls are covered with metallic, shiny Greg Brady groovy wallpaper.

In the reflection of the wallpaper, I see a Brightness. A white glow.

That instant, the room becomes cold.

Bone-cold.

Then, I smell it.

His scent. The scent from the curve of Mick's neck.

It envelops the space as if it's a fine vapor filling the room.

I know.

I know.

A rush of warmth, liquid heat, pours through my body, streaming into my limbs, from my toes up my spine and out the center of my skull.

Fear seizes me. I rise, rigid and upright.

"Mick? Mick, I know it's you," I whisper to the glow in the wallpaper.

Liquid heat rushes. The air is bone-cold. The light reflected in wallpaper pulses.

"Mick, you're frightening me."

I am frozen on my bed, my knees clasped to my chest, my eyes wide and staring.

"Mick. Don't. Don't go. I need you. You are my Everything. Without you, I don't exist. Mick?"

The glow reflected in the wallpaper pulses.

"I love you more than Life. You're my Soul Mate. If you stay, no matter what, I will take care of you. I will never leave you. Stay, Mick. *Stay.* Please, stay. *Please.*"

My forehead hits my knees, and I wail and whisper "please" over and over again.

Then, it is gone.

The room is dark again. No light. The cold is gone. The room is humid, hot.

I fall onto my back, looking up at the ceiling, afraid to move.

I close my eyes, squeezing the hot wetness down my temples into my hair.

It's over.

***

Early, the phone rings.

Michael.

Mick died late in the night.

I know.

The following evening, my phone rings again.

I don't answer it. I am deep in a coma of my own.

My mother calls from the other room,

"Pick up the phone, honey."

"Hello?"

"Is this—?" It's a woman's voice. She says my full name, first and last.

"Yes."

"This is Wendy, Mick's wife."

I am silent. My heart goes *boom, boom, boom.*

She sounds younger than I had imagined. Her voice is warm and soft.

"I know," she says. "I know about you and Mick."

I don't speak.

My heart bangs hard against my ribs.

"I'm calling to invite you to the funeral, if you want to come. I thought it would mean something to him, and to you."

Was she really saying this?

I hadn't even thought about a funeral.

And her, inviting me?

Was it a joke?

Was she going to have me murdered when I got there?

Yell at me? Tell me off?

Was she really this kind?

"I would like to. It would mean so much to me," I say.

"Michael's Funeral Home. Tomorrow night, seven o'clock."

"Thank you so much for asking me," I whisper and hang up the phone.

– 22 –
GONE

The funeral parlor. Many familiar faces fill the building—everyone we knew from the health club—the twenty-eight-year-old girls, Rick, and Michael and his wife, Patty.

I am wearing the only black dress I own: a second-hand black skirt and matching top with pink elephants running along the bottom hems.

In my sweating palms, I carry the pictures of our relationship.

In the front of the room is a closed casket heaped with flowers. I stand at the back, unable to move. The room hushes as people slowly begin to notice me standing in the back.

A petite brunette with black-framed glasses walks back to me. Her smile is delicate, her teeth slightly crooked, her face lovely and understated. She reaches out her hand, touching my forearm.

"Hi. I'm Wendy. Mick's wife."

The corners of my mouth, hesitant, rise up, waiting for what might come next. I look at my feet, then up at her with my eyes only, my head still facing the floor.

"Do you want to go up to the coffin?" she asks.

I nod.

She puts her arm in mine and leads me up to the front.

I feel the eyes of the room on us. When we arrive at the front row of seats, Wendy releases my arm, and I proceed alone to the polished mahogany casket that holds my life, my Soul Mate, captive within it.

Kneeling on the resting block, I close my eyes, placing my free hand, the hand without the photos, on the cover, feeling the smoothness of the cold wood beneath it.

I speak to him loudly in my head, silent to all but myself, "Mick? Why did you have to go? I would have cared for you. I would have never left your side. Why did you go?"

There is no answer. No sound.

My forehead rests on the hardness of the casket.

Very soft, a whisper, almost, I sing to my True Love captured within this eternal prison I will never be able to physically penetrate. I whisper the song he sang to me. "Three Times a Lady." It comes out in halted breaths and swallowed words, ends of rainbows and wishes for a chance to do it all over, this time just the two of us together for a lifetime

"I love you" my final sigh.

When she puts her hand on my shoulder, I hear myself sobbing softly out loud.

"Come," Wendy says. "Let's go downstairs and have a cigarette together?"

I climb away from the kneeling block and let her help me up.

Together, with all eyes on us, we walk arm-in-arm down the stairs to the basement.

She seats herself in a folding chair at the head of a long table. I sit beside her. There is coffee and cookies. There is ham and bread. There is cake.

She removes two cigarettes from a fresh pack, hands me one, and lights both with a match.

We take a drag at the same time.

"Mick would be so pissed if he saw us smoking," I say.

"Well, we're really pissed that he died," she answers.

"So there?" I ask.

"So there," she concurs.

We drag. Inhale. Exhale. We scan each other.

"What do you have there?" She points to the photos now pasted between my thumb and fingers.

"Just some pictures of Mick and I," I answer, embarrassed.

"Can I see?"

I hand her the stack, leaning in to look at them with her, and I narrate each one. She lingers over each shot, asking questions, bringing to life again my lost love.

My energy revives.

I am telling the stories, forgetting the uniqueness of the situation, who I am telling them to.

Her eyes betray no hurt. She seems to look at me maternally, with sympathy, never letting on what this must mean to her.

We laugh again about how naughty we were being, smoking.

How Mick must be looking down at us in disapproval.

He hated when I smoked and was always trying to get me to quit.

We take drags and look at each other, bursting into giggles like two naughty girls sneaking a puff in their parent's bathroom.

By the time we get through the pictures, I am relaxed and laughing, the first time since Mick's accident.

For one brief moment, I don't feel the weight of the loss.

A middle-aged Midwestern-looking couple comes up behind Wendy. They take her hands, hugging her deeply and kissing her.

They take the seats next to me at the table.

They have Ohio accents, stretching their "o's" and flattening the rest of their vowels.

They are, I learn, Mick's parents.

In my own tight, young, seventeen-year-old narcissistic world of grief, everyone else is a character in this tragedy I am experiencing. I had never thought about him having parents.

I am shoved by an urge to be "known" to them, to have them know what an important part of their son's heart I had been. In this moment, it doesn't occur to me how devastating I might be to them. Me, at the funeral of their beloved son. This seventeen-year-old girl their son had betrayed his marriage for.

Wendy introduces me, and I launch into a picture-showing episode like I'd done with her.

His parents are not as receptive. They grow more and more uncomfortable, shifting in their seats, their eyes diverted, looking at Wendy and then around the room. I notice, but I am completely, selfishly unaware of the extraordinary pain I must be causing them.

I thank Wendy.

Michael and Rick take me out to my car.

I drive home to an empty, black, echoing hole.

Mourning.

Morning.

A morning.

I don't know when or how many days it's been since the wake when my parents call me into the other room.

They're sitting at the dining room table, an open newspaper spread atop it.

"Daughter," my father says, "did you know that Mick was thirty-one years old?"

"Huh?"

"That bastard," my father mutters.

"What do you mean?" I ask.

"It says here: Michael Daggett, beloved husband—did you know he was married?"

I nod.

My father's eyes shoot bullets at me. At the situation. At the deceased Mick.

"Beloved father of three. Children, too?"

My mother looks at me, puts her hand on my father's wrist, and emits one of her back-of-the-throat groans.

Thirty-one years of age. Three children."

I am in shock. Thirty-one?

Mick had lied to me.

***

Michael calls. He wants to see me, needs to see me. He's desperate to talk about Mick. Patty, his wife, is out of town for the weekend.

Maybe I can come over and he'll make dinner and we'll talk?

He welcomes me into his suburban home, furnished in Nautical style; there are pictures of sailboats and rope tchotchkes.

I show him my ever-present pictures of Mick and I, and reminisce about Mick's glorious hands, his fragile eyelashes, his champagne laugh, the way his spirit seemed to pirouette and shimmy, the way he sang his thoughts.

We laugh and toast to Mick and drink Chablis, the kind he and Mick liked. For a moment, I feel like my old self again: the woman Mick loved. For the moment, I am not the woman who withered and disappeared after he was gone.

I stare at Michael as he talks about times he remembers. Character traits he shared with Mick—they were best friends for so long—come alive in front of me. Michael shares with Mick some similarity of movement and inflection I had never noticed before: the movement of his hands, how he holds the wine glass, the rise and fall of his vocal pattern. Perhaps they inherited these things from each other over the years.

Hope washes over me, through me, and I lean into Michael's aura. He isn't Mick. I know that, but it's close enough. He is a fine substitute, and maybe he can restore me, restore my life, pull me out of the tsunami I am drowning in, yank me back onto a safe, recognizable harbor.

Just for a moment.

Just for a moment.

We talk until we have no more to say, until stories begin to repeat themselves. I look at my watch.

"I think I should go. I have to be home by midnight." I reach forward to hug him goodbye.

"You know, Mick was thinking about ending it with you."
The air crackles.

"What do you mean?" I am stunned.

"He told me. He was concerned about your age. That the relationship couldn't go anywhere."

"I don't believe you," I say. "Mick and I talked about it. He said he could never leave me, that I was his True Love. We're Soul Mates."

"I know, but he was getting tired of the age thing. Of having to sneak around."

Why is he saying this to me?

"We had to sneak around 'cause he was married, mostly," I answer him without flinching, but I feel as if sharp tweezers are pulling my heart apart one piece at a time.

"I know he wasn't going to leave me. He loved me," I say, demanding this be the last word.

"He wanted you to go on with your life. He really believed in you. He always talked about how much potential you had. Maybe he just didn't want to stand in your way. I know he loved you, but maybe he loved you so much that he wanted you to fly and felt you couldn't if you stayed with him."

"I don't believe you," I say again, standing, grabbing for my purse, gulping back impending tears.

"Hey, I didn't mean to make you cry." He comes to me, wrapping his arms around me.

"Well, what did you think saying that would make me do?"

"Hey, hey," he says, pulling me close to his chest. "C'mon, don't cry."

But it's too late. I'm shaking against him.

He clutches me tight until I calm.

He takes my face in his hands the way Mick did the first night I met him.

"You really are so lovely," he whispers, and, for a moment, with my eyes closed, I imagine it is Mick speaking.

Hearing those words again is like a warm, soft breath in my ear. The world falls on its head. Time stops, and Mick is not dead.

My body, weak, falls into his arms.

A salty tear drops into my mouth.

He brings his tongue down to my lower lip and licks away the wetness.

Then he opens his mouth, covering my lips with his.

I am terrified and overcome at the same time.

It is too soon.

Too soon.

He is not Mick.

Mick would be looking down from Heaven and hating us.

Hating me.

Wondering how we could be doing this so soon after.

Yet Michael's lips are restoring me to the woman Mick loved.

I am *She* again.

240

I am the Goddess only visible through Mick's eyes.

His lips are still hungry, still feeding on mine. He walks me into the bedroom, laying me on his bed. Quickly, he enters my body, moving fast above me, in and out.

I feel the wetness dripping out the sides of my eyes into my ears and hair. If I open my eyes, I'll see Michael's dark-brown hair. If I breathe in, I'll smell Michael's scent instead of Mick's. So, I lay with my eyes squeezed shut, holding my breath, imagining it is Mick on top of me making love, a sensation I thought I was never to feel again.

When he finishes, he lays next to me, silently running his fingers through my hair.

"Do you think we should have done that?" I ask, breaking the quiet. "Do you think if Mick were looking down at us, he would be mad at us?'

"I think," he says, smoothing a hair away from my forehead, "that Mick would understand."

"What? What would he understand?"

"That we both were just looking to get close to him again."

Michael turns over onto his back.

We lay staring at the ceiling, up beyond the ceiling to where Mick is, lying there together, missing him.

INTERMISSION:
GRAB SNACKS,
SILENCE YOUR PAY PHONES.

ENJOY THE REST OF THE STORY.

PART TWO

AN EDUCATION

- 23 -
SOMEDAY

Memories of Mick are everywhere. Every place hurts except, once a week, during my Saturday night babysitting job, for those few hours, real life goes away. I'm able to forget I had a true love, and he's dead.

Every Saturday night, I babysit for a couple whose baby is still in a crib. I don't know much about them. They live in a two-story townhouse. Upstairs is the master bedroom and the baby's room connected by a bathroom. In the bathroom, on the toilet is a box labeled "Hemorrhoid Wipes." I have no idea what hemorrhoids are or how you get them except that it seems like you can wipe them away. I'm not sure which one has them or if they both do. Are hemorrhoids contagious? This is the only personal thing I know about them.

The husband is a big man. Maybe two or three hundred pounds. My dad said he's fat. My mom says heavyset. The wife is teeny-tiny thin, a little taller than me but even skinnier. So, they're an unusual couple. I can't imagine how they made the baby, but I try. Wouldn't he squash her?

By the time I arrive in the early evening, they're ready to go, and the baby is fed and in her crib in the tiny nursery. On the counter, just for me, they've laid out all sorts of snacks. Not just cookies and chips, but Mystic Mint cookies and *Onion Sour Cream* dip *for* the chips. There's Orange Fanta pop and more selections in the fridge. They're very kind to me. They tell me to eat anything I want. Which is one of the reasons it's a great job. One of the reasons.

The other reason is, on these Saturday nights, sitting cross-legged on the master bed, (because that's where the TV is), eating a buffet of snacks, I watch the lineup:

7:00 *All in the Family.*

7:30 *The Jeffersons.*

8:00 *The Mary Tyler Moore Show.*

8:30 *The Bob Newhart Show.*

9:00 *The Carol Burnett Show.*

It's magical. The raw emptiness that is me, quiets, and I laugh. Hard. Out loud. Till I cry. It's the only time since Mick died that I laugh anymore.

That's when I have the discovery. In the middle of the TV lineup, watching Mary Tyler Moore, the world seemed to stop, as if saying "notice this moment; this is meant to be."

What do you want to be when you grow up? This. To be on a TV show, or my own show, like Mary Tyler Moore, like Carol Burnett. Part of a TV family, making people feel good, making people laugh, the same way these shows are saving me every Saturday. I want people to feel safe, to forget real life, and feel everything is ok, at least for the time my show is on.

It's inside me to be an actress, but I wasn't sure what shape that took in the world. It seemed vague. Now, when I say I want to be an actress, I mean this.

Oh my god, I'm buzzing. I haven't felt hopeful since before Mick died. Since then, my only goal has been to just get through. But right this moment, I have a purpose again. I can't wait to get home to tell my parents, when I say actress, I don't mean vague fantasies of being a glamorous star or rushing from photographers. I mean the actual job of acting. There are jobs. Careers. Once they understand, they'll be excited and help me figure out how to get started. Because right now, they're insisting I go to college in the fall. They're not paying for me to take acting classes. When I get serious about what I'm going to get my degree in, we can discuss it. I'm taking student loans anyway, and a summer job will pay for the rest. I know they love me, but them not believing in my dreams makes it hard for me to believe.

Usually, when the couple gets home, it's after *The Carol Burnett Show*. I'm conked out on the master bed surrounded by snacks. But tonight, I'm vibrating. I can't wait to get home.

***

My parents are awake in the living room. My mom has on her zip up modesty robe over her nightgown. Her feet are up on the hassock, and the long yarn blanket she's crocheting is draped over her lap. My dad is watching the news.

I rush up the stairs, bursting, high on my epiphany, possibly also the five hours of super sugary snacks. It blurts out of me, "There is a job for actors! I know the job! I'm going to be Mary Tyler Moore!"

I sit on the edge of the couch, holding my breath, waiting. I get hit by another wave, "That's what I want to be someday. Not just an actress, but an actress on TV. The minute it hit me, it felt meant to be."

My mom hooks a loop of yarn.

"You have your whole life ahead of you," she says, pulling the long yarn strand. Which seems like it's not the point and exactly the point.

"Exactly," I say.

I'm confused. It's a goal. It's a great goal. It's an actual job. My dad loves *The Carol Burnett Show*. He laughs until he has to take his glasses off to wipe his tears. This is what I'm telling them I want to do someday.

"You have to have something to fall back on," my mom says, moving her crochet hook, hooking and looping.

"When I *don't* make it? I haven't even tried, and you think I'm going to fail," I say, trying to be calm.

"It's a very selfish life. Actors need lots of attention. They have to be very self-absorbed," my mom says.

Why? Why do they have to be selfish? Does that mean I'm selfish because I want to be one? The argument I didn't anticipate has begun. Everything we haven't said. Everything that's been hinted at and tiptoed around.

"It's because of these shows I'm laughing again. These shows save me. Nothing else in my stupid life does!" I yell, unsuccessful at being calm.

"I'm glad they help you," my mom says, her fingers tracing the loops, counting how many she's completed.

"How is it self-absorbed to want to help people escape? What's wrong with wanting that?" I'm on the verge of tears.

"That's not what you want," my mom says. "You want to make yourself feel good goofing around. You're going to waste your college years. It's time to grow up."

"I am grown-up, and I'm not goofing around and—I can't even talk to you guys. Why is it so hard to even imagine that I might have something special enough? That maybe, just maybe, I could someday be a famous actress?"

"Oy. Enough yelling. You're gonna wake the neighborhood," my mom says.

"Listen, daughter," my dad says. "You're a smart girl. Why don't you think of doing something that could make a difference in the world?"

"Like what? Being a lawyer or a doctor?" They always want everyone to be a lawyer or doctor.

"You would be a very good lawyer," my mom says. "You love to argue."

"I'm only arguing because you won't hear me."

"What about a psychologist? You like people—"

"I do! But I don't want to fix people, I want to be with them the way they are."

It's like they know me only as their daughter. It's like they don't want a whole part of me that's not an extension of them to exist. Or maybe they do know me and just don't think I have what it takes.

"Harvey made it," I say, "and he's in our family! So, it's not such an impossible dream."

Harvey Korman, from *The Carol Burnett Show*, is my second cousin, my mom's cousin. She told me he used to sometimes sleep on my grandma's couch when he was a starving actor. Before he made it. So. It can happen. Harvey's famous, and he's related. Regular people can make it.

"Harvey struggled a long time before he was discovered. He had a hard road," my mom says.

"What's wrong with a hard road? If there's a will, there's a way. Right?" I ask.

My dad always told us, "If there's a will, there's a way." His mother said it to him, and he would say it to us whenever we were giving up.

"I don't want to see you suffer. You have to go to college so you have something to fall back on. That's what it is," my mom says. Her crochet hook grabs and pulls some yarn through a loop.

"You're always telling me that I'm so dramatic and so oversensitive that I should be an actress. Now that I want to be one, you don't want me to be? Oh, that makes sense," I say.

I cannot understand why they have such bad feelings about acting and me in acting.

"All right, it's late," my mom says, gathering her crochet, stabbing her needle through the holes of the patterned blanket.

"I don't want to go to college. I want to go to TV acting school. Or just be an actress." I say.

"Listen, kid," my dad says, "I've had enough for one night. My eyes are closing."

They always leave mid-argument.

"Oh my god! You're so frustrating. I came in all excited, knowing what I want to be in my life, and now I just feel stupid, like I shouldn't have told you."

"Listen, daughter, we can talk about it in the morning. I'm getting a headache. So, let it be written," he says, biblically, rising from the couch.

"Fine, I'll find my own way to get acting jobs. Maybe before college even starts," I say to their backs as they head down the hallway to bed.

I won't even have to go to college to become whatever. I'll be on my way to fame. When I'm a famous, successful actress, they'll be like "we should have believed her."

Maybe it's shallow to want to be a famous actress. But I want that. People care what happens to famous people. If someone dies in a famous person's life, the whole world mourns with them. It's on every magazine cover. It's in the news. People talk about it at work. If someone dies in a non-famous person's life, no one cares for long. They think you should get over it. A famous person can feel however they feel for as long as they feel it, and people care and talk about how they must be feeling. So, yes, I want to be famous someday.

– 24 –
JOBS

A new restaurant named Corfu is opening in our neighborhood. A Greek diner. I apply, and I'm hired with all the new
hires. There's meetings and training and uniforms, then the
grand opening. The restaurant is packed from the minute
they open the doors. We're non-stop racing. Somehow, all
the other waitresses know everything about the menu, where
things are, what goes with the menu items, like soup or salad,
and what to bring to the tables and when. Why don't I know
any of this? I was at the meetings and the training.

"It's all Greek to me," I say a few times when I'm
confused. It's funny the first day, then the other waitresses
stop laughing.

My skills are: greeting the tables, taking the orders, and
writing "thank you" and a smiley face on their checks. And

bringing food that's not complicated. Not like soup. Oh god, soup.

Soup is always complicated. First off, you have to remember to bring the special spoon and the side crackers, and two, you have to remember to bring it in the first place because you don't get it from the kitchen. Then, you have to get the bowl or the cup. Oh, and you have to remember if it's a bowl or cup, so that's four. Then, you have to ladle it yourself, and you have to not spill it or get your uniform in it. (Especially your boobs. Trust me. It's a hazard.)

I hate when people order soup. Or anything that has a side to it. I always forget what sides go with what and to ask what dressing they want if they say salad. I know to be the cheerful me, the giggling funny one that everyone likes, talking to my customers, laughing with them.

I work three days on lunch shifts. On my third day, a table of four truckers sits in my booth. I spend a lot of time flirting. They're so happy. They say so.

"Oh, man," they say, "we're coming back here all the time."

They say it loud. I'm sure my boss hears. They leave me a ten-dollar tip. Most tips are around one dollar. I think if they give me more shifts, and I get more tables of men, I could get rich this summer.

The boss calls me into the back office. He tells me to change into my regular clothes and turn in my uniform. I'm fired. I cry. Why? What did I do? Customers love me. Isn't that the job? I'm so confused.

He won't tell me why. I thought being a good waitress and being good for the restaurant is when the customers loved you.

"The customers love me. Isn't that good?" I ask through tears.

In his thick Greek accent, he says, "Family restaurant. No sexpot."

I don't want to be a waitress anyway. I want to be an actress but, oh my god, how? I just need a start. Why does no one seem to know how to do that? Not teachers, not counselors, not magazines on acting. Not one how-to book at the library. You have to have that *it* factor, they say. You have to have inborn talent, they say. It's either meant to be or it's not, they say. You have to be discovered, they say. Ok, but how do you get discovered?

Maybe in the "Wanted" ads? I borrow my dad's Sunday paper, and there they are. Not for acting but for modeling. Models probably get to be actresses.

The ad reads:

"Photographer with national publication seeking models. No experience necessary. Must be eighteen. A+ to look 12-18yrs."

I'm seventeen, so, yay.

At my best friend Suzy's house, I dress up in my red slacks and my tight white t-shirt that says "Jailbait" in red letters across my breasts. We Farrah Fawcett my hair. Suze takes Polaroids of me, and I send them with my letter where I fib and say I'm eighteen.

I wait. I check the mail for a reply. I keep checking the "Wanted" ads.

Another ad is for aerobics instructors for a brand-new women's health club named Spa Petite. This would be good. Mick would be so proud of me. He was a fitness fanatic. I apply. They teach me an hour routine. Thanks to my cheerleading background, I memorize it fast and try out for the woman boss. I'm hired.

Spa Petite is in a strip mall just a five-minute drive from our house.

Our uniforms are black, high-cut zipper-front leotards that say "Spa" over one breast and "Petite" over the other. Underneath, we wear beige tights.

The all-female staff has several jobs. One is to sign up new members and receive commission. Two, they have to guide members through their personalized workout programs. Designed by us. Scary. With three of us working from opening to close, we are each to teach two of the six aerobics classes offered daily.

Three of us worked full-time. Me, Helena, and a girl named Cal. Cal is short, a bit chubby, and is supposed to also teach aerobics classes, but when her time comes to teach, she pats her belly and says, with pain in her voice, "You guys, I can't teach today. I'm too bloated. I'm filled with poop."

Which always seems way too revealing and personal. I can't even admit I poop in the first place.

Then, she begs me or Helena to teach her class. Every day. Every single time. And we do. Helena and I alternate teaching three one-hour high impact aerobics classes of the six total each day. Meanwhile, Cal sits behind the check-in desk drinking pop and signing people up for memberships. And getting commission.

Helena and I bond over this and become friends outside of work. She's my first friend I didn't have from school. We hang out like adults in real world places. We have fake ID's for the local disco where we order Pink Squirrels. We have no idea what's in them, but they're sweet, they require an ID, and they never seem to get us tipsy. We spend time at Corfu, the Greek diner I was fired from, drinking coffee, smoking, talking, and, at some point in the many hours, ordering. Me, a banana cream pie. Helena, one scrambled egg and a half piece of dry toast.

When Helena initially said to meet her at Corfu, I suggested Denny's instead, but Corfu was closer. We sit, drinking bottomless cups of coffee. I confess my firing incident. She listens, posture forward, smoking. When I finish, she leans back and taps an ash from her cigarette.

"Oh my god," she says in her thick Midwestern accent. "Well, 'cause it's a family restaurant first of all."

"I know. But so?" I ask.

"So, you're seventeen. The pervert truckers were like what?"

"I don't know. We weren't doing anything," I say.

"I mean, the owner didn't want people to be uncomfortable."

"But the truckers would have come back. And they might have told their friends?"

"Forget it. You wanna still be working here? Forgetting soup?"

I definitely don't.

"Spa P is better anyway," she says. Then, she looks around. "They don't even recognize you here."

I look around. Waitresses I knew just a couple weeks ago walk by. Taking orders. Carrying soup. Ugh. It's true. And weird. I was just fired a few weeks ago. If I'm not in uniform, they don't know me.

Helena is the most symmetrical girl I ever saw. Beautiful that can't be seen as anything but. Poreless skin. Thick wavy blonde hair that requires no bobby pins or hair spray. Her nose is thin and straight with flared Sophia Loren nostrils. Her body is model thin but not unhealthy looking. She looks beautiful without makeup and more beautiful than any Miss America I've ever seen.

I expected her to either be stuck up (she's not), or have plans to go to New York City to become a model (she doesn't). She could have had anything she wanted in the world of men just based on her beauty. But she's so practical, a Midwestern girl from a lower income family like me. My dreams are to save the world and be an unforgettable actress. Or vice versa. Her dreams are to be a model but to stay close to home. Also, to get married, have babies and have a house in the same neighborhood where her family lives. Maybe work in an office. Way too unglamorous for me, but that's what's so nice about our friendship.

I tell Helena about Mick.

She says, "Wow, yeah. Your heart is broken. It's like you're a widow at seventeen."

She's my friend that never knew him or me the way I was. Just two months ago. She's new, so I'm new. We build something new.

– 25 –
POSE

Scoping the want ads, just in case, I see:

Director seeking talented actresses. Star quality only. Send picture and résumé. Include twenty-five-dollar cash application fee.

Aha! And eeeek! This could be it. My break!

It takes me a week to save up the twenty-five dollars. I wrap the twenty-five singles in notebook paper and tape my Polaroid to it. Since I don't have a resume—I'm not sure what a resume is—I include a letter saying how much I want to be an actress and why. It's two pages front and back.

A week later, I get a call. I sit under my desk in my room to talk so no one in my house hears. I don't want my parents to know.

He has an accent that isn't American. Not German. Maybe from Europe. His name is Willem Oster. He has been a famous director in Sweden for many years, he tells me. He was Ingrid Bergman's director and mentor and practically discovered her. Do I know who she is?

I say, "Yes! She's the famous actress who is in the movie *Casablanca*."

He seems pleased I know this. And then he says he is now making his next big film in the US. It will be a remake of the film *Gone with the Wind*.

I say I know that movie, even though I don't. But I say I know it. I do know the famous line from it.

He says he's on a talent scout to find his perfect Scarlett O'Hara. He asks do I think that could be me?

"Yes. Of course," I say.

He asks if I want to come for an interview. He's holding in-person interviews in the lobby of the Palmer House in the city, in Chicago. On Sunday.

And I say, "Yes. Of course."

He asks if I need directions.

I think about how I am going to do this. I'm not sure what I'll tell my parents where I'm going with the car. But I'm excited because maybe he'll discover me.

I say, "I've never driven into the city, but I can borrow my parent's car."

He says it sounds like it might be too much trouble.

I say, "Frankly my dear, I don't give a damn."

261

We both laugh because it's the famous line, and I know it.

I hang up and jump up and down in my room, silently screaming my joy. This might be my famous date with destiny.

***

The Palmer House is the fanciest hotel I've ever seen. The sign outside is made of gold. After entering, there's another entrance of two velvet curtains parted in the center that threshold the lobby. On the ceiling is an elaborate hand-painted mural. The carpet is lush green with a large swirling pattern. Everything looks old and stern as if it is only for important people. In front of me is a double staircase with a gold railing in the center, dividing it. The stairs are covered in the same elegant carpet.

I imagine I'm the movie star after being discovered years ago in this very spot, and I'm about to meet my dear director, Willem Oster. I raise my chin and only eye the steps as I walk down slowly. I wonder if walking with elegance down staircases is practiced in acting school. My neck grows higher, and my posture lifts, balancing an imaginary book on my head. I'm a princess, kind and beautiful, smiling a warm, closed-lip smile to the crowds as I descend. On either side are gold pole lamps that blossom into chandeliers. As I pass them, my head tilts down, and my eyes look up with "come hither" heavy lids as if the camera is pulling in for my close-up. It's impossible not to imagine I'm already famous.

I see him sitting in a little area with two leather chairs and a wooden coffee table with lots of papers spread out around him.

He looks much older than the picture in the newspaper clipping he mailed to me, the one showing him with his arm over the shoulder of Ingrid Bergman. He's an old man with white hair. Maybe like fifty or sixty or seventy or eighty?

He sees me and stands and says my name. We shake hands. My heart is going hummingbird-crazy. I'm giggling way too much.

He opens a scrap book of fading newspaper articles taped with crackling yellow tape. He speaks English tinged with, I guess Swedish? He repeats what he told me about himself while showing me articles illustrating everything he's saying. The articles are for proving what he's saying is true.

Pointing at another article, he juts his chin, urging me to read, and I pretend to. I'm too nervous to actually read. He watches me for reactions. I nod, impressed. *Impressed.* I believe him without reading. You can't make up being in the newspaper. I nod and believe him so we can move on to the important parts: the acting role and how I apply for it.

He asks me if I want to drink anything, but I can't think of anything. Also, I only have a dollar twenty-five which is for gas on the way home. My parents don't know I took the station wagon all the way into Chicago. I have to come home with almost as much gas as I left with.

"Tea?" he asks.

But I don't know if he's paying, and I don't know how much tea is, so I say no thank you to the tea.

He closes the scrapbook and unzips a leather pouch that's fraying on the edges. He must be too busy to buy a new one. Famous directors are like that, probably. Only poorer people who haven't made it yet have to care, I think. Because they don't want to get caught with their slip showing, my mother would say.

He sits back. I sit up straight, my hands clasped so hard against each other I can feel my own heat and bones.

"So, you are an actress?" he asks.

His front teeth seem to click forward a few centimeters then his tongue clicks them back again. I try not to notice or focus on it. I imagine it must be false teeth instead of his regular teeth being loose. I hope. It would be terrible if it was his regular teeth and they pushed out during a meeting with me. Then that would be all he would remember me for. The girl he was talking to when his teeth fell out.

"There's going to be a big remake of *Gone with the Wind*. Do you know that movie?"

I say yes. But I don't.

They are on a talent search for the next Scarlett O'Hara. I remember this from our phone call.

"Oh!" I exclaim.

Doesn't he remember telling me? And my funny response?

We are searching for the right look, the right tonality.

I nod, understanding how important it is for them to get this just right. There will be several phases to the audition process. The first will be the look. How you look on camera. Am I available for a photoshoot, test photos, on Thursday of this week?

I say yes. *Yes!*

I know I'm on the schedule for work, but I'm pretty sure Helena can cover me. Or I can just call in sick. This is so much more important. This could change my whole life.

He gives me the information where to go for the test photos. Downtown Chicago. More scary city driving. He stands as I say goodbye.

I'm giddy the entire way home, so floaty in my head, imagining the scenario of me in front of the camera and all the movie crew gathering around, looking at the pictures.

"She's so photogenic."

"She's got that special something. Charisma."

"There's something about her."

And Willem saying, "I discovered Ingrid and gave her her first break. I'm going to do the same for you." There are newspaper pictures that proclaim, "The New Scarlett O'Hara, discovered by famed director Willem Oster."

I tell no one. All of me wants to believe this is how it's done. This is how actresses are discovered. All of me wants to believe I'm special. Isn't that what you have to be? Special? That some people are and some people aren't? But you don't know your secret future until the curtain is drawn and your fate, your destiny, is revealed. Like a game show. Isn't that how it works?

***

I am standing on a box against a bulletin board where he has thumbtacked articles of him and Ingrid Bergman. He has me wearing a light-blue polyester leotard with a wide collar, open buttons that lead down past my sternum, and thick snaps at the crotch that pinch into my "vv."

He's pulled the material of the way-too-large leotard to the back, fastened with three safety pins to tighten at the waist. He is way below me. I feel way above him. He likes to take the pictures from down below, as low as by my ankles when I'm standing on something—like right now on the box of books—and point the camera up at me.

The Polaroid zooms and spits out the pictures, and we see it form itself. He shows it to me with pride, nodding, studying the results. I look terrible. Not at all like the model I'm supposed to look like. My head is bulbous as my koi fish eyes stare down at him. My round breasts are uneven and diagonal in the framing. Instead of accentuating my waist, the fabric, pulled too tight, is crinkling and makes me look fatter. If this is the way they take pictures of models, why don't I look good? I did my makeup and hair before I came, and I looked pretty in my bathroom mirror. I practiced movie star faces and did their poses in my mirror.

He mutters for me to turn around; I know it's so he can readjust and make the pins tighter. I questioned him about this once, asking, "Aren't models on photoshoots supposed to have clothes that fit?"

He said no. The clothes were the clothes. The way they made them look good in pictures is the safety pins. You can't see the pins in the pictures, so it creates an illusion.

Who knew, right? You never know what goes on behind the scenes.

I ask why the photo shoots take place in his apartment. He says it's the way they get the first impressions, before they go into production and have to have crew and studios and big money involved. They take care of the things they can on their own at first. He has to see how I screen test in front of a camera before he gets me in front of a real set with so much at stake. This is my first peek behind the scenes in the movie biz. Seems like there's so many unglamorous "behind the scenes" scenes of a glamorous world.

From the box, I watch him rummage through piles of old, wrinkled clothing. The apartment floor is thick with crumpled clothes and scarves and shoes and items scattered a sundry. Like a busy thrift store. It makes me wonder.

But I read that many creative artists, writers, and geniuses are a mess, their lives cluttered, living in chaos because of their creativity. Willem must be a genius director.

Every week I come, he's picked out a few new clothing pieces from the piles and piles. Usually, it's a leotard with snaps at the crotch that doesn't fit right and needs to be pinned. Then, we make our way over to the box by the bulletin board near the kitchen, or the kitchen step stool by the entrance hall. Usually, those two perches lift me out of the piles. I try to pose in some of the styles I've seen in books of old-time movie stars.

At home, before the next time, I memorize the way Greta Garbo looks into or away from the camera. The tilt of her head. The heavy-lidded expression. I practice in the mirror, the vibrant aliveness of Katherine Hepburn projects to the camera, and I project that as Willem crouches on the floor below my feet, pointing the camera up toward me, his tongue making his front teeth click back and forth.

When he's positioned just right, and I've hit an expression he especially likes, he says don't move, and I hold my breath and stare at him, unblinking. Weird sayings come into my head as I observe him below me. Like "he's drowning in a *schmatta* mountain." *Schmatta* is rags in Yiddish. I think.

He asks if I can come on Saturday. I have my babysitting job on Saturday. He says he will give me twenty-five dollars if I come on Saturday. When I get home, I tell my babysitting job I can't come this Saturday. I am involved in a high-stakes interview for my future.

***

On Saturday, he has something special for me: a triangular shawl made of tiny soft colorful threads that weave a silky pattern and fray off into a long, trickling fringe at the end. Instead of going to the box or the ladder, he moves me toward the other room. I've never been to the room which I guess must be the bedroom.

He asks if I'm ok with partial nudity, and I know that that's a question they ask actresses in contracts because I read it in biographies of famous actresses. They have clauses in their contracts. That's one reason Marilyn Monroe got so famous is she was ok with nudity. Betty Grable showed her legs. Most of the famous, most glamorous actresses started out not being afraid of nudity. Most except Bette Davis, Katherine Hepburn, and Audrey Hepburn. Willem tells me to take off my clothes and cover myself with the shawl and, when I'm ready, to call him.

I'm sitting at the foot of the bed covering myself with the triangle. I've never been naked or partially naked like this before. Both my hands hold up the top of the shawl above my breasts. The triangle part falls in-between my legs and partially covers my thighs.

He asks me if I would lie back, but I can keep my feet on the floor.

I do. He tucks the shawl tight under my right side and tight under my left side, then tight down between my legs. Kinda like the same thing he does with the bodysuits, making them skin-tight against my body. He starts adjusting his position on the floor to get the perfect angle.

I lay looking up at the ceiling. I hear the *click, click* of his teeth as he presses them forward then back with his tongue. I hear the *click* then the *wiz* of the Polaroid shooting out the picture. For a second, I think this is all this is. He's not directing a film, and he's not taking stills for the studio. He's having me here to take pictures.

He tucks and untucks and rearranges the fabric. I don't want it not to be true. If it's not true, then not only have I been used, but my dreams, all my imagined outcomes, will crumble, and I'll land, humiliated, back into my life of just me.

I ask him, "When will we be going to the studio with the pictures? Will I get a script to memorize soon?"

He says he thinks these pictures, with the shawl, are the winners. Finally! I'm so happy. I get dressed as Willem spreads out all the pictures we've taken since the first time. There's fifty at least. He likes all of them. I don't see what he sees. I've taken some pretty good pictures in my life and, in these, I can only find maybe two that don't make me look distorted.

Willem says it's the style. The camera has to find the most interesting angles. I understand. I think. He asks me if I have any girlfriends to bring that want to get into modeling. I feel sick. I thought he was priming me to be his next Ingrid Bergman. Why would he want me to bring a friend?

He must see my hurt, because he says, "Not an actress like you. Not for the role of Scarlett. It would just be for modeling."

It helps him to practice on different subjects. He will pay us both twenty-five dollars and, to me, an extra twenty dollars just for gas, just for coming. Saturday afternoon is best. But I have my babysitting, and I feel so bad having to cancel. I say I'll see.

I know my friend Sue wouldn't want to do it. She might, but she'd ask too many questions. Questions I ask myself on the tense freeway drives into the city and home. Questions I have Willem's explanations for that sound right at the time but lopsided once I'm alone.

I decide I'll ask Helena. In the diner, I tell her everything. How he would pay her twenty-five dollars. I tell her how he's helping me eventually to play Scarlett O'Hara. She's excited for me and for her and, most especially, for the twenty-five dollars, which is the least exciting part for me. Yes, it's money, but I want the career. I want to be discovered. I want the extraordinary. I want the world to vibrate because I was here. How can anyone not want that?

***

Before the next time with Willem, when Helena was going to go with me, I get a call from the first "Wanted" ad I answered. The photographer from the national magazine. He wants to know if I can come for a photoshoot, and of course I can. The dam is bursting, and the opportunities are rolling in. Things are finally starting to happen for me.

His apartment, in a high rise with parking right there in his building, is so much more modern than Willem's old brick walk up. It makes me wonder why Willem, a famous director, lives where he lives, and this young photographer lives in this elevator building with a fountain out front.

He seems like he's maybe thirty, a lot younger than Willem, but still a grown-up. His apartment has white carpet and white counters, and everything is white and tidy except for the black camera and stand and lenses and all the equipment.

I can tell just from the way he looks at me when he opens the door, I'm not exactly what he was hoping for. Maybe I'm too short? But he saw my picture, so I don't know.

He tells me the pictures will be nudes. Tasteful, he says. I'll show you, he says. We can start and end with partial nudes, he says. But you have more chances to get into the magazines with nudes. He asks me if I'm still interested.

I say yes. I'm thinking of Norma Jean—Marilyn Monroe—who got her start posing nude. Soldiers liked her poster, and she got famous enough that Hollywood came a callin'.

He hands me a thick terry cloth bathrobe with silky material inside. He tells me to put it on and lay my clothes over there. On the white table. That way, the crease marks from my clothes will have time to ease off my skin. Which makes more sense than most of what Willem says.

We sit at the other white table and there are magazines kind of like *Playboy* but not *Playboy*. Magazines with nude girls in tropical places. He has me look through them. Then, he pages through the contract. A contract. Wow. I'm going to sign a contract. This is real. He says he's freelance. I'm not sure exactly what that means, but I make a serious face and nod and pretend I do. The pictures we're going to take will be his property. He will send them to the magazines and, if they publish them, he will let me know, and then I will get paid. Otherwise, neither of us gets paid.

I sign on the line on the bottom of two pages, one that says I'm eighteen. Ha-ha. I'm not. But from my fake IDs for the bar Helena and I both have, it says I'm twenty-one. I know that year by heart, so I put that down. The other signature is that I consent to him owning the pictures until we sell them is what he tells me.

He positions me on the white bed against the white wall and has me drop a shoulder of the robe. He holds a tiny cube with a dime bulb by my face, and it pops when he presses his camera. Now, he's ready. He hides behind the camera that's not way down by my feet shooting upward. He's level with me. And he tells me to move in whatever way I want. At first, I feel shy, but as I smile into the camera and turn my chin down, my eyes look up from under heavy lids, and the photographer whispers "yes, yes, that's beautiful—beautiful sexy, oh, yes."

And with every "yes" and "you're beautiful," I let the robe slip more. The movement flows, and I think about all the movie stars I've been studying for Willem, and I start doing all the faces and the poses. It feels like we're on a ride.

I work my way from vertical to horizontal to vertical again on the white bed. Every so often, he reaches a hand to move a hair out of my eye, off my forehead, away from my mouth or to flatten the white bedspread that's rumpled up. When I can't think of another pose, he has me sit down at the edge of the bed. He asks me if I would mind spreading my legs apart. My toes touch the white rug that sits on the white carpet on the floor. Even though I'm sitting with my legs straddled apart, I stand on my toes as if I'm a ballet dancer on point. That way, it makes my thighs lift so they don't squish on the bed and look fat. He tells me to place my hands on either knee. I do. And I can feel the wetness, the heat between my legs. Dripping. Dripping out of me.

I feel like I'm in the mirror game I used to play when I was little. I feel like he's the man in the mirror watching me, spying on me, seeing more of me than I noticed him seeing. It's making the heat in my center glow red, warm and hot, moving up and pulsating out through my body. He reaches his hand forward and asks for permission to touch me between my legs. He tells me he just wants to shape my lips for the camera. I nod. His finger touches my labia and spreads them apart. His touch is so light, so tender as if he's trying not to touch me at all. As he does, I feel myself dripping. He lays his camera down, grabs a towel, and lays it on the floor below my dripping wetness.

He takes some pictures from far away, moving closer to me, moving closer to my face then pulling wide again, Then, finally, a close-up of just my vagina. I can hardly stand it. He puts down the camera and puts his finger between my legs, and I let him. I lay back on the bed, and I want it. I want it so much. I wasn't sure if this was the reason that he brought me here. If this is what he does. If he is a legitimate photographer. A freelancer. Or if he fucks all the models that come over. I don't know. I don't care. I just want him to fuck me. And he does. It's fast. I think. He fucks for himself. But then, that's how men fuck, isn't it? It's so hot. But I never have the honey pot moment with men. That's only something I can do with myself. I know in porno books, or dirty books like *Coffee, Tea, or Me*, or in *The Happy Hooker* or in *Penthouse Forum*, the ladies talk about them coming together. Or the guy made them come. But that's never happened to me.

When he finishes, I'm even more drippy wet and still humming inside, but it's over. I wash up and re-dress in his bathroom which is also all white. Even the soap is white. And when I come out, he's dressed and the room looks as if nobody's touched anything.

He thanks me and shakes my hand and tells me he'll be in touch if the pictures sell. I hope they do. It's not an acting part, but it might get me started.

***

With Helena in the car, the drive into the city doesn't feel like such a tense panic ride. We sing radio songs and talk about modeling careers. She's truly the model type. She's getting a model portfolio put together and taking modeling classes in the city with Barbizon. It's just a starting point for her. Someday, she'll be in the JCPenney catalog, and I'll be on TV.

We park and walk to Willem's faded yellow brick building. My pace is brisker, bouncier, more outgoing while walking with her to his apartment. I'm an old pro at this.

I buzz, and we head down the stairs to his basement apartment. Willem greets her with a big smile, clicking his front teeth forward and back. He goes through his routine picking a bodysuit for each of us. One at a time, we head into the bathroom to change.

Helena's body looks so much better than mine in the bodysuit. In our Spa Petite bodysuits, we both look good. But she looks good in anything. She wears the light-blue polyester one, his favorite, and looks so much better in it than I did. Her body is tight, slim, with nothing extra. She has small breasts and hips and legs like a ballet dancer. She doesn't have to be at any special angle. Any position she's in looks like a picture in a magazine.

She steps onto the kitchen step stool in front of the white closet door. I think about how perfect she is, but Willem still feels the need for the safety pins. However, instead of having her turn around, he pins tight from her waist in front down to her hips so when she turns around, the butt part is really tight and lifts up so you can see her butt cheeks. He tells her to stay facing the wall and to turn around looking over her shoulder as he takes pictures from behind. First over her left shoulder. Then her right. He's crouching, finding different angles. Usually, it's very quiet when Willem and I take pictures together. He doesn't talk to me much; he just moves me from this place to that place or adjusts the safety pins. But, with Helena there, it's now us giggling, chatting.

"This is like our Spa Petite uniform," Helena says. We both laugh. It sort of is.

It's my turn. We make our way through the piles of clothing on the floor. I'm up on the box by the kitchen. Helena lights a cigarette and watches. I feel silly doing my movie star faces and poses in front of her. Willem doesn't seem to notice. He just keeps shooting from down below, and I hear the *zip, zip, zip* and see the flash of the Polaroid. He struggles up to his feet and readjusts the safety pins at my back making the bodysuit tighter and tighter.

Finally, we're done. Willem gives us each a Polaroid to take with us and hands us both twenty-five dollars.

We giggle all the way to the car, counting our "easy" money.

"What did you think?" I ask as I drive us onto the freeway.

"Oh, he's definitely not a real director," she says. I suddenly feel nauseous.

"Really?" I ask. My right hand digs into my bag, loosening a cigarette from the pack in my purse. I light it with the car cigarette lighter, and I quickly roll down the window with my left hand. I'm not allowed to smoke. At all. So, I definitely don't want the smell in my parent's car.

"He's a real director," I say.

"Definitely not," Helena says, examining the Polaroids. "These are not what model pictures look like. We look terrible. Model pictures are not Polaroids," she says.

"No, I know," I say, not knowing but remembering what Willem told me. "They take Polaroids first to get the right angle and the right lighting and the right shot and the right look. They do that before a real shoot. Because real film and real cameras cost a lot of money."

"He told you that?" she asks.

I nod.

"That's bullshit," she says.

She doesn't know the hopes I built up around this. I told her a little. But not everything. I never told her about how deep I hooked my dream to Willem Oster.

"He's a hoarder. His apartment is a mess," she says, laying out what I didn't know how to interpret.

"He's an old, oddball kook. I get my model pictures back from Barbizon next week. I'll show you what model pictures are supposed to look like."

"But these are not supposed to be model pictures," I insist. "They're stills to get the shots right for the screen test."

She lists the reasons why Willem Oster is not legitimate. Not real. Every protest I make, every counterargument I state using Willem's answers, Helena comes back with something logical, practical, and now that I think about it, true. I just listen, give as much of a laugh as I can muster, and nod.

I'm embarrassed. Humiliated. Devastated. Fooled. *Fooled*. A ridiculous *fool*. Did I really think I had the "it" factor? Did I really think "oh, I'm 'special'? The Universe is giving me my dream!" Ha! Really? You believed that? Thinking this was meant to be? It could be this easy? The reason the Polaroids look ugly is because I am ugly. The reason he was searching for a good angle is because I don't have one. I'm not photogenic. I'm not charismatic. Why do I believe what everyone says? Stupid. So stupid. Because you never know. It seems like everything is possible. I can see how anything could be true. I see the person I believe. Not the lie or the untruth. I'm empty. Queasy. There's a ditch where my dreams were.

At the coffee shop, I say, "He really did once direct Ingrid Bergman. It was in the newspaper, in black-and-white. Newspapers have to print the truth. That's their whole job."

"He's not. A director. Of movies," she says. "Maybe he was. Now, he's just a kookoo oddball."

I crease my eyebrows and nod.

She lights a new cigarette and begins the long list of things that weren't right. And why. The truths deflate me. The hope I placed in Willem slide onto the dirty coffee shop carpet.

We talk until we've both smoked all the cigarettes in our two packs. It's time to call it a night. We both have four aerobics classes to teach because, "Oh, you guys, I'm so bloated. I have too much poop in me," we say together, imitating Cal.

– 26 –
PURGATORY

I stop going to Willem, and there is no more Saturday baby-sitting job. They replaced me with someone dependable.

During my hour lunch break at Spa Petite, instead of hanging out having my Perrier and a peach, I drive the five minutes home. Our refrigerator is stocked. I never noticed how stocked. I didn't eat much. I was always doing gymnastics or writing or playing or doing things. I never noticed. Our freezer is especially stocked. Ice trays, meat, popsicles, a gallon of Neapolitan Ice Cream. Not my favorite. I don't like the chocolate, strawberry, and vanilla touching.

I shouldn't have ice cream in the day. I shouldn't have ice cream before I have to exercise. Or teach. I shouldn't have ice cream because my mom didn't say I could have it. I just shouldn't have ice cream. Buuuuut. If I just had a shrimp fork of it... That wouldn't even be noticeable.

Below our oven is the silverware drawer. Below that drawer is the silverware "for company" drawer. In that drawer are these special teeny-tiny forks that my mom said were shrimp forks. I've never had shrimp but just the word alone says it, so. Go figure.

I take out the gallon. The cardboard top is frozen to the brick of tri-colored ice cream. White steam fogs off the top as I peel it back. I take the shrimp fork, with its three mini prongs, and run it along one straight edge of the rectangle, letting my lips close on the sweet cold. My eyes close, my mouth takes in all the senses. I almost moan. Was ice cream always bliss?

I run the shrimp fork along just the very melted frame of the frozen block, and I slip it in my mouth. Ecstasy creams around my tongue. I'm not even high. How is this so good? I feel a quiet elation. Everything is sliding away. Everything's going to be ok.

The milky edges are deeper now. I make sure every skim is perfectly level and, if it's not, I scrape the extra, evening it off. With every forkful, a wash of euphoria relaxes me, and the heavy lead grief blanket that's been flattening me lifts and floats off.

I dig lower, skimming at the outside edges of the melted parts. My tongue is numb. The sweetness isn't as electric. But I can't stop. I scrape the tiny fork until it hits the bottom of the container. The ice cream is now a round ball, the chocolate and vanilla almost whittled away. The strawberry stands alone.

It's enough, I've eaten enough, I tell myself, but my hand skimming the fork won't stop. There can be no pause in the icy sugar bliss. The box is finally empty. I realize what I've done. It's time to go back to work. I teach my class at one. The box condemns me from the counter. I schmoosh it into itself and push it down below all the trash in the garbage can under the kitchen sink. No one will find it. Probably, my mom will think she bought it but then think she didn't. No one will suspect me. I leave for work, feeling worse than I did when I got home except for the time of euphoria between when it was just me and the intimacy and pleasure of the ice cream.

It's every day now. I come home for lunch, stopping at the store on the way, buying my own gallon so my parents won't know. I set it on the counter and wait for it to melt. I open a diet book and write out the diet I'm going to go on—not today—to lose the weight I'm starting to gain. Even though I'm teaching three high impact aerobics classes a day, and even though I'm working out on weights, nothing can compete with the gallon of ice cream I devour at lunch every day. Holding my shrimp fork, I feel relief, peace, relief, gratitude, overwhelming gratitude for the relief.

Every day I tell myself I will stop. I'm going to start fasting. Perrier only. Lose a pound or two a day. But every day, I come home.

Now I'm like Cal, asking whoever is on if they'll cover my aerobics class for me. I'm bloated. I'm not feeling up to teaching. Even Cal steps in for me. My bloat is more than hers. We compare pregnant bellies.

One day, no one can take over my one o'clock, my right after lunch break class. I make my way to the front of the studio and face the mirror. The class spreads out behind me. It's a full studio. I press play, and I start giving my enthusiastic commands over the music.

First, it's easy, smooth, just stretching, warming up. In the mirror, I am no longer the ninety-eight-pound athlete I was when I began this job. My uniform pulls, the zipper strains. My beige tights are uncomfortable, pushing out on my outer thighs. Saddle bags. Under my eyes puffy, there are dark half-moons. What is happening to me? I watch myself as I instruct and watch my class behind me.

Jumping jacks. We move into the jumping, hopping, bouncing portion. The reason they call it high impact. No matter how bad I feel, my many years of cheerleading and gymnastics save me.

"All right, ladies, here we go. Jumping jacks. And up and up and up. Switch it out. Legs closed, hop, arms going up and up and up. Switch it out. And up and up and—"

And suddenly, I poot. I poot. I poot.

With every landing, I poot. And poot. And fart. Little milk toots.

I can't make it stop. The music's loud. They can't hear me, I tell myself. I look up. In the mirror, they're trying not to look up at me. I know the routine so well, it's a moving train. I can't stop! The music won't let me. Habit won't let me. I'm mortified. Girls don't fart. Girls are a fantasy.

Class ends. Avoiding eye contact with everyone, I grab my purse from beneath the counter, and sneak out the door.

Once I'm home, I call and leave the message: I quit.

I don't want to quit. I love this job. I love Helena. I love the ladies that go there. It's been my refuge since Mick died. But I'm too humiliated to return.

Only two weeks before I go to college, I lock myself away, writing poems of Mick in elaborate calligraphy with a metal quill and jar of ink onto various sizes of parchment. I burn the edges of the parchment on a flame then blow them to ashes. I attach Mick's pictures then laminate the parchment tributes so they'll live forever, so *he* will live forever. We will live forever. Him and the me I used to be. I will bring them to my dorm and hang them. When people meet me at college, I won't need an ID. They will know. This is who I am.

– 27 –
FRESHMAN

I am fat. I am *fat*. Fat. Fat.

Shrimp forks and ice cream have done me in.

That and quitting smoking.

And Mick's death.

I have never been this fat. People are going to think this is who I am, that this is who I've been. But this is my first time being fat. And I have to start college this way.

I try to eat healthy.

The healthier I eat, the fatter I get. Completely unfair.

The only upside to being fat is that my hair is amazing. It seems to grow faster and be thicker.

If it wasn't for my fatness, I could be in a Pantene commercial. I have never had such great hair.

Five feet, four inches. And, at one time, ninety-eight pounds. Now, still five feet, four inches (unfortunately, that didn't change), I'm now 138 pounds. Only my skirts with elastic waists fit me.

I buy my first size eight, a pair of jeans that bite into my bulbous thighs and feel too good when I peel them off, leaving road marks from my knees to my crotch that last for hours.

I hate myself.

I hate my life.

I hate God for taking Mick away.

But here we go.

I start at Western Illinois University because it's a state school, and my grades aren't good enough for any place else. I want to be an actress because I feel it inside me. Because I want to be on TV. I want to be an actress even though I have no concrete experience. In truth, I have never acted before.

I check in at the all-girls dorm.

Security snaps an official photo, laminates it to my official Student ID card, and shows me to my room. Home for the next year. I yank my heavy bag through the door, letting it slam behind me.

The room is a box. A musty, airless box.

A box with two twin beds with plastic-wrapped mattresses on opposite sides of the room. Yet they're still almost touching. Beds with puke orange bolsters against the wall so they can double as sofas. The bolsters pull open for storage. At the foot of each bed are two small built-in desks with shelves above for books. Next to the desks, directly opposite the door, is a full-picture window overlooking the campus. At the head of the beds, near the door on either side, are two closets with wooden doors. On the wall hangs one phone with a long, curly cord—a party line to be shared by the entire floor of girls. Down the hall are the shared bathrooms with stalls, showers, and sinks.

My roommate will not be in until morning.

I unpeel my jeans, rolling them inside out until I am able to kick them off with my feet, groaning with pleasure as I scratch the seam lines indented in my thighs. I take the left bed, tossing my stuff on it. I remove the scotch tape I was diligent to pack for the dozens of poems I created in calligraphy, each one laminated together with a picture of Mick, and I design a memorial covering the entire closet door, inside and out.

I unpack.

I light a candle.

I fall asleep, watching the flame flicker across Mick's dancing smile reflected in the glow of the laminate.

– 28 –
KULI'S GIN MILL

Cindy Victory, my roommate, arrives looking and acting just as her name implies. She's peppy cute with a button nose and a short bouncy haircut, although mousy-brown. She wears shorts that have been pressed, gym shoes with lacy bobby socks, and a tasteful white t-shirt that barely reveals two small breasts, self-contained and of manageable size.

She has the body of a track and field athlete, able to wear shorts without shame for she has thighs that have not yet known the tragedy of cellulite.

Her disposition is one that has never been acquainted with pain or self-doubt. Within a few minutes of our meeting, I learn she is a virgin and proud of it.

Being near her makes me want ice cream. Gallons of it. With hot chocolate sauce and spirals of whipped cream.

Cindy and I spend our first night as roommates on our beds, leaning back against our boosters, giggling too loud as we expose our "whole entire" lives to one another. Cindy dips economically into the peanut butter jar with her one toasted-wheat cracker. I polish off the jar with an enormous tablespoon. We plan to be the best of friends.

Within the next few days, the rest of the girls on our floor take up residence. We share a bathroom at the end of the hall—all thirty-nine of us—except Kittie Peas, the RA (Resident Assistant) who has her own bathroom attached to her private, no-roommate box.

New environment. New People. Like Germany, this could an opportunity to recreate myself.

I go to classes.

I observe and listen.

Observe and listen.

During the daytime, I walk from class to class, my eyes on the pavement and my thighs sticking together, gathering sweat on my cellulite. I feel it roll down to my fat knees, my cankles.

I eat meals with the other "kids," participating in conversations I can't remember the minute I leave the table. I am not for them, no matter how hard I try to be pleasing.

I decide to try. I go to campus parties to fit in, to be a college kid and not think about being a love widow at seventeen. I laugh too loud and seem super eager to hangout when the girls on my floor yell "frat party." I join in the gossip and seem super interested at the smallest hearsay, with dramatic takes and gulps and sad glances. I pile into the bathroom with them as we all squint one eye and mascara the other, as we tease and hair spray and lip gloss. I hold out my wrist to be stamped at the beer-soaked thresholds of the frat houses and beg to be a little sister.

"You guys, did they choose us? Did they choose me?"

To be a little sister of a frat house is the intern rung on the road to being popular with college boys.

I go to their dorm rooms and have sex on the top bunk or the bottom bunk or the natty sofa while their roommate is sleeping—or not—in the other bunk.

The next morning, I give them my number. This one might be my new boyfriend. Or that one. Then, I can relax. I can leave this circus of desperation. I wait for the promised call that never comes. I see them on campus. They ignore me, embarrassed they slept with me. They don't recognize me because they never really saw me in the first place. It's impossible to ignore how unmoored I am. Nothing I can do or be will be enough. I wasn't a keeper. I don't know how to reconcile the me that swept away a grown man's heart with the disposable me I am here. I am not young enough to be with kids my age.

I stop going. I try to study, but I'm immobile with grief, despair, a longing for Mick. I don't know who I am without him.

I don't know who I am.

I only know who I was.

What I don't want.

Unlike my peers, I'm done with the drugs, the drinking, the "pulling all-nighters." I've had lots of sex and been through an abortion. I've been part of an adult relationship and have experienced the death of my lover. I don't know how to shrink myself enough to fit in. I am alone. With my past. My unfamiliar cellulite. And lots and lots of food.

By November, Cindy Victory has a steady beau.

And I, a much-needed job.

***

Although I'm underage, thanks to my fake ID, I get a job as a bartender.

Kuli's Gin Mill, a Fraternity/Sorority hangout. Kuli's is shaped like a hollow wooden gymnasium. Lots of empty space for the crowds to pack into with a rectangular bar in the center surrounded by a few billiard tables. Even before the customers are let in, the always soaked floor reeks of the stench of industrial cleaning fluids, wet cigarettes, and old sticky beer.

Drinks are easy. Beer in cans. Beer in bottles. Beer from a keg. Served to privileged Fraternity boys who show their metal guzzling canned beers, crushing the cans on their foreheads, whooping to a chorus of "woah, cool, man!" Wine with a twist off cap. Generic liquors: vodka soda, vodka tonic, rum and coke.

The only specialty drink to learn is Long Island Iced Tea, served mainly by the pitcher to groups of Sorority girls who drink until they're standing on the bar stools arm-in-arm singing loud and drunk to "We Are Family."

I got all my sisters and me!

With limited funds and limited self-worth, working at Kuli's is a blessing. It's an excuse to be in the nightlife without having to invest in the "goings-on." There's no way to reject me. I'm part of the scene but not in the ring. I can flirt but be distant. Hey, I'm here to work. If nobody hits on me, that's ok. I'm here to work.

But I'm also on display. Apart from the crowd. Easily noticed and somewhat more desirable because I'm not part of the masses. I'm behind the bar. Am I a student? Am I a local? Only a mystery because most of these kids don't have to work their way through school. I'm an anomaly.

Kuli's is a comfortable fit. My shift, four days a week, runs from four o'clock happy hour, when locals and truck drivers pass through town, until the wee hours, when all my peers arrive. Different from Corfu, Kuli likes when I'm playful with the customers. Good for business, Kuli says. I flirt with the men from the safety of the bar between us.

Among the locals are two truck drivers, Dennis, "Denny," and his partner, Bob. Two rigs, one in back of the other, driving in tandem.

Bob is much younger than Denny. Black hair, thick-framed

black glasses, flannel shirt, dirty well-worn blue jeans. Scrappy handsome.

Dennis appears sixty. In his sixties. Gray and dehydrated. He reminds me of one big cigar ash. His face, so furiously wrinkling, is like a snake's skin, molting. Sharp gray bristles of a two-day-old beard poke out from the top of his bony cheeks near his eyes down to his pointed Adam's apple. The only saving grace is his stark blue eyes that seem to have no pupils.

In the many twilights in the bar, when the sun blinds me as it sinks beneath the picture window and the barroom fades to darkness, the shocking blue of Denny's eyes hang like small iridescent balloons, alone in the air.

– 29 –
No

Kids go to "Kegger" Parties. Frat Parties. Get stoned.

Kids have one-night stands that end in high fives in the male-dorms,

Tears and whispers in the female dorms.

"Did ya hear she pulled a train at Alpha Beta Omega last night?"

Slut.

"Did ya hear she got smashed and blew the entire eleventh floor of Basey Dorm?"

Whore.

"Did ya hear he popped Sally Snowball's cherry last night? Way-ta-go!"

Prostitute.

The school has a mandatory self-defense class for all women to attend. About fifty girl coeds in gym clothes line up along the outside square perimeter of the wrestling mats. We're nervous and giggly; this is silly. We're all still teenagers. Most of us are seventeen, eighteen, or nineteen. Undergrads.

Two men stroll onto the mat. One is dressed like a gym teacher, the other, like the Michelin Man. Or the Pillsbury Doughboy. Head to toe in what seems to be thick Styrofoam armor. We're going to beat him up. That's what it seems like.

They ask for a volunteer. A girl comes to the center and kicks the Michelin Man in his balls. Or where his balls would be. He grabs her foot and fells her to the mat. The normal man blows the whistle. Now all the girls want a turn.

"We'll get there," says the not-Michelin Man. "We're gonna build up to it. First things first: today, we're going to start with the exercise 'NO.'"

For the exercise of NO, we are all to stand at the edge of the mat, and the Michelin Man will come to each one of us and get right in our face and go to grab us, and our job is to yell 'no!' in his face, loud and fierce enough to make him back off.

And we begin.

Across the mat from me, the Michelin Man charges at a tiny girl in purple shorts but, before he can reach her, she yells a "no" so loud and so definitive, I can imagine that if it happened in real life, her would-be attacker would run away. Ding, ding, ding. That's the purpose. Get him to back off.

Around the mat he goes, each girl stepping up, screaming, yelling, shouting, blasting him backward, protecting herself, "No!"

No, no, no, no, no, no, no, no, no!

I'm one of the last. There he is. He's close now. I see his eyes through the space in the helmet. Inside the suit, he looks like a regular man. He has eyelashes. Eyelashes are so vulnerable. So human. Monsters don't have eyelashes.

I step back, preparing for my "no." He backs up then comes forward, ready to charge me, grabbing at me. I hop back and giggle. No "no" comes out of my mouth. I stand, giggling.

He shakes his head and stops right in front of me, looking at me. He asks me if I understand what to do. I do: I yell "no." Yes. That's what I need to do.

He backs up and comes in, threatening, his hands ready to grab me. Now is when you say "no." I know that. I plant my feet. I don't back up. I ball my fists. I'm ready to yell. I open my mouth.

Nothing comes out.

Like in a dream when you're being chased, and you scream, but nothing comes out.

I giggle to cover.

Ok. One more time.

He charges, hands out, ready to grab me.

I just stand this time. Still. Paralyzed, willing my voice. "No!" I hear in my head. "No!" I urge my voice to say.

But nothing comes out.

"Yell, 'no!'" the man in the gym uniform says.
"No," falls out between my lips in a whisper.
"Now yell it," he says, willing me.
"No," I say, a little louder.
"Ok, let's take it again," he says.
And the Michelin Man charges.
And I stand.
Silent.
Unable to say no.
To an attacker.

– 30 –
EUPHORIA

Why is she even here?

That's the look I get from the actors who've been here.
The theater department is a clique. I can't act. I'm not
welcome.

Pictures show colleges sparkling, with everything new
and expensive. The theater classrooms seem all olden and
wooden. The desks are short with built-in tops like for
children. The rooms are dim with old-fashioned blackboards.
The bathrooms are like the ones in older elementary schools
with low sinks and scratchy paint on stalls with worn-out
locks. Not the glamour I was expecting. Neither is acting
and the theater. I thought taking acting classes would be in
front of a camera. This dusty building with no cameras, just

empty spaces and rescued furniture, is confusing. Maybe we advance to classes with cameras?

This semester, besides the regular requirement classes like Biology 101—all the 101's—I can take three theater classes, and I can be in plays if I get cast.

There's a rule that the teacher/director has to give everyone a chance in the plays so the acting teacher, who so far mostly ignores me, gave me the role of a Spanish flower seller in the next production, *A Streetcar Named Desire*. My part is to walk across the stage selling flowers to mourn the dead, saying, "*Flores para los muertos.*" She has nothing to do with the main people in the play. She just walks through the play and out again. It's a small part, but I relate to her. She's in grief, wearing black, selling flowers for the dead. I understand grief. I don't just understand it, but I *feel* it. She lives in mourning. I live in mourning.

What I don't understand is how to bridge the gap between my feelings and the acting lines. The part isn't me. The lines aren't my actual words. How do I know who she is? How she should be played?

I ask the acting teacher in class, "How do you take a feeling you have, like, maybe grief, and translate it to a feeling your character has, like grief, so it melds and becomes the same feeling and comes out in the lines?"

I don't think he understands what I mean. He gives a short answer I don't understand, so I put in my notes that it's something I'll look up in the acting books before the show. It's a tiny role, but I want to be good in it. I want the teacher to think I have talent. That I'm worth knowing. That I'll be somebody someday.

***

"*Flores para los muertos,*" Mim Canny, the Voice/Diction teacher, takes me into the girls bathroom "because of the acoustics" and helps me with how to pronounce it.

We look in the mirror at the shape her mouth makes in slow motion over each syllable, and I try to copy. She has me place a cork between my back teeth, to try to shape the sounds so the cork is undetectable. I sound drunk. I'm slurring and drooling over the cork. I pop it out to laugh so I don't swallow it and choke.

"I think I'm ruining your cork," I say.

It's the first time I've laughed, not fake laughed, the first non-effortful laugh since I got here.

Mim Canny. The sound of her name seems like the best name for anyone. Beige hair, beige lashes, beige baggy trousers with beige pockets, and beige loafers, yet she is the least beige. The way she is with me. A protector. Seeing me. Caring that I learn. She's the first person here who sees more than the awkward, mournful, fat, thus far untalented teenager I appear on the outside. She is fuchsia kindness.

***

Before each show, I arrive at the dressing room three hours early. I'm learning from scratch. I lay on the floor and meditate on my character. I think of myself growing old, being unloved by anyone but Mick, who's now dead, and I'm all grief, needing to bring flowers for all the broken hearts I intuit. My cry, "*Flores para los muertos*," is not just mourning, it's a reaching out of empathy.

I try to meld my understanding in my head and heart into the person I'm supposed to be on the stage. I don't know if any of this makes a difference when I'm on the stage, which is the scariest thing ever, but I don't know what else to do to learn. There's an invisible force field gap that's beyond what I know how to bridge.

After the show, or in class, the acting teacher/director never tells me if it was good or bad. Or what to do. Or how to act. I'm not even sure he knows my name. Or that I'm there. So, this is all I can think of to do.

When the other girls come into the dressing room to get ready, they give me sideways looks, surprised I'm here so early. As if I'm in their bedroom they suddenly have to share with this foster kid.

I watch them from the side of the stage, and I wonder how they can be on stage so long and how they remember all their lines and where to go and not be so scared they'll forget. I wonder at the language of theater, of the acting they speak of that's so above me, my intimidation tuning me out. I watch them act and rehearse and wonder how they got from a know-nothing like me to where they are. They don't want to know me, but I admire them. I'm in awe.

***

Just before the Christmas break, Mim is directing her show—*You Can't Take It With You*—a screwball comedy with many characters, so a lot of people in the theater department get a part.

Mim casts me! I'm the part of Gay Wellington. Not a lead but a great part. Gay Wellington is an actress, a nymphomaniac, an alcoholic, a singer, and a drunk with a broken heart, desperate for her dreams to come back to life. Which seems like a part I can play. She spirals out, drinking and singing, "Peg O' my heart, I love you, we'll never part, I love you." I think she's mourning her past love, too. I relate to that even though this is a comedy.

It's opening night. There's an auditorium filled with university students, professors, their spouses, and people I would never get to meet. Even locals from the town.

It's time for my entrance onto stage. Before I even say a line, a roar of laughter from the audience gusts the stage. A *roar*. Is it because of me or some look another actor gave? One of the leads?

Every time I speak or do anything, there's laughing. Loud laughing. Bursts of laughter. But I keep going. When I get off stage, Mim is waiting and whispers, "When you hear them laughing, hold."

"Hold what?" I whisper back.

"When they laugh, don't speak. Hold your thoughts, hold your actions, and wait. Let the laughter die down.

Otherwise, they can't hear your lines," she says, squeezing both my upper arms in a firm hand hug.

I make one more entrance down the stairs, bringing chaos with me as I sing and fling myself wide-legged onto a bench. I have tights under my skirt and fan myself with the hem of the skirt, teasing, as if I'm unaware a peep show might happen. The audience roars with every dangerous close call. Swinging a bottle of booze, I sing, both happy and sad, singing loud and mournful, "Peg O' my heart, I love you." I waver each line of the song in an unpredictable way, tricking the audience who thinks I'm going to keep singing it one way, but I zig another. This is the first time it's really a good thing that I can't sing. I can't sing at all. I sound like a mournful cow.

I, Gay Wellington, am on a couch downstage. Downstage is theater lingo which means on the stage at the very closest part to the front of the audience. (I love every new theater language word I learn.)

I'm singing with my legs swaying open, and the laughter is so loud, hitting the stage like waves, it's almost making me laugh. So, while I'm holding, I have to bite the sides of my cheeks to keep from breaking up. I've never felt anything like it. I've laughed like they're laughing. I've laughed till I cried. They're doing that. I'm cracking up hundreds of people. Hundreds of people are crying and laughing. Howling. Because of me. It must be what a conductor of an orchestra must feel, creating the rolls of music that move emotion in the audience.

I want this. I want this more than anything. This is what I want to do for the rest of my life. Harvey Korman, Tim Conway, *The Carol Burnett Show*. *The Mary Tyler Moore Show*. It's like that, but this is stage. The audience is right there. I can feel them, and they feel me. Would I someday be able to do this as my actual job? Can an actress do both stage and TV? I would do this even if I wasn't ever famous. I would do this even if I never got paid.

That night, all wound up, unable to sleep, I look up in the thesaurus the word for the feeling I had. The feeling I want as my job. My life.

Euphoria.

I want to do things that make me feel euphoria.

Making people, including myself, laugh until we cry is euphoria to me.

– 31 –
Movement Class

The movement teacher is Joseph. We don't have to say his last name. He's hip and young and cool—maybe in his twenties—with long, thick, curly black hair that goes past his shoulders and a V-shaped, tight body. All slim muscle, no fat. During class, he's barefoot and wears only black tights, no shirt. Swashbuckle-y.

One day during our first week, there will be pictures taken of our bathing-suit-clad bodies. We must enter the room one at a time. We will be photographed from every angle in front of a board of horizontal and vertical lines. These are going to be our "before" pictures revealing to us our posture and where we need to improve. We will aim for a neutral stance from which to move freely and be able to create our characters from. At the end of the year, we'll retake our picture to see how far we've come.

I don't want to do this. I really, I mean almost-throw-up-in-my-mouth *really* don't want to do this. I have big cellulite thighs because I tried to eat my way out of my grief. Why was my idea of what acting school not at all what this is? How is this board standing posture thing useful to act in a TV show?

It's on picture day, when I'm in line with everyone, when I realize I didn't bring a bathing suit. I forgot. Also, I don't have one now that I'm F. A. T. I tell Joseph. No problem. Bra and underwear is fine. Oh, super. Facetious. Then, I remember, I wore a sheer bra and underwear. It's not even sexy. A white roller coaster of realization zooms from my throat to my stomach. It's just the biggest underwear I own that fits me right now.

I whisper to Joseph, "May I postpone?"

But there's only one picture day. As an actor, you have to be willing to be vulnerable. Not afraid to be emotionally naked. Be exactly yourself, loving all that you perceive at your best and worst and everything in-between. Then, and only then, will you become an extraordinary actor. Then, the world of acting will open up, and you can play anyone. It's terrifically exciting to hear. Ok.

But right now, I'm wearing too-tight sheer underwear over this foreign body I'm living in. I understand emotionally naked. But physically naked, too? Especially now that I'm fat? But I do it.

Afterward, Joseph meets with each of us individually for a few minutes to discuss. We sit side by side, like artist to artist, as he points out on the Polaroids the areas we'll be conscious to improve. I have a million questions.

Joseph invites me to his off-campus house for dinner, to answer all the questions I have about acting and the theater. It's so incredible of him. Like Mim, he seems to think there's something in me worth teaching. It feels so affirming to have me as I am and to have my dreams taken to heart. By Mim and Joseph.

***

It's electric to walk to someone's actual off-campus house after dark. Macomb is a small college town, and there are only a few reasons to leave campus if you live in the dorms. To Kuli's for work. To the frat houses for parties. To a store. These were the little houses I walked by, wondering who lived there and what it looked like inside. They all seemed so cozy. Made of wood. Painted white or green. With tiny porches. One or two steps up to the front door. Lawns with windmills or chimes. Married people housing. Graduate students. Teachers. Townies. Locals. Here I am, invited to a dinner by a professor. Me. I'm now walking to a dinner with a grown-up to talk about being an actor. I see the number. I walk up the little sidewalk. Despite my shunned status, this feels like a step in a good direction.

There's so much stuff squashed in his little house; it's tinier on the inside than it looks from the outside. Kinda messy. Like he cleared a space for the table that we're to sit at. There are shelves of books, a sofa, a coffee table, and a TV. The usual stuff. A stereo. Albums. A barbell by a full-length mirror tacked to the back of the open closet door. Inside the half open closet, hangers are draped with uneven clothes. Seeing him from the inside of his house, he seems like a person more than my professor.

He puts two waters on the table then offers me wine. I take only a tiny sip. He stands, leaning against the oven. I go back to his bookshelf. Acting books. Stage combat books. History of the Theater books. Scripts. Books with secrets that could unlock the mystery of acting.

"You're doing great in class," he says.

I am? I feel so lost in this college. I feel so lost in the theater program.

"Really?" I ask. "I feel like I'm a ladybug on a windshield hanging on to the wiper for dear life."

He raises his eyebrows. "Well, that's specific. Being specific is good for acting," he says.

"Um," I say and nod. I should know what that means, but I have no idea and don't want to seem too naïve by asking.

"College can be scary at first," he says.

I nod again and giggle, taking a sip of my water.

He brings our plates with one chicken breast on each. I sit at the square wooden table on a not very comfortable

309

wooden chair. Here, just like in school, his feet are barefoot. It seems nice to have a job where you're mostly barefoot.

He tells me how the theater became his "mistress."

"Are you married?" I ask.

He laughs, so I laugh. I think I know what he means but not exactly.

He speaks in such sophisticated terms. I'm not familiar with what he means. Someday, I'll be able to speak theater fluently. I just nod and say "huh" as in "that's interesting."

He finishes his chicken. I only have a few bites of mine because it feels weird to chew in front of him. He finishes his wine. I finish my water.

"The theater," he says, "is part of a tradition. The theater has a language unto itself."

I nod. That's for sure. I'm glad he said it.

"Once it's in you," he says, touching his chest with all ten fingertips, "you're part of a community."

It does feel like a closed community. A private clubhouse with a secret password. I'm just not a member yet.

"I felt like that when I was in *You Can't Take It With You*," I say, taking a small sip of my wine. Because my water is empty.

I laugh, remembering Mim rushing backstage the first night to tell me to hold for the laughter.

"It was funny," I say, "because when we were doing that show, normally I just walk to my classes and am in my classes for like, biology or psych, or I'm in the Union, and no one knows me. But when we were doing the show, people would point at me or say, 'Gay Wellington! Man, you crack me up!'"

I laugh when I tell him that.

"And it made me happy that I could see that I made them happy. And it made me feel like I finally had hope," I say.

"Hope?" He asks, surprised. As if he doesn't know what I mean when I say hope. Does he not see I am only hope right now, hope like a torn, wind ravaged sail clinging to the mast?

"Can I ask you a question?" I ask.

His pressed lips smile, and he nods.

I press my lips, smile, and nod. I take another teeny sip of wine.

"If everyone that saw me in that play got joy from it, if it made them laugh and forget anything they were hurting about, for right then, at least..." I trail off, trying to configure what I'm trying to ask.

He brushes a coil of black curl from his face back over his head.

"...Then why is wanting to be an actor such a shallow goal? Or selfish? Or self-involved? Do you know what I mean?" I ask.

He shakes his head and furls his brows.

"When I said to my family, people I know, or *anyone*, that I want to be an actress, everyone's like, 'you just want attention,' or 'hardly anyone makes it,' or 'you have to be

311

special,' or 'you just want to be famous.' Which I wouldn't mind. Is that shallow?"

He stares at me, listening, but not answering.

"I mean, is being an actor a shallow thing to want? When I was Gay Wellington and people were cry-laughing, I felt it was the least selfish. I felt it was euphoria for them and me. So why do I feel wrong? Ashamed, even?"

We sit knee to knee, his knees pressing into mine. He looks at me, unblinking, then, he tilts his head, about to say something. I try to hold his gaze. I feel like I'm under a spotlight, waiting. My tummy growls.

"You're an intense girl," he says.

I guffaw. I don't mean to. Obviously. It just comes out. It's not really an answer. Now I just feel dumb.

"You're not shallow. And intensity is important. All great actors are *intense.*"

He leans forward, elbows on his thighs, his mane of hair swooping over to the front of his neck and face. Unblinking. *Intense.*

It's hard for me to look at him.

I look down, not knowing what to do with what he just said. I remind myself, out of all the students in his class, he chose to invite *me* to dinner.

Joseph keeps looking into my eyes. I think it must be a test of how intense I can be, so I stare back. *Intense.* His black eyebrows, thick, *intense.* With black strands in the space between his brows. His nose is hawk-like. Like mine. Our noses make us even more intense.

Suddenly, he takes my hand. We stand, and he leads me to his bed as if this was a conversation we had with our eyes, and I wasn't paying attention. As if we just had a whole wordless conversation in two different languages.

"You have to believe you have a gift," he says, placing himself on top of me.

"Oh," I say, not stopping him. Not stopping him because he wants it to happen. He did take the time to be a mentor. Not stopping him because the weight of a man always feels so euphoric at first. That first moment of weight. That first feeling of his erection pushing against his pants at a tantalizing, safe distance. Not stopping him because the feeling of his desire makes me feel I am treasure. Not stopping him because I don't know what else to do but be amenable.

"You have a gift," he says.

Maybe he means my "vv" is the gift.

What does this mean? Has he wanted me even though he saw my cellulite in class? Even though I'm not a good actress yet?

I'm aware of him moving inside me. I'm also wondering how he got his shirt off with me not noticing. Was there a moment I didn't notice? What was I noticing? Was he even wearing a shirt? He always seems like Tarzan, shirtless and shoeless.

He has a fluffy comforter. Most people only have bed spreads, but his is like the kind they had in Germany. Made of feathers. And lots of pillows. Like a comfy nest, this bed. Does this mean we will be dating? It's so smooth and wet between my legs as he strokes in and out. I'm always wet. Too wet. I still have on my skirt. I turn my face into his hair. His hair smells clean and feels damp underneath. As if he took a shower before I came over, and it hadn't fully dried. He moans louder, moves faster. I moan, too, suddenly involved. Then, he relaxes, his full weight flattening me.

I feel safe in this one moment. Covered and safe. Like a helium balloon rescued by gravity.

Underneath him, his chest expands into mine. I turn my head to the other side and open my eyes. He kisses my forehead and rolls off to the side and talks. I don't know about what. He's casually chatty. He goes in and out of his bathroom.

I take in the room again. The messy bed. The clutter on every wall, in every crevice. Between the pillows, there is a small black elastic hair tie. Could be his. I don't let myself wonder.

Dressed and brushing his hair, he sits on the edge of the bed. He squeezes my ankle. He seems very concerned whether I can get home ok.

"Will you be ok walking home alone now?" he asks. He's asked a couple times; it occurs to me that this is my cue to leave. Pulling my underwear up and my skirt back down, I wiggle myself up and off the bed.

Smiling.

He's smiling.

I hold out my hand to shake, making a joke. A not a joke-joke. Because I don't know how to speak what I am feeling in this last casually chatty, "get home ok" moment.

"Thank you, Professor," I say.

He hugs me. Like a brother. I pat his back, too.

As I wander back, I feel him drip down my thighs. My calf. At the dorms, I wash him from between my legs. I put on my flannel PJ's, open the bolster where I store my snack food, sit cross-legged on my bed, and eat the entire jar of peanut butter.

– 32 –
SIEMPRE

"Phone!" one of the girls shouts from down the hallway. All the floors in the dorms have phones in their rooms that share one phone number. It's called a party line. Several of us snatch up the phone.

The voice asks for me. My heart bangs. I haven't heard his voice since Mick died.

"Yes?" I ask.

"This is Rick," he says. When I don't speak right away, he says, "Mick's friend."

"Hi. Hi!" A white wind blows an energy through my body that I haven't felt since I had last seen Michael. Rick's been writing to me since I arrived, big, sentimental Hallmark cards with roses and swirly letters and generic "how much you are loved" romantic poems already printed on them. He writes in a signature that has swirl, and his letters are so fancy, they seem to be written by a girl. He must be Spanish or Italian because at the end, he always writes, "*Siempre*, Rick." I think *siempre* must mean "always," but I don't want to ask him because to ask him would mean we have to say it out loud, and I don't want that word alive between us. I only know him through Mick. I only saw him at the health club with Mick. And the only person I feel *siempre* about is Mick.

It feels like a penetration, that word. Like he's trying to make me take it and say it. Like he's forcing it on me. He's probably just being nice, but I don't know how to tell him I don't want him, so I just never write back. But then he sends flowers, too, and I have to write him to say thank you. Every time a card or some flowers come, and all the girls on my dorm floor "oooooo" and "ahhhhh" and wink, it makes me cry. He's not my love. He's not my boyfriend. He's not my *siempre*. He's not Mick. My true love lives on my closet door and inside me. *Siempre*. So, I always have, "Write Rick back" on my to do list. It never goes away because the minute I finally write him back, he sends more flowers or cards.

"How's school?" he asks.

"It's the coolest!" I say. "My roommate is the coolest roommate I could have ever wished for."

Cindy is sitting at her desk.

"I started theater classes and have been in two plays already. One, I was really funny in," I say.

"Cool," he says.

"Yeah, it's really cool," I say, tittering through every word.

"Are you going anywhere for your semester break?" he says.

"Um, I don't know. I have a job," I say, "so maybe I'm just gonna do that."

"Can you come to Chicago for a few days?" he asks.

"Umm, umm, well, why? I mean, I don't really have enough money to," I say.

"I want to see you," he says, as if that's reason enough.

But in his voice is the promise of Mick, alive again in memories shared. In his voice is the recovery of my old self, both getting fainter as the days go by.

He offers to pay for the Amtrak from Macomb—where WIU is located—into the city. A three-hour ride.

But Macomb doesn't have a train station.

He offers to pay for the taxi to the station.

I don't have enough money for a hotel.

He offers to let me stay with him.

So expensive, all this.

Perhaps he is missing Mick and needs to reconnect? Maybe we'll talk about the old days. When we were all friends. At the health club. When Mick was alive. Maybe he'll tell me things about Mick, funny anecdotes that happened before I met Mick that I never knew. Maybe he'll tell me the way Mick told him that he loved me. Maybe I'll feel the way I felt back then, only a year ago. Was it a year ago?

I agree to go up for the weekend.

Rick is waiting on the platform. He wears a three-piece suit. His short black hair is thick, slick, and groomed straight back from his forehead with pomade. He wears a gold necklace and a pinkie ring. He's a rich "man of the world." He strides to his Caddy as I follow behind, transforming. I am Mick's lovely lady. No longer nothing me. It's magical, the mirror of his reflection.

He talks to me about nothing really. Weather. The train ride. I watch as he unlocks his gas tank with a key, then, once inside the chamber, unlocks the car doors. Mysterious and cool. He has none of the exuberance of Mick's nature. He is pre-possessed, edge and danger lurk somewhere in his life. There is no spark between us. No past life recognition. No innate intuition drawing us together like there was the moment I met Mick. He just likes me. I feel dizzy. Swaying. Like an autumn leaf hanging onto the branch not ready to be torn into the wind.

But I am three times a lady, and I hold onto that.

He is thirty-one, like Mick.

He is thirty-one and wants to spend time with me.

He is *paying* to spend time with me.

I can't even beg men my own age to spend time with me. Unless, of course, I was "putting out," and as soon as that was done, I would be disposed of.

I am Mick's true love.

A few minutes from the city limits of Chicago, he pulls into the lot of what appears to be a two-story motel with steps running on the outside. I follow him up the stairs as he carries my suitcase. He unlocks the door. From the threshold, I survey his home.

A one-bedroom apartment, all plastic and chrome furniture of four colors: red, white, silver and black. How sophisticated. And so grown-up to have his own place.

He offers me a drink. I ask for a diet soda. He says I can have alcohol. I say the first thing I remember from Kuli's: a seven-seven. I ask for an ashtray. I had quit smoking in Mick's honor and substituted ice cream instead. Now, working at Kuli's, I took up smoking again. Rick doesn't smoke, so he hands me a salad plate. I sit on one of the plastic kitchen chairs next to the refrigerator, facing the flower wallpaper with my back to the room, smoking.

I had hoped we'd talk about Mick, but we don't. I don't know what we're talking about. He leaves the room several times to take important phone calls, because, even though it's a vacation for me, he still has to work. I smoke more. I press the red ash into the salad plate, snuffing it out. I light another. I finish the entire pack.

We go to dinner and, even while I'm there, I'm not remembering a thing about this restaurant, this dinner, what he's saying. I don't remember. We go back to his apartment. I fall asleep on one side of his bed.

***

In the morning, I awake in a fetal position facing the closet, my back to him, my newly-Goth black hair flowing over my pillow. Something hard, wet and fleshy is poking, rubbing up and down, from the dip in my bottom to the separation between my legs.

I move forward a bit, hugging the side of the mattress.

A hairy arm encompasses my waist, pulling my back into his stomach, soft with tufts of hair.

The poking rubbing wet hardness slips inside.

Moving. Moving. Smells like sour mornings.

I make the requisite moans, knowing this is the price paid to be interesting enough to spend time with. This was the price of the trip.

He finishes.

Wet stickiness gushes out between my thighs, flowing down to my knees.

I shower, dress, and sit at the kitchen table, chain-smoking as I stare at the wall, waiting for Rick to take me to the train.

I am invisible.

I am vapor.

– 33 –
DETOUR

It's February, the middle of my second semester, in the icy Midwest. Fierce winds and wet-cold air. Two days before Valentine's Day. I want to go home to Chicago to surprise my parents. Maybe Helena.

In truth, I can't bear to stay on campus for the festivities.

I have no sweetheart.

At least, not one with a body.

Money earned at Kuli's pays for food, books, supplies, housing.

I have thirteen dollars. Not enough for a train ticket.

Wearing my most stylish high-heeled winter boots and a thick coat, carrying an overnight bag and my purse strapped across my chest, I trudge down to the main road in front of my dorm building, and raise my mittened thumb.

A few cars zip through the fog of my breath. More cars. I breathe hot into my mittens, hobbling back and forth, shifting my weight from one foot to the other. I raise my thumb again.

A truck pulls its eighteen wheels to the side of the road.

A second truck follows, parking in front of the first.

The driver's side door of the first truck opens.

Dennis, the happy hour trucker from Kuli's, leans out. He's dressed in stained white long johns, yelling over the rumbling of the engine.

"Where ya headin'?" he yells into the wind, his breath white.

"Home," I yell back. "Chicago."

"Going there. Get in," he says.

I'm thrilled.

Thrilled to get out of the cold.

Thrilled its Denny, someone I know.

Super thrilled to get a ride in a "big rig."

Something I've never done before.

I can add this to the list of all the remarkable things I'm going to experience in my lifetime that will add up to be a fascinating life led by a remarkable woman. I'm at just the start of that list, but every new experience matters.

I tiny-step fast trot over the slick snow to the passenger side of the truck. I grab the door handle like a saddle horn, hurtling myself up onto the high metal step and into the passenger seat. The cabin is warm and filthy. Dennis is wearing full-body long johns that used to be white and fading jeans that, even though they're over long johns, are still loose.

"Thanks so much," I say. "I lucked out."

Dennis, both hands on the top of the steering wheel, bouncing up and down a little in his seat while revving the idling engine, says, "Get in, get in." He has a wide smile and wide eyes as if he's a little boy and gets to show off his big truck. "Ever ride in a big rig before?" he asks, his eyes sparkling through the sharp gray bristles that porcupine out all over his face.

"Nope," I say, leaning forward, looking out through the enormous wide pane. It's like having front row seats to watch the world. "First time."

"Get comfy. We got hours in ahead of us," he says.

"How long does it take?" I ask.

"'Lease four hours," he says. "But me n' Bob gotta stop 'long the way n' pick up a load. That all right?"

"It's an adventure," I say, and I slide my coat down from my shoulders, put my feet on the dashboard, light a cigarette, and watch the road as if we're in a plane hovering above it all. I never felt so safe on the highway.

Dennis and Bob drive in tandem. Sometimes Bob is lengths ahead. Sometimes it's Dennis. Sometimes they're side by side, and they blow their horns loud, startling me, as they laugh and wave and pass.

Looking out the enormous window, sitting up so high above the world, I say, "It's like God on wheels."

Dennis laughs hard and grabs his CB radio.

"Like God on wheels!" he wheezes into the microphone.

"10-4, Denny. You got some Spice of Life in there with ya!"

"Sure do. Ain't you sorry? Over."

I'm laughing, having a blast. This really is an adventure. Dennis hands me the speaker.

"Try it." He lights a new Salem with the butt of the one he's finishing.

"How?"

"Just press this button and say who ya are."

I hesitate then push the button in with my thumb.

"Breaker, Breaker, this is Spice of Life..." I giggle, flirting safely over the airwaves at eighty-five miles per hour.

Dennis smokes a constant stream of Salems.

Two hours into the journey, he grabs a clear sandwich baggy from off the dashboard full of black capsules and pops one in his mouth, tossing the baggy onto the ashy dashboard.

"Black Beauties," he says in answer to my raised eyebrows. "Want one?"

"What is it?"

"Black Beauties."

"But what's that?"

"Speed. Necessary part of the job."

"Oh. That's ok. No thanks."

As the newness of the truck ride wears down, I rest my head on the palm of my hand, leaning against the chilly window. I doze off.

The truck bumps hard, hitting my nose against the glass, and comes to a full stop. I open my eyes, but it's not the cramped building to building city-ness of Chicago. We're just off the highway—with few buildings at all—in the parking lot of a small, one-story L-shaped motel. A large wooden hand-painted sign of red letters on a white background reads Chief Motel.

"Are we in Chicago?" I ask, scooching myself upright, looking around.

"Naw. Keokuk," Dennis says.

"Iowa? Isn't that the other way?" I ask, unsure. There could be a Keokuk, Illinois, too. I don't really know these states. When I moved to Western Illinois University in Macomb, one of the first surprises was the morning radio. Instead of soft rock or the weather, it was twenty minutes of hog futures and other farm animal and seed predictions and warnings. It occurred to me how just four hours away people's lives were spooled around such different things.

"Too much ice on the roads," Dennis says. "Had to turn it around and head west. We'll make Chicago tomorrow."

"Oh. Ok," I say, reaching into my bag for a stick of gum for my sleep breath. "I've never been to Keokuk before. I can add it to my list now."

I wait in the warm cabin as I watch Dennis and Bob go into the little cabin area and check in. A few minutes later, Dennis comes out, gives a sweeping overhead wave to me, and I grab my purse and follow Dennis, carrying my bag, to a little room.

He tosses my overnight bag on the flimsy faded bedspread and tells me he and Bob are headin' to the bar. He tells me I should come if I want to.

A dark tiny hot box, the room's four walls are floor-to-ceiling fake wood paneling. The double bed has no headboard and sags deep in the center. At the foot of the bed, against the back wall, is an old wooden stand in which someone has carved their initials. On the stand is a heavy iron phone with no numbers on the circular dial of its belly and a weighty receiver. Since there is no other floor space, the TV is suspended from the ceiling.

There are no windows.

The bathroom sink is the circumference of two fists. There's a toilet and a stand-up shower.

I decide to join Denny and Bob.

***

The bar is lit only by the glow of the television and the neon signs proclaiming various beers. I am the only woman, so when I walk in, the bar explodes into a chorus of howling wolves.

Seating myself for safety between Bob and Dennis, I order one drink—something with a cherry floating on top—smiling, nodding, and listening to a conversation yelled above the music, about "routes" and "sawbucks" and "weigh-in stations." It reminds me of being in Germany when I didn't speak the language.

I pluck the cherry from its stem, mashing the juice out with the flat of my tongue, then, I swallow it whole. I finish the drink, cracking and swallowing every last ice cube, then excuse myself and go back to my room.

I slip on my yellow terry cloth spring dress that doubles as a nightgown, crawl under the stiff itchy sheet, and drift away.

***

Fists are banging on the door.

My eyes open to a darker blackness than in my sleep.

Pounding, the door vibrating, Dennis's voice slurs and he yells, "Open the fuckin' door! It's fuckin' freezin' out here."

I stumble to the door, turning the latch in the doorknob.

Dennis barrels past me and flops down on the bed.

I stand, watching the outline of him, not knowing what to do.

"I thought you got this room for me?" I ask softly, confused.

Dennis growls, clears his throat, and coughs.

"What the fuck? You think I'm made a' money?"

I stare, my eyes adjusting to the darkness. He leans on his elbow and stares back.

"Get in," he says, breaking the standoff silence.

328

"No, that's ok. I'll just sleep here on the floor." I reach for the thin hole-y bedspread.

"Gimmee it," he says, snatching the blanket from me. "Jesus H. Christ. Fuckin' uptight... I'll sleep on the floor."

"I'm not uptight, it's just that I don't feel comfortable."

"Blah blahblah. Blah blahblah," he snarls at me as he hurls his body to the floor between the bed and the door.

"Dennis?"

He's snoring.

***

I wake a few hours later. It's morning. I am sleeping on my stomach.

My face is in the pillow.

My mascara that I didn't remove the night before is making my eyelashes stick together.

The room is almost as dark as it was the night before.

I am half asleep and half awake.

The weight of a body is lowering the mattress to the side of me.

A slow hand on my thigh is quietly working its way upward.

I breathe heavy on purpose, thinking maybe if I don't move and pretend I am asleep, he'll stop and go away.

The hand keeps moving.

I lay still. Play dead. Stop my breathing.

The hand reaches my heat.

Instinctively, I squeeze my thighs together.

It's all over.

He takes my shoulder and flips me onto my back to face him.

"C'mon. I know you're awake."

Brown breath exhales into my mouth.

I turn my head away.

His bony fingers pinch my face, pulling my mouth to his.

I make my lips hard, and he bites them.

He tries again as I turn my head back and forth.

My heart is banging against my ribs, my blood is flowing fast.

His crustaceous body pins me, his bony elbows dig into my forearms, and his skeletal knees bruise my thighs, trying to press them apart.

He wins.

He jams it inside me.

The room begins a dizzy, slow-motion spin.

I mark the TV as it goes around and around, a merry-go-round on the ceiling.

He is moving, in and out, in and out.

I have no words. I have no breath. I have only my eyes to plead with.

I look to find his eyes. They are closed.

If he sees my eyes, sees them begging "please stop," he will.

He won't want to do this if I don't want him to.

"Dennis." My mouth moves, my breath finally allowing words.

His eyes look at mine.

Two blue stones—two blind shark eyes—turn my way.

His lids are open, but he is not there.

Stones. Shark eyes.

He is pumping.

I am not in my body.

I could grab his head and, with my thumbs, poke his eyes out.

But what if I don't manage it, and he gets angrier and kills me?

His sharp Adam's apple bobs near my eyes.

I could punch it in.

But if I do, and he dies, I will be a murderer.

This is only rape.

I will survive this.

But I won't survive being a murderer.

In and out.

The sharp edges of him cut my flesh, stabbing my bones.

My Spirit, like a vapor retreating into a bottle, hisses small inside a secret chamber inside me.

Wetness splats on my face. He has spit on me. He is out of me and standing above me.

"Fuck you." His face is contorted. "Can't you even get into it? Fuck you! You're the worst fuck I ever had."

I watch the crêpe-y skin of his buttocks go into the bathroom.

I listen to the water go on in the sink.

He comes out dressed.

I haven't moved.

"I'm headin' with Bob to pick up a load. We'll be back in an hour."

The metal screen door creaks and slams behind him.

I am paralyzed.

I lay there just as he left me, staring at the water-stained ceiling.

The TV is on.

How did it get on?

Good Morning, America.

There's a guest, someone famous, talking about what makes a great marriage.

How is life just going on?

How is a normal day starting right now?

Life is oblivious to me.

I am nothing.

I am invisible.

The world goes on as if I never breathed.

An hour.

332

He'll be back in an hour.

I get myself into the bathroom and take the longest shower.

I look at the wash rag, white with the words "Chief Motel" embroidered into it with bright blood-red thread.

I hide the washcloth in my purse.

I notice the phone.

Time becomes real again.

I hold the phone to my ear. Two rings, three rings. Will the front desk pick up?

Ring fourteen, ring fifteen, ring sixteen.

I listen to the rings.

No one is answering.

I will go to the police.

I will get dressed and go to the front desk, and they will call the police.

I have no clothes but the yellow terrycloth dress I wore to bed. No shoes.

I look for my bag.

He took it with him.

It is gone.

***

The screen door croaks.

The white door bangs into the wall.

Dennis stands, framed in the doorway.

"We're ready. Let's go."

I am meek. My head is down. I whisper, "I don't have any clothes."

"They're in the truck," he says, turning to go.

"I don't have shoes," I say.

"You can put 'em on in the sleeper," he says, and the metal door slaps closed behind him.

Barefoot, on tiptoe, I sprint on the hardened snow to the rumbling truck three hundred yards away. The icy layer on the metal step to the passenger side door threatens to tear the flesh from the pads of my feet.

I don't look at Dennis. I look up in the sleeper area of the truck. My bag is sitting on top of disheveled three-day-ripe male-odor sheets. One has a light-blue teddy bear pattern.

I climb up and change horizontally.

Fully dressed with my coat buttoned up to my throat, I climb down to the passenger seat. I stare straight ahead out the foggy dash window.

Dead bugs hit by the wipers get shifted to a new resting place.

Dennis finishes writing on a bill of lading, takes the glasses off his nose, and tosses them to a bag next to him. He starts talking about nothing. Talking about the weather. As if nothing happened.

He wants things to be cheerful, an adventure again today like it was yesterday when I first got in his truck. He wants me to be a "Spice of Life" as if nothing unusual happened. Yes, he was drunk last night so he might not have remembered how his personality changed. But he was not drunk this morning.

My fingers twiddle a loose thread on my coat seam.

"You raped me," I say softly, contrite.

But I say it.

Nothing.

Then, suddenly, he says, "This is what we're gonna do." His shark eyes are penetrating. "We're goin' ta breakfast with Bob. You're gonna order biscuits and gravy and coffee and that's all you're gonna say at breakfast. I'll drop you in Chicago. That's it. I didn't rape you," he informs me.

At the diner, I do as he instructed. I order biscuits and gravy.

I don't eat.

I stare, unblinking, at Bob, sending him an SOS with my eyes. Bob just smiles, chats, chews, and sips. He doesn't get it.

Back on the road, I huddle close to the door, resting my forehead on the freezing window.

I am silent, thinking only of getting to safety.

Dennis chats and jokes on the CB.

His laugh makes me want to vomit.

I watch the day fade into darkness, the car lights go on. We should be close to Chicago by now.

We pass a city sign that says "Cedar Point."

"Where are we?" My voice comes out hoarse.

"Roads are too bad to go further north. We're spendin' the night."

We pull into another motel parking lot. My stomach fills with a bitter orange fear.

***

At the front desk, Dennis gets a room. For him *and* me. Bob signs in for himself. Everyone working at the motel seems to know them; there are high fives all around.

"Denny! Bobby! How's it hangin'?"

I stand in the corner, gripping my purse and bag with white bloodless hands, alert for an opening, a chance to call the police, a moment without Dennis near me. He doesn't let me out of his sight. His hand closes on my arm as we walk to the room.

"Throw your bag there. These are my friends. We're all goin' out to party. Smile. Cheer up. It's Valentine's Day. Jesus."

The owner's eighteen-year-old son has a Park Lane car. We all pile in: Denny, myself, Bob, Mark (the owner's son), and a girl named Joyce whose dejected posture makes her look like she has lived in a small town too long. I make eye contact with Mark. I know I have to get away. I can't spend another night alone with Dennis. Either he will rape me again or he might kill me. From the sudden change in his personality from the Dennis I knew at Kuli's to the furious rapist, I don't know what's coming. I think maybe I can tell

Mark, and Mark's parents can somehow get me away? I don't know. I have no money and, therefore, no way to escape.

We arrive at a cheap disco that looks like a lodge or a lunchroom with a mournful, low ceiling, somewhat damaged colored lights, and a disco ball that moves too slow, out of sync with the music. Dennis gets up to dance with a girl we don't know.

I scan the room for a pay phone.

There's one by the restrooms. I need a dime. I ask Joyce. She's already drunk. She searches her wallet but instead of a dime, she pulls out a picture of her boyfriend, her newly *ex*-boyfriend, and begins to weep. She yells the saga over the music into my ear. With my arm around her shoulder, nodding with pitying eyes, I pretend to sympathize, one eye tracing the whereabouts of Dennis.

I could just call the operator. I wouldn't need a dime for that.

I excuse myself to go to the washroom. As I stand, Mark comes over and asks me to dance. We sway to the slower song. The world is surreal. Valentine's Day in a small-town, sad disco the night after a rape, maybe before a murder. Am I being dramatic? I am not here. This can't be me. Then, a lightbulb goes off in my head.

I lean into Mark and whisper, "Please listen. Dennis raped me this morning. I'm trapped here. I have no money. I have to stay in the room with him. Could your family give me a separate room? Or could you call the police for me?"

I don't know what response I was expecting but it wasn't:

"Denny? Our Denny?" Mark asks a little too loud.

I pull him back to me.

"It's the truth. Or, please, just stay up tonight and watch the room. It's just one night of your life. If you hear anything, you could bust in or call the police."

I am pleading.

"I've known Denny all my life. He would never do something like that. Man, are you drunk or somethin'?"

"What's goin' on?" Dennis is breathing on us. I stare hard at Mark.

"No, man. She's just drunk or somethin'."

"C'mon. Let's get outta here." Dennis throws me my coat then grabs me by the scruff of it, leading me out to the car. We all pile in. When we pull up to the motel, I keep my eyes on Mark. Pleading. Hoping he will, actually, one night of his life, security guard walk by our room all night.

In the room, it's just Dennis and I. I sit on the edge of one of the double beds, the one closest to the bathroom, boots and coat still on, my purse and bag in my lap.

He undresses down to his long underwear, a grown-up onesie, that sags loosely around his bony body. He climbs into the other bed, pulls the blanket up and looks at me, waiting.

"Take your clothes off," he says, pissed.

"I don't want to," I say, chin down, the words falling into my coat.

"I said take your clothes off," he says.

"No," I say.

I stare at my bags.

He sits up.

"If I wake up in the morning and you still have your clothes on, you're dead."

My breath stops. Did he say *I was dead?*

He turns out the light.

The moon falls on his bed in slats.

His snoring begins.

Do I leave? In the middle of the night on the empty highway in the below zero temperatures? Where would I go? Hitchhike again? If I had money, I could get a separate room and barricade myself in. If I had money, I could call a taxi and take it to the next town until I was far away and safe. If I had money, I wouldn't be here in the first place. Maybe. If I had money, I'd be safe.

I lay on my back on top of the polyester bedspread, fully clothed. My eyelids fight to stay open. I stare at the ceiling and pray, "Mick, if you are there, please help me. God, if you are there, please let me be safe tonight. Mick. I miss you so much. I need you. I don't know who I am without you. I don't know how I got here. Mick, please watch over me tonight. Mick?"

The brightness of the room opens my eyes. It is morning.

I am untouched and still dressed. Dennis is not here.

Maybe he is at breakfast with Bob?

This is my chance.

I don't know where I am going to go. I'll just run.

I have to pee.

I hurry into the bathroom, grabbing my purse and bag. I pee. I wipe. I zip. I buckle. From inside the bathroom I hear, "Get in the truck!" Dennis yells into the room and then leaves, the door slamming. My chance slammed shut.

Dennis is sick of me.

I'm no fun anymore.

Out in the parking lot, I'm in my coat, my high heel boots, and my purse is strapped across my chest. Holding my overnight bag, I lean into a fierce icy wind that is bullying the parking lot. It lashes my face, pushing me backward. Snow is falling so thick it seems there is more white than air. Cars on the highway zip by. I move to the rim of the road, staying lower than the shoulder of the highway, trying not to be seen. Maybe I can walk to town?

Escape Dennis.

Stay out of his truck.

Push against the wind.

"Get in the truck. Jesus," Dennis says. I stop. We stare. Him from by the truck, and me from the road. Freezing air numbs me. Numbs me. It feels right to be numb, grateful for the icy gusts. There is nowhere to go. There is the truck. There is the motel. There is the highway with no buildings. I get in the truck.

We drive less than a mile into a suburban residential neighborhood. A white Victorian style house takes shape up the road.

Dennis parks on the road in front of the house. Bob's truck belches then hisses to a stop behind him. Dennis takes me to the door. An older man and an older woman peer from behind the cracked open door. They look like the kind of older people you'd call folks. Like they'd be in jelly commercials. Or breakfast ads.

They know each other, this couple and Dennis.

They say things like, sure, no problem, we'll get her home, take care, good to see ya, talk soon, right-o then. And Dennis leaves. They hold open the door to their home to me. We watch the trucks pull away.

Their names are William and Marlena Crawley. They are retired. They usher me inside. Their home is a mountain of stuffed animals. Stuffed animals everywhere. There is nowhere to look that there isn't a stuffed animal. They make them at home for extra money, they explain. I am hoping they'll give me one. I don't know why. But they don't. We sit on their hard, cushioned, frilly-skirted, busy-patterned sofa, not knowing what to say once the stuffed animal conversation ends.

"Did ya have a nice Valentine's Day?" Marlena asks, leaning in, clasping her hands, waiting for a young person's gleeful recount. I want to say something polite and sweet, but tears, hot and wet, surprise me, and they roll down my cold cheeks against my will. I look down at my palms pressed together between my knees.

I can feel the Crawleys exchanging glances. I try to speak above, over, out, around, and through the lumpy stopper in my throat holding the rest of the hidden iceberg of emotion in place. But I cannot without loosening it. Marlena gets up and comes back, handing me a burgundy-colored wash cloth. I nod a "thanks" and wipe my face until I can speak.

"Dennis," I say. They stare at me. "I think I should go to the police," I say. Their eyebrows raise.

"Well, it's Sunday, darlin'," Marlena says.

I nod. And wait. Trying to reformulate what I am trying to say. I didn't know police were closed on Sundays. I never thought about it.

"Dennis raped me," I say, looking to their eyes as I say "me."

It's not the nurturing reaction I guess I didn't realize I expected. Marlena laughs, good-natured and polite, as if I surely must be joking, or I caught her unawares with my joke. She's hoping. And then says, "Denny? Why, he wouldn't hurt a fly."

"I'm not a fly," I think.

"We've known Denny, what, dear?" Marlena asks, touching her husband's thigh. "Well, most of our lives. He's a good egg, that Denny."

I nod my head because the lump has grown and the tears keep rolling. I don't know what to say, how to disagree. I can see saying anything else not only won't be believed but is downright impolite and this is my only port in the storm right now.

Finally, Mr. Crawley breaks the silence.

"Could drive her to the Amtrak in Streator," he says to his wife. Then, to me, "S'about twenty-five minutes from here. You could get the train back to the university from there."

"I have no money," I say, "but I could send it back to you when I get back to school?" I offer and mean it. The Crawleys agree. Marlena writes out their address in blue ballpoint practical swirls. Mr. Crawley buys the ticket at the station booth.

Three hours later, I'm back at my dorm room in Macomb, Illinois. I only see the details I need to see. I feel like I'm in a haze. I shower. I ache everywhere. I fetal position myself under the covers in the middle of the bed and remain there. All night. All day. All evening.

Late that night, Cindy Victory arrives, chirping the news of her romantic weekend with her beau. I unwind myself from the fetal ball, pull the covers up, and listen with only my eyes peeking out at her.

"So, how was your Valentine's Day?" she asks, ready to cheer for me.

"I was raped," I say.

This has nowhere to go in Cindy's idea of the world. I can see her struggling with it. She puts her hand gently on my thigh. We both just sit. Then, I allow myself to cry. Out loud. Sobbing. Ugly tears. She lets me finish, sitting next to me with her hand on the cover on my thigh as my sobs turn into hiccups. As my breath regulates, she leans in and hugs my shoulders. And then, in a quiet, nurse voice she says, "This is the kind of thing that can happen when you are kinda wild in your life."

I press my eyelids tight.

"I don't mean it to be mean. I just mean that if you are, well, out there, then other people get the signal and think it's ok. You know what I mean?"

I say, "Um hmm." And Cindy gets herself out of the room.

Is that what happened? Did I give the signal that it was ok? To have sex with me? To hurt me? To not care what I feel? Is that what I've been doing and not knowing it? All I want to do is be open and be loved and have an extraordinary life. Does that mean I give people the wrong signals?

I skip class. I call in sick to work. I go back to bed. Then, I get up. I get up and look at my Mick door, and I remember what he said. Women lose their beauty when they get hard and cynical. The more open you are, the more compassionate you are, the closer you can get to unconditional love, the more spiritually enlightened. Everyone you meet is your mirror. Is that true? I don't know how to process that. I'm not enlightened enough yet. But you have the choice. I want to be beautiful and charismatic. I want to be an actress of great consequence. I can't do it being bitter and angry.

No. I refuse to let them win.

They can violate my body.

They cannot touch my Essence.

344

I refuse to allow my Spirit to change because of what they did.

If they can't touch my Soul, they don't win.

To get bitter, to get angry, to get hard-hearted, is to get ugly.

I will not.

This very moment, I declare I will stay soft and loving and kind.

I am far from unconditional love.

But I will put it on my horizon. No matter.

I declare myself the winner and refuse to remember it.

Refuse any thoughts of any of it.

I win.

***

A month goes by. I come back to the room after picking up my mail. A bouquet from Rick. The second batch of wasted flowers after a barrage of five Hallmarks, all saying the same thing: He loves me. I am beautiful. When can I come back to see him? All signed the same in luxurious handwriting:

Siempre, Rick.

I throw them all down the garbage chute.

***

The phone rings once. I am the first on my floor to pick it up.

"Hello?"

"You forget about me, Spice o' Life?"

Dennis.

I'm paralyzed.

"Don't see ya at Kuli's."

I returned to work but only do the late shift to, on purpose, miss the locals and truckers at happy hour.

"I wanna see ya again," he says.

Angry, frantic tears blur my vision.

"Why ain't ya sayin' anythin'?"

Silent tears stream down my face into my blouse.

"Hey, you gave me the crabs, you know that?" He spits the words.

The room feels like it might be moving in a slow spin. I hold the wall. "I don't have crabs so I couldn't have given them to you. Maybe you got them from someone else that you raped." Both hands clutch the phone.

"I gottem from you, and I want to come give 'em back."

Silence.

Click.

I sit on my bed, shaking.

Why didn't I go to the doctor? To the police?

What's wrong with me?

I have no money for a doctor.

Yes, but there was the student nurse.

What about the police?

Lying in bed those two days afterward, I debated on whether to further my shame by going to a doctor or the police.

I hitchhiked.

I was wearing high-heeled boots and tight jeans.

I've had sex before, so what's the big deal?

I flirted with Dennis and Bob day after day when they were at Kuli's. I stayed in a room with him, not one night, but two.

I have responsibility for some part of this.

Yes, it was rape, but no one was physically injured.

It wasn't *violent* violent. It had to be or it wasn't rape. Right?

All that really happened is I had nonviolent unwanted sex, and I felt it wasn't fair. Right?

I could have hurt him during the act, stopping it, couldn't I?

Part of this might be my fault.

I don't know what rape is supposed to be like.

I knew I was raped, but I didn't die.

I thought people died in rapes.

Now, it has to be my secret.

− 34 −
A RESISTIBLE RISE

I start skipping classes. I don't know why. I skip biology. Psychology. Math. Every day I promise myself I'll go next class. But I don't. Same for acting class. The teacher doesn't even know me. The class clique ignores me. So, I skip that. I skip movement class. I know it's my ego, and I should just get over it. I mean, did I really think that just because Joseph slept with me that I meant anything?

I end up failing his class. The acting teacher passes me. Maybe because he doesn't know if I'm there or not. Mim gives me a "B" in her class. She would have given me an "A," she says, but she has to count my absences. She looks at me with sad eyes.

"You'll do better next quarter?" she asks.

I will. I'm still in the theater department.

The next production is a play that's picked to make a statement. *The Resistible Rise of Arturo Ui.* It's competition time for the university's Theater Departments. It's so important to the university that we rank high that a guest director is hired.

He's intense. Lean. He paces like a panther. He wears wire-framed round glasses. Tight to his scalp is curly dark hair. He has an aura of aggravation. His first upset is that he has little say in casting. All or as many as possible theater students must be cast, male and female. However, there are nineteen or twenty parts for men and only two female roles. Well, really, one. The prostitute is a female. The barker could be a man or a woman. There's a lot of actresses, so we're not sure how or if we're going to be cast. Mim Canny is at rehearsal as Assistant Director.

We take the stage to hear our casting. First, "The Prostitute."

Cassandra. I don't know her. I've never seen her. She must be a year or more ahead of me. She's a tall, voluptuous dark-skinned woman with a wild afro. Cassandra. That's her real-life name. Three syllables. I've always longed for a name with three or more syllables. Lyrical. Ethereal.

"The Barker will be played by Fame Fetuna!"

Fame Fetuna is her real name. Her parents believed in her that much that they named her Fame. And she's not skinny and she's not tall and she's not beautiful like a movie star. She's better. She has short, loose, feathery, cut-for-ease brown hair. She wears loose-fitting, nondescript baggy sweats with pockets that can't be defined as any style at all. She's a bit overweight like me, but my overweight is tight, clinging to a once athletic frame somewhere underneath. Hers has been jiggly and loose for years as if sports were never a part of her growing up. But it seems like she's comfy that way. Not concerned that professional actresses have to be skinny. Doesn't even think about her fat as an enemy invader, the way I think of my fat. She laughs when she feels like it, not to please anyone else. She's been acting since she was a kid. And she likes me. Well. She smiles at me every time I see her in the theater building halls.

Fame strides downstage, smiling, her hands in her pockets.

"Hey," she says to the new director, to Mim, and whoever else is sitting with them in the audience rows. She puts her hand over her forehead blocking the bright stage lights so she can see them. "Thanks," she says, smiling. And she walks upstage again, smiling and winking at me as she passes. At me.

The men's parts are cast. The main roles are given. What's left is a group of characters called "The Chicago Grocers" who are supposed to be men, but there's a bunch of us, all female, still standing. The director is not happy with this.

He points to each of us and yells, "Grocer 1! Grocer 2!"

It's as if it doesn't matter who plays who. We're all the same. Annoying because we're female.

"Grocer 10!" he says, pointing at me. Last, but I'm in.

***

Fame knows Cassandra. Fame knows everyone. Everyone knows Fame, and Fame is the lead. She already knows most of her lines by the first rehearsal. Even when I'm not called to rehearsal because there's no Grocer scenes, I go anyway.

I sit in a velvet theater seat in the back of the auditorium, leaning forward with my arms crossed on the wooden frame back of the seat in front of me, my chin resting on my arms. I try not to move too much so my seat doesn't creak. The director is very testy, and I'm not certain that we're allowed to be watching rehearsals we're not in.

Watching Fame rehearse is inspiring. I'm learning so much. More than I learned in a year of acting class. I see how she's coming into this character from the lines on the page until the lines were never on a page but inside her. There's no page, no stage directions on the page anymore. She's swallowed them, and now they are coming out of her, *through her*, in whatever surprising way she wants.

***

The Chicago Grocer costumes are so ugly. Brown trousers with suspenders, big suit coats and barber hats. Underneath, fat padded bellies. We pin our hair up under short hair man wigs. We stipple our jaws to make us all look like men in need of a shave. Finally, tight ace bandages to flatten our breasts. We must help each other. There's no way to do them tight enough by yourself. We giggle and moan. It's painful, but we're all in this together. Mine are the hardest to get flat because I have larger breasts, but once I get the suit on, I imagine it'll just look flatter and fatter.

Tech rehearsal begins. Our first Grocer scene. We stand together in two rows. We begin. Grocer 1, Grocer 4, and Grocer 6 say their lines.

They tell us to hold. We're told to move over a foot. Lights are adjusted. We're told to begin again. Grocer 1, 4, 6, 9, 10—that's me—2, and 3 say our lines. We're told to hold. We're told to say our lines again.

My turn. I tuck my chin into my neck to help get my voice lower,

"It's our own fault! We don't stand up to them!" I yell to be heard in my deepest voice.

I hear something smash like the director bashed his clipboard on the seat in front of him.

"Freeze!" the director yells. "You!" he yells.

We freeze. No one breathes. Everyone is frozen, afraid to ask which "you" he means.

"Which one is she?" We hear him ask then yell, "Grocer 10."

His loud impatience reaches inside me, pulling my stomach to my throat.

"Line!" he commands.

I step forward and tuck my chin.

"It's our own fault—"

"Goddammit!" he interrupts again, smashing the clipboard. "No. Out. I want her out. I want her gone. Not in my play. She's a goddamn brick shithouse. Get off the stage. Get off. You're out. Out."

Inside me, my bones shake. I feel sparks run through my veins, almost like the zapping of electrodes. I'm unable to move.

"Get off!" The clipboard clanks to the floor.

I'm paralyzed. My eyes are hot, foggy, and wet. I can't see. Everything is a haze around me, like I've been in a crash, and I don't know what to do. The lights are blinding, and everyone staring, hushed.

I feel something gentle on my arm. A hand. A soft whisper brushes against my ear. Mim Canny's voice.

"Come with me. Come," she says. Mim Canny leads me down the side steps of the stage, up the red-carpet aisle of the auditorium, through the exit doors, down the linoleum-tiled hallway, and into the girl's bathroom. I stand, shaking, unable to see her or myself through the fog in my eyes. Unable to hold the sink to steady myself.

Mim is cooing. "You're in the play. He's a hothead. He was out of line. It was uncalled for." She takes one of my hands in hers.

"I'm not a good man," I say, the words coming out in chunks. Tears plop out onto the bathroom tiles.

"Everyone was convincing but me. Everyone has talent but me. I'm a bad actor," I say, condemning myself, confessing to a crime.

We all knew being a bad actor was a crime. How dare you be not good at acting and still attempt it? That was the feeling. Here it was. Like a hard slap in the face. I knew it was true. The director was just the first one to say it not behind my back. How dare I attempt being on the stage when I'm not good enough?

"What's a brick shithouse?" I hear myself asking and, suddenly, I'm sobbing. It sounds like such a terrible ugly thing to be. Does it mean I have no feeling in my acting? Or did he call me an outhouse? Made of bricks? What does it mean?

"It's not important," Mim says. She places her hands under the faucet, then washes the wig hairs from my forehead and the tears from my cheeks. She pats my face with the coarse paper towel. She dries her hands and holds her palms open. I place mine on top. Look at our feet. Her practical loafers. My man costume shoes. The cuffs of my trousers. A long brown hair spiraled by the floor drain. My breathing calms.

"It will be ok," she says, pressing her thumbs softly into my palms for emphasis. "You're new. You have a passion for this. It takes time. And you're very funny."

I let myself laugh a little. Mim shares it with a closed-mouthed smile.

"And you do have talent," she says.

I shake my head hard in denial. This makes me cry again. "Then why?" I wail.

"He was out of line," she says again.

"But he was saying the truth," I say.

"No," she says. "No. This is not the right part for you, but he was wrong. Acting can be learned. Be willing to stay vulnerable. That's a brave act. It will serve you. I promise. Try not to hold onto what he said. I will make sure you're still in the production."

Hand in hand, we walk back into the theater. I sit in my seat in the back rows where I had watched Fame rehearse. I watch Mim talk to the director. I watch but cannot hear the back and forth. She turns and waves me up, pointing to the stage. With my head up, eyes straight ahead, I take my place with The Chicago Grocers. No one says anything to me about it.

Fame and I walk back to the dorms. She digs her hand in her pockets, and she blows a bubble that pops over her lips. "I feel like we gotta good shot," she says, talking about the judges coming to see the play.

We walk, watching our feet marching in even strides together on the pavement. Same rhythm. Left-left. Right-right.

"Acting is what I'm meant to do," I say. "I just don't know what I'm doing."

Fame laughs. "Yet," she says.

"Yet," I say. "But you do," I say. "When you get a part, how do you know how it's supposed to be played? It seems like it could be anything. Did you feel lost in the beginning?"

"I mean, I was a little kid when I started. I just said the lines and pretended," she says.

My eyes well up with tears. "Maybe it's a language too advanced for my brain," I say. Then I laugh and say, "I should probably just quit."

Right-right.

"But if I'm not going to be an actor, what am I supposed to live for?" I ask and laugh too loud as I watch the pavement go by.

Left-left. Right-right. Left-left.

"A brick shithouse means you're hot," she says. "Solidly hot. So what if you suck at being a guy?"

"Meryl Streep could play a guy," I say.

"Yeah. But Marilyn Monroe couldn't. She's a brick shithouse."

– 35 –
Born Again

There might be something wrong with me. Also, it's the Fourth of July. I'm looking out my dorm room window onto the grassy quad below. All the kids are down on the lawn. In shorts. All of them. The guys and the girls. Some of the girls who never had the "freshman fifteen" are in bikinis. Some are playing frisbee. Others are lying on the towels from spring break with alligators or palm trees. There are even kids BBQ-ing. Boys. Not BBQ-ing boys—although, *yum*—but boys BBQ-ing. They all look so young and care-free. Tonight, they'll lay on blankets on the lawn and watch fireworks.

PS, I hate the Fourth of July. Because of my cellulite thighs. On the Fourth of July, you have to wear shorts so you can participate in outdoor sports fun with coed groups of pals that just go out and play volleyball and tag football. I don't know how to be friends with those people. People with no neurosis. People who are never self-blaming or self-hating. Who wake up cheerful, ready for sport. I have never been like that, and I can't wear shorts. I am just inside when I should be outside in the sunshine like a normal person on a holiday. So, I'm not going down to the quad. And if I'm not going down, I should be filling out my application, which I've been procrastinating on.

In the *American Theater* magazine, there was a full-page ad for a Theater School of Mime. Mime, I'm pretty sure, is acting without words. Studying it in an intensive program could teach me to deeply express myself through my body, teaching me to act from my flesh and bones, making my acting intense.

I sent for their application, and even though it was all the way from Boulder, Colorado, it came pretty fast. I've been waiting for a free day to fill it out. Like today. But it's summer, and summer in Illinois is a big deal. So is the Fourth of July. You don't just waste it like a zombie sitting indoors filling out applications.

Somehow, I've forgotten how to enjoy life. The only thing that feels fun is accomplishing. Frisbees and BBQs do not accomplish things, so they do not feel fun. I have so much to become. I have a list, pages long, of things to master to become extraordinary. A lot of kids my age just want to graduate and get a job in the field of their major and that's it. Do that job forever. But to be an actress, successful and even famous, you have to develop star quality.

I'm reading the *Handbook to Higher Consciousness*, a book on spiritual enlightenment, which is necessary for charisma. For having that "it" factor. Only a few people make it, so I have a lot more work to do. Inward and outward. Time is ticking. I'm already almost eighteen. Plus, I have to work. A lot of kids my age don't worry about becoming. Or work. Or cellulite. Just look at them on the quad.

I'm gonna go down. I am. I should. I can enjoy a sunny day among my peers. I can wear my terry cloth beach cover dress. I wear it almost everywhere in the summer night and day. It's bright sun yellow. It has no straps, just elastic across the chest and elastic at the waist and comes down to mid-calf. It's so comfortable, I don't have to wear underwear or a bra under it if I don't want to. It shows off my breasts, makes my waist look smaller, and covers the fatness of my thighs. I look like an hourglass in it. Like a brick shithouse. Ha-ha. If it's clear I'm not down there to play frisbee, it'll be fine. I'll just look summery.

With my application on a clipboard, my journal, my pens, my theater magazines, my towel, a diet pop from the mini fridge, matches, and my cigarettes, I wander out on the crunchy lawn of weeds, crabgrass, dandelions and bare hard dirt, and I find a patch with a circle of aloneness around it. A couple boys look over. I lift my chin, not noticing them noticing my bralessness. I lower myself like a dancer melting, legs together, knees side saddle, to my towel. I lay on my back and wait until I feel their eyes are no longer on me, then I squinch around on my towel to find the right arrangement of not too clumpy dirt beneath me for my head and not too pokey of crabgrass coming up through my towel. How does no one else think this is not icky? I find a position and put my knees up so any cellulite falls under my skirt, invisible at the top of my thighs. I close my eyes and exhale.

Ok.

Ok.

This is ok. It's the Fourth of July, and I'm among my peers, doing what everyone is doing, participating in the day off. My palms skim the tips of the grass blades, making them tickle, then itch. The smells of cooking meat, charcoal lighter fluid, and coconut tan lotion float me back to when summer was just summer. When I was little, just experiencing was joyful. When did everyday life stop being enough? When did I become so lacking?

I sit up again and reach for my cigs. I hate smoking outside, but I need them right now. Smoking is my friend. Smoking is a way not to be alone. If I'm smoking, I'm doing something. Smoking gives me time to think without having to speak. Something to do so I don't feel lost or alone. It jacks up my metabolism when my mind is fading. A buoy when my emotions trample me.

"Don't smoke. It doesn't make you look cool," a male voice says from right behind me so I have to crane my entire body to see him.

I look. I see. I take an on-purpose drag. I blow it out in front of me and take up my journal as if he interrupted already in process writing. Why do men think they can just tell you how to be? Would he say that to another guy?

He sits himself in front of my towel. He's about my age. He's got the body of a young boy, all lean, nothing extra, still kiddish, wearing clothes so tight I can see the outline of his outie belly button. The only protrusion on his rawboned frame. I give him a glare, my eyebrows furled together in an "um, what are you doing" look. I don't know what he wants. He's not saying anything. I'm still going to smoke, so.

"I'm doing some things, so," I say and start filling out the application. Name. Address. Phone number. I keep it close so he can't see my personal information.

"Going to the fireworks tonight?" he asks.

I circle "Female" and "Single." I fill in "Age: 17."

"Give me your number." He's searching his pockets. For what? Maybe a paper to write on?

"I'm not going out with people right now," I say.

"I'm not good enough for you?" he asks, crossing his arms. He's confrontational. Pissed. He thinks I'm that attractive?

He *is* kind of cute. But all boys to me are cute because every boy is a possibility, and you never know. Unless you get to know them, you could be passing up Mr. Right. But he's very demanding, and I never met him before. He's bossy but not in a sexy way, and I don't know what to do.

"That's not what I meant," I say. I didn't mean to make him feel bad.

"Then write down your number. I'll make you dinner at my apartment. You live on campus?" he asks, reaching for my journal. I quickly press my hand on it.

"What are you doing?" I ask.

"You can write your number here. Just tear it off," he says.

"I'm not going to tear my journal," I say.

"You want me to take you out, don't you? I'm growing on you," he says. And laughs. Smiles. It's the first time he smiles. Is this just his weird way of telling me he's attracted?

But I smile, too, and I write my number on my journal and tear it off anyway.

"You live in the dorms? Is this a party line?" he asks.

I nod.

"In August, I'm moving off campus for sophomore year," I say.

"I've lived off campus since sophomore year. Same apartment every year. I'll have you over. Ok?" he asks. The first time he's asked me anything he actually expected an answer to.

"Ok," I say. "Are you a senior?"

But he's already walking away, shoving the torn paper with my number into his pants pocket.

I return to my application. I wasn't trying to hurt his feelings when I said that I'm not going out with people, meaning guys, anymore right now. I feel bad now. I hate being misunderstood. It's just I miss Mick. I miss who I was with Mick. Plus, the past year with guys has been kinda super hard, to put it mildly.

The application is all essay questions. Questions about how you feel about acting and theater and mime. Questions about why you feel you'd be right for their program. They only sent one form, so I decide I'll write it out in my journal then onto the form.

I write until I'm shaking my hands and cracking my knuckles. The kids are getting louder and rowdier as dusk descends. I stay, transferring my words onto the application page.

I write: Acting is the art of emotion. I am often tsunamied by my emotions. Being an actor would be a way for me to control those forces, to distinguish and move through them like a painter with a palette of nuanced colors. It would be to use them in the creation of something higher, something beautiful. To capture the chaos that life feels like and frame moments, give them meaning. Holding them as meant to be is to harness life and say "there is God; 'tis not all meaningless chaos." What better way to spend a life than to be devoted to mastering this?

There's one more question, but it's too dark, and I hear the fireworks and lose my concentration. I gather my things, mulling the last question: "Picturing your life in the arts, visualize yourself and your life ten years from now. How will our program make a difference within that vision?"

I don't know. I don't know who I am right now. I can say what I wish for. But I can't project the me that I will be in ten years. Also, I'll be twenty-seven. I could be dead by then.

The fireworks spill across the black sky in the distance, whizzing up and bursting open. Everyone is listening to the explosions. The kids, now louder and drunker, scream.

"Woah!"

"Oh, man!"

"You guys!"

I stop to watch before I go into my dorm building. They're pretty, but they're the same every year. Delight exploding in the sky. Maybe in ten years, I'll have changed so much, the Fourth of July will be joyful.

Or it won't have to mean anything at all.

***

He calls. The guy from the Fourth of July. Yes, he was weirdly bossy, but he's the first guy my age that's asked me on an actual date since I got to college, and it would be such a relief to be someone's girlfriend and be cared about.

His name is Christian. Not the religion. His actual name. Although it might as well have been because as we walk to the pizza place, all he talks about is being a born-again Christian.

"What does it mean?" I ask.

"I accept Jesus Christ as my personal Lord and Savior," he says.

"Isn't that what all Christians do?" I ask.

For a moment he stops walking to look at me.

"I mean, it's so ironic your name is Christian, with you being so Christian," I say.

"It's what my parents named me," he says.

"I know, but it's such a coincidence that you turned out to be like overflowing Christian." I say, trying to make him smile.

"My parents are Christians. I'm Christian. They named me Christian," he says.

"I thought you were just born, and they named you Christian and, by chance, you decided to be a born-again Christian. Which is ironic. Like you doubled down on your name. Oh, wait, but your parents might be born-again. Doink. I'm thinking you picked to be born-again to go with your name. Like matchy-matchy. Ha-ha-ha." My hands are fluttery, making a fuss. I'm giggling.

"And you're not even blonde," he says, not laughing.

I stop laughing. I'm going to have to get more serious if we're going to be compatible.

Two more weeks to the end of summer session. Two more weeks until I can move into my off-campus apartment. Almost two weeks of sexless-dating Christian. Not even a kiss. Which feels like maybe he likes me-likes me and wants us to be special.

We walk. We eat. He's very serious which makes his boy face even more adorable. We have deep conversations. He listens to me as if he's listening for a lyric he can't remember. He's really attracted to me but, for now, he is keeping a Christian distance. He cares about my improvement, so he's helping me become more self-aware.

But there seems to be a lot that needs improving. It's strange how differently he sees me than how I am. Sometimes, he compares me to Mary, Jesus's mom, and it makes his eyes well. Other times, I'm a fallen angel, open and vulnerable to evil forces. This is why I should accept Jesus Christ as my Lord and savior. It's a force field against Satanic energy seeking a host. I'm the perfect host.

It's ridiculous but when I lay in bed at night, I think of the night Mick died. The light of him glowing against the metallic wallpaper in my bedroom, the bone cold, his scent. Mike's call that Mick died in the night. I know it was Mick. His energetic form. His Spirit. I believe what Christian says: if there can be good spirits, why not malevolent ones?

He tells me when the Born-Again meetings are. He assigns me a special Bible to read. He says if I don't, how do I expect him to take me seriously and have an intelligent conversation? I don't have a good reason for not going to his meetings except I don't want to. I don't think I can believe in Jesus in the Christian way, and I definitely don't think I can accept him as my personal Lord and Savior.

***

I'm sitting with the mime application. Christian calls me for a date. He asks if I read the book, if I feel I can accept Jesus Christ. I say I can't. He says that he doesn't want to see me again. I say ok, because I'm kind of exhausted by it. Then he says I have a lot to learn, so he will make an exception, and we can get a burger.

If he likes me, why does he need to admonish me all the time?

I say maybe. To the burger.

Back to the application question: "Picture yourself ten years from now." I can't. How can I see myself someday when I don't know who I am today? People treat me so differently than who I think I am, I must not be who I think I am. Is my identity who I am or how I affect people?

Like with Christian. I think I'm a nice person, but he sees me as a heathen that needs to be saved because "Satan hides in the angelic." Which totally confuses me. That means bad could be good and good could be bad and there's no way for anything to mean what it is. I strain to see what he's seeing when he sees me.

I can get no further on the application, so I agree to the burger.

And, PS, if I am Satan, why are we having a burger?

At the burger place, who knows why, I tell him about Dennis the trucker.

I ask, "Was it rape?"

It's the first time I've told anyone other than Cindy what happened. He intertwines his fingers with mine. We both drop our foreheads like in prayer. I can tell he feels helpless after the fact. He puts both arms around me, as if to protect me from men who would do such things. I feel cocooned in this moment of kindness. He whispers "sweet lost Magdalene," then he asks me to his house for that dinner he promised when we first met.

Wasn't she the prostitute?

I dress up. Candles flicker on the table. Flame reflections dance on the walls. We eat, and he talks about having been a sinner before. How his whole life changed when he was saved. I put my hand on his. He puts his other hand on mine. I think he's going to kiss me, but he says, "This is why it's important to me to save you."

Ugh!

Then he says, "I want to be with you."

"You do?" I ask, flirty, shimmying my shoulders.

He nods. "I want you to be safe from Satan. So, we can be together."

I lean in to kiss him, ignoring the part about Satan.

He leans back.

"I don't believe in Satan. I don't believe in Hell. Or Heaven. I'm Jewish," I say.

"The Jews killed Christ," he says.

"Christ was a nice Jewish boy," I say.

He gets up.

I get up then plop cross-legged on his floor.

"This is what I believe," I say, running my fingers through his carpet. "I believe God is a powerful universal force. Like unconditional Love. Not a person. I believe everything has a spirit. Animals. Insects. Trees. Toads. And none of us are heathens. I believe we're all vibration in bodies. Every time our spirit chooses to be inside a body, it's so we can grow to a higher consciousness. To be more like God. That's what we're here to do."

It's the first time I say that. It's what I've been thinking since Sissy. Since Hebrew School. Since Mick died. Since I saw his light the night he died.

Christian is staring at me. The energy between us, circling. I think he's going to lean in and kiss me.

"Those are the words of Satan," he says, so close to me, speaking his words into my lips. "I accept thee, Jesus Christ, as my personal Lord and Savior. Say it now. Banish Satan from this room."

His voice is pitched deep, and he's leaning into me. He's scaring me.

"There's no such thing," I insist.

"You don't think a manipulative energy—an *evil* energy— can sneak inside you?" His energy is intense and dagger-like.

I don't know what to say. Anything is possible. We know so little. I have chills. The energy in the room has shifted. I'm frightened. I do believe in things we cannot see. I do believe it's possible there could be evil energy just as much as loving energy. I don't think it's Satan, but I do believe in spirits.

This is getting scary. It makes sense. Energy can overtake energy. I am open, I am vulnerable. My imagination is too open. I have no force field. He could be right. But I know I'm a force for good. I'm starting to shake. The room seems darker.

"I want to go home," I say. Tears are starting to run down my cheeks.

I'm trembling. He octopuses his arms and legs around me, between me. He rocks me, saying, "Shhhh. Shhhh."

If the Devil is near, trying to meld inside me, is Mick here, too? Is he protecting me? I'm dizzy and so, *so* spooked.

"Although Satan can't read our thoughts like God can," he says, "he can enter into us by tempting us." I am wide-eyed, keeping myself pressed safely in a ball into Christian's torso, trying to hear how to keep the negative spirits that are in this room from claiming me.

"Just because you're Jewish or don't say that you accept him, you to Hell? Even if you're a good person? I ask, pleading my case. "Can you protect me?" I ask, almost begging.

He nods. "Say it, and he will be banished," he says.

"Even if I don't mean it?" I whisper. "Isn't that worse? To say a deception?"

To say it seems like blasphemy to everything I believe. To say it is a lie. I stare at him. My teeth are chattering. His torso is wrapped around me like a cloak. I can feel the negative energy of other entities closing in around us. I'm terrified of being swallowed by forces I cannot see and don't understand. Desperate and weeping, hoping the evil spirits cannot see through my passion to the lie underneath, I say it.

"I accept you, Lord Jesus Christ, as my personal Savior."

Christian hugs me closer. He weeps too. We stay in a ball together on his floor. We don't move until it feels like the air around us is the way it was when we first came in. Before this talk began. We stay, breathing into each other.

I didn't mean what I said, but the room feels different. Like the evil thing blew past. And Christian seems different than he's been the entire time I've known him. Relaxed. He kisses me for the first time.

The kiss grows until we're gyrating against one another on his floor. My pelvis grinds into his. I don't feel his hard-on pressing back. I reach down for it, but he takes my hand and leads me to his bed. I want to dry hump longer until I can't stand it anymore, but he asks me to get undressed and get under the covers. He says he'll be right back. I do. I lie naked, waiting for him under his sheets.

He enters in a cotton robe tied tight at the waist and slides himself next to me under the top sheet. We start kissing again. My thighs separate and wrap around his thigh, rolling my heat into it. I don't feel the erection he should have demanding license with me.

"Do you want me?" I breathe into his ear.

"I do. I just needed you to say it," he says.

"I did," I say, holding the edge of his earlobe with my lip.
"Because Satan—"

I kiss him full on his mouth to stop this talk of Satan in the middle of soon-to-be sex. To him, I am an angel who was maybe the Devil. But aren't we all a bit? Enough Bible. It's sex time.

My hand rides up to his cock, expecting hardness that isn't there. What's going on? I'm slow and cautious, careful not to change my expression from warm and happy and passionate.

He's on his back. I open his robe. His eyes are squeezed shut as if he can't look at me.

His penis. Oh, this poor man. This poor boy. His penis is smaller than my pinky. How is this? I never knew this was possible.

I bend down and put the tiny pinky with the tiny mushroom tip in my mouth. He keeps his eyes closed and lets me. I have to keep my eyes open and looking at him. I have to see that he's a grown man because my mouth is feeling an infant penis, and that churns my stomach. I take it out of my mouth and straddle him instead. There's no way to put a condom on it. I doubt he has one.

I try to slide him inside me, but it's not big enough to enter and stay. I don't want him to get self-conscious so I keep moving, placing the tiny penis between my lower lips and sliding slowly, warm and wet, forward then back, forward then back, stroking him. His face lightens then softens, no thoughts making it stone-hard argumentative.

I close my eyes, getting close to orgasm when I hear him. A loud "umph" escapes his cemented-together lips. His extra gooey wetness spreads on my clit and pubic hair. I want to lay with him, but I better wash off the cum before any of it sneaks inside me.

"I'll be right back," I say, and I prance to the bathroom on my tiptoes so my thighs don't look as fat as they do when I'm flat-footed.

He knocks on the bathroom door.

"Your clothes," he says, handing them through the opening.

He's so abrupt. But maybe now, with enough affection and sex, he won't be so paranoid about life. Or his penis. Was that why he needed to be born again? Because of what he felt about his penis?

I exit the bathroom with a naughty smile. He's leaning against his front door, ready to go. I must have given him a quizzical look because he says, "I'll walk you home."

We walk without talking. I keep looking over, smiling at him. I reach my hand to his and hook my pinkie on his. He lets me for a block then scratches an itch on his chin and walks with his arms crossed.

As we get close to the dorms, my eyes well up. What did I do this time?

"Here. It has meeting dates in it." He hands me the palm-size Bible or book of born again or whatever it is he carries. I don't want to take it. I feel like whatever evil energy I felt in the room is in this book. I don't want it in my hand. I don't want it in my room. I know if I don't take it, he'll be mad at me. I know he wants to see me at the meetings, and I don't know what to do.

"It's ok," I say, leaving the book in his hand.

"Oh, now you don't want me?" he asks.

How does he even think that? I circle his torso with my arms. He pulls my arms away.

"It seems like *you* don't want *me*," I say. Tears are rolling, and I don't care. "I thought it was a really nice time. Didn't you?" I look into his eyes.

"Crocodile tears," he says. "You lie so easily."

"What did I lie about?" I ask, my voice harsh, demanding.

"Yeah, you are a good actor. You picked the right major," he says.

"You told me to say it!" I yell at him.

"Not that," he says.

What did I lie about? Does he mean his penis? Does he mean I faked enjoying his penis? Does he think I'm lying about liking him and his penis?

"I would not expect to recognize Satan. He masquerades as an angel of light," he says. Then, he takes a step backward and points at me.

I don't know what to say. To think. I stand there in the dark, outside of the street light beam, feeling my face get hot with tears streaming down my cheeks, my neck, and my chest into my blouse.

It's as if
He projected upon me
What he wanted to see
The demon he wanted to fight
And I projected upon him
What I wanted to see
So I could have someone to love, me.

"Tempting," he says. He turns with a sideways smile, then clicks his pointed finger together like a fake gun as if he just defeated me. As if I misinterpreted the whole thing.

– 36 –

Bad Roommate

There's a very cute boy. *Very* cute. He has blond, floppy hair. Every time I come back to my new apartment he seems to be returning to his. We catch each other's eye from across the lawn and flirt.

And the next time, we wave.

And the next day, we meet at the picnic table that sits in the middle of the weedy lawn between our two buildings that face one another. Something I say makes him laugh. You're funny, he says.

The semester hasn't started yet. We both moved in early. He's majoring in Econ. He admires that I'm in acting. We compare our upcoming class schedules. He says at some point he has to take a liberal arts credit. Maybe he'll take theater so he can see me. We lean back next to each other with our hands on the table behind us, close our eyes, and smile up at the sun.

His name is Mitch, which is very close to Mick so this could be meant to be. And we're neighbors, so we can see each other often. It's been over a year and a half since Mick died. I still think of him every day. I moved his memorial from my dorm room closet door to the wall above my desk in this apartment. Maybe Mick sent Mitch to rehydrate my heart?

I've changed. I don't have the freshman fifteen anymore. Maybe just the freshman five. I feel more independent. More adult.

The next day, we kiss outside by his front door.

He leads me into his apartment where he has a full-size waterbed. Waterbeds are so groovy. I've never been on one before. There's a lot of waving from side to side. It's like making out on a canoe. When Mitch climbs on top of me, we dissipate the water until it's like a taco shell around us, like Moses in the middle of the parted sea. My spine is planted all the way down to the wood platform frame. My naked flesh scrapes away with his motion. Later, the bones of my spine are bruised, and a thick, hard scab has formed. The throbbing pain becomes a reminder of our passion. My war wound. My love wound. My spine hickey. Such are the perils of sexy blond possible boyfriend neighbor love making with the groovy waterbed.

Fame arrives. Then Kittie. My roomies! Kittie was the RA in charge of our whole dorm floor. Fame and Kittie will share the bigger bedroom, and I have my own room. We swivel our stuff around to accommodate what we each brought. Dishes and plates and an afghan for the daybed. Food for the cabinets, food for the refrigerator. Dishwashing soap and laundry bags. Salt and pepper. Even placemats. For all three of us, this is our first apartment in the real world. The night before classes begin, we stay up late, sitting cross-legged in a three-way circle on the living room daybed, comparing class schedules, confiding secrets in each other while drinking pop and eating bowls of potato chips with sour cream onion dip. We squeeze each other's hands, excited to be sophisticated sophomore roomies in our own apartment.

***

The note on the kitchen table in Kittie's handwriting is waiting for me. I avoid it all morning. I know I have to open it. I don't want things to be wrong. My hands shake. It's a list. The things I do they can't live with. The "sexual exploits" in my room are disruptive. The food I ate and didn't replace makes me selfish. The dishes I let build up in the sink, letting them spill onto the countertops, make me thoughtless and irresponsible. I sleep late in the morning and stay up all night. The list goes on.

I'd been unconscious of my awfulness. Unaware that anyone paid attention to me. Unaware anything I did affected anyone else. But it's true. It's all true. I'm busy. Work. School. Boys. Mitch. Studying acting on my own. I'm afraid if I stop, I'll never accomplish all I need to do before I get too old. So, I'm in the moment, juggling the important things, ignoring the day to day mundane.

But their accusations about my "sexual exploits"? Don't people love sex? Do Kittie and Fame not feel what I feel? Am I un-normal not being able to imagine life without sex? Needing sex, desiring sex, imagining sex all the time? It's primal. It's blissful. It's spiritual. What age do you have to be for the slut-shaming to stop? When are you allowed to like sex? At what age does my sex life stop mattering to anyone else?

I say I'm sorry. I'll change. Fame hugs me. Kittie hugs me. Sort of. She hopes there will be changes. If not, she will move out. That's not a threat.

Fame goes home to visit her mom for a few days. Kittie is moving out. I don't change enough. I apologize to Kittie. I didn't mean to be neglectful. I didn't mean to have her think me awful. I didn't mean to be a bad roommate.

For a few days, I, again, have the apartment to myself.

– 37 –
NOT REPORTABLE

Exhausted, I return to our apartment after dance class. I'm wearing a skirt and a leotard over my tights and ballet shoes. It's a small college town, so I don't lock the door behind me. I only have an hour to rest before I need to go back for my evening classes. I don't change clothes. I just plop down on the daybed in the living room. I close my eyes and drift.

A heavy weight lands on top of me. I hear my breath exhale "*uuk.*" There's a man in my apartment. On top of me.

My brain is trying to filter "this is not normal."

He's not a huge man, but he's bigger than me. Harder than me. He's heavy and determined, pulling to lift my skirt that covers my tights and leotard. Pulling it up. Pulling it down. But his whole body weight is on top of me, so how

380

is it going to come off? It's like he doesn't dare to *not* pin me with his body weight, but he can't accomplish anything if he does.

I don't know what to do. My heart is pounding fast, but my thoughts are slow, thinking through everything that's happening.

As he's wrestling with my skirt, my hands push at his waist. He's wearing old black corduroy pants. I can feel the ridges worn at his pointy hip bones. There are round coins in his pocket. I can smell the unwashedness of the white-gray tip of his collar poking my turned cheek. He's skinny. His clothes are tight. He doesn't have a weapon. Except for himself.

"A man is on top of me. A man is on top of me." I want my brain to tell me what to do, but my brain is stuck. "A man is on top of me!"

His hands are under my skirt, yanking at the crotch of my leotard. This makes something in my head *bing*. Somehow, it's funny. I don't laugh, but while all this chaos is going on on the outside, with clothes being yanked and tugged and his bones poking into me, it seems absurd. It's a moment of absurdity—funny—because of my clothes. These *ridiculous* dance clothes. I can't even get them off to pee. I have to make sure I don't drink anything before or during class and pee before I get dressed because even *I* can't get them off. But, right now, they're saving me. Funny how life is.

I almost laugh, but I don't. Why am I so slow? What's the opposite of panic? Slow motion? Hypothermia? The feeling that he doesn't have a weapon? Feeling he won't get the clothes off? I'm sensing absurdity.

My eyes are at his neck. I'm looking at his Adam's apple. My brain decides to work, reminding me that if you punch a man in his Adam's apple, you could kill him. I think about doing that, but I don't. Because, I think, if I punch him in his Adam's apple and kill him, then I am a murderer, and I can't live with that. I mean, I can live with being raped. I don't want to, but I can. I can't live with being a murderer.

I don't punch him in his Adam's apple. Instead, I pat him on his head. It surprises me. His hair is bouncy. Springy. I'd never felt an afro before. I never imagined what they would feel like. I never imagined bouncy. Hm.

He seems more panicked. Frantic. To get these clothes off me. Manic. Yanking, pulling, tugging, swearing, mashing his body from side to side. I'm scared, but I'm calm. My brain won't work, but something in me is working on its own. My arms go around him. I hug him, pat him, "shhhh shhh" him. He feels desperate. I pat his head again. It's soft. I didn't imagine it being soft either.

The soft bounciness of his hair makes me think how vulnerable we all are. Our hair being out of our control. We're just born, and it becomes whatever it is. It's ours. Our hair experience. For life. And we feel ways about it. It's a human thing. He's a person who, when he was little, had a boingy afro. Maybe there were days when he hated it, and he wished for different hair, and he cried. Then there were days when he was happy for his hair.

He's so human to me right now. I pat his head. I say, "Shhhh shhhh."

I put my palm on his shoulder blade because I feel the little boy. I feel the human. I don't know why I do this.

I'm thinking, too, he doesn't have a weapon, so it's just him and me, and we are just two humans. I hug him like a mother or a friend hugs somebody who's in distress.

He stops struggling with my clothes, calming into my arms for a second, and I don't know if he's gonna get calmer or rile up again, so I take advantage of the calm and say, "You don't want to do this. You don't want to do this. You don't want to go to jail. You don't want to have a criminal record that's just going to mess up your life, and for what? Why, this is so silly. This is so sad. All the people in your life who know you, your sister or your cousin or your mother—"

He pops up and looks at me—for the first time, *looks at me*—with the heavy weight of his body still on me, saying "Shut up, shut up, just shut up! You shut up!"

I get scared because now he seems sadder and confused and that makes him angry. Angrier.

"Don't talk about them. I don't give a shit about my—"
That shocks me.

I feel my heart banging.

It causes him to sit up. Off me. He starts to cry, and he pounds his fist into the mattress as I scooch away toward the wall. His tears are making tracks where they roll, shinier than the rest of his skin, and I don't know what to do. My back is stuck to the wall behind me. He hits the bed, and he digs into his crotch and punches the mattress and says, "Fuck! You ruined it! Now I can't."

"I'm so sorry, I'm so sorry. I'm sure most times you're fine," I say. "This is probably just better that you can't. Probably."

And I turn my head past the paneled walls, faking that I'm looking at a clock out of sight that I don't have, and say, "Oh my god, my roommates are going to be home any minute, and if they see you, they'll call the police." I look alarmed. I am alarmed, but I look even more alarmed with emphasis. He looks at me. I look at him.

We have a conversation with our eyes, lasers, like we're fencers, pausing in a duel. We're breathing hard, waiting for the other. The focus is so intense, my small apartment turns to gray haze. We are floating, he and I. The only sound, our labored breaths, in syncopated rhythm. I sense this is my only moment. This precarious balance will tip one way or the other.

"Just go," I say urgently. "Go. Go now. Hurry. I won't tell anyone."

He searches my face. Am I lying? His skin is still glazed under his eyes, down his cheeks where the tears were. The odorous collar that scraped my cheek and grazed my lips is flipped up on one side. There is a quarter next to his knee that had fallen out of his pocket.

He bounds off the daybed, swinging open the door. He is gone. I force myself away from the wall, pouncing to the door, snapping the lock. I sink below the window that goes to the waist of the door. I sit on the carpet and listen to my heart smash into my chest.

I don't know what to do. I don't know what happened. I don't know who to call. I don't know how to move or how long it will be before I will feel safe enough to stand up.

***

The police come. First, there are two. Then, one leaves when I say I was not raped. Meaning, there was no penetration. I still had my clothes on. What happened really? A wrestling match, really. The one that stays takes a report. I guess. He asks questions. Mostly about what happened on the outside. I ask if it was called attempted rape. At least. Would that be something?

He takes his description. The corduroy pants. The soft afro.

"But is it something," I ask, "if a man breaks into my apartment and tries," I say, looking at my feet, realizing my pink ballet slippers are still on my feet, "and I don't feel safe anymore?"

He wants more information. How I escaped. Why he stopped. Instinct tells me, if I explain leotards and hugging and talking of his mother, if I say I caused my would-be rapist erectile dysfunction, no. No.

"I don't know," I say.

– 38 –
AFTERMATH

I can't sleep. I can't be anywhere in the apartment. Nowhere feels safe. I keep the lights on in every room. I lock every window in the bedrooms. I put a glass filled with spoons on every windowsill in case I doze off and someone tries to come in through a window. That way, I'll hear the noise and have a chance to run out of the apartment. I sit on the living room sofa and stare at the front door where he entered.

After hours of pop-eyed vigilance, I lay on the sofa and let myself watch with just one eye. Until I doze.

No, *no*.

Have to stay awake. Keep watch. He could break the window on the door, stick his hand in, turn the knob, and this time—

This time.

Or maybe someone else.

I stay awake until morning. No one would break in when it's light. Just four nights, then Fame will be back. I can stay up four nights. The only reason he got in was because I didn't lock the door.

I take out the mime school application. No. I can't think about "someday" when I don't know if I'll survive tonight. Criminals return to the scene of the crime. I heard that. Maybe on TV. I turn the TV on but low volume so I can hear if any window or door creaks. I don't dare get up from the couch to change the channel or put new tin foil on the antenna. I just watch whatever is on, however zitsy the picture is, until the light from outside becomes brighter than my lights inside. I let myself fall asleep.

***

I don't get up in time to get to classes. I call in sick to Kuli's because what if I was coming home from work late at night, and he was waiting and forced his way in? I don't leave the apartment. I watch TV on low volume. I stare at the application. I sleep. As it gets dusk, my throat tightens, and my eyes widen. Three more nights till Fame comes back. I turn on all the lights again and stare at the front door. I get up, tiptoe to the front door, pull back the curtain just an inch, and peek.

Kids are in the grassy area. Kids are coming home from school. I should feel safe. But that was what was happening a few days ago. It was bright afternoon. Kids were in the grassy area, coming and going to classes from their apartments. All that was happening when the man came in. I stay, staring out. Two columns of nostril breath fog the glass. I see him.

Mitch. My sort of boyfriend lover. Going into his apartment.

I shouldn't say boyfriend. We hadn't decided on that status yet. But he did come over to the drama department like he promised. I was taking Directing 101. I cast him in a three-minute, two-person scene I got to direct. After rehearsal and after the presentation in directing class, he'd wait for me, and we'd walk back to our apartments together, most of the time ending up sharing lunch or dinner. And the waterbed.

But we had opposite schedules, and it just would be too hard to be dating-dating.

Besides, it was different from last year when I would sleep with guys and get my heart broken because I thought they liked me-liked me. Now, I was just having fun, too. Most of the time, dry humping. Dry humping was the foreplay, the sparks that ignited ravenous desire. Desire made me feel alive. To be passionately desired, to passionately desire, was all. Desire was euphoria.

After the guy left, I'd lie on my bed, slide off my wet jeans, and roll my fingers over my throbbing wetness until I came, usually within minutes.

I heard that couples could cum together. The only way I knew how was the very specific way I could do it to myself. How do I stop everything and teach a guy that?

Only one time, when a guy was over and it was super late and it would have been noisier to let him out of the apartment than to let him sleepover (this was when Kittie still lived here), did I almost come close to cumming with a guy.

I had changed into a deep-blue silk kimono robe from the thrift store, and he was in his underwear, and we climbed under the covers. In the middle of the night, I felt his hands, very soft and timid so as not to wake me, feel my breasts, my nipples and linger there. The softness of it, the goalessness of it, the tentative touch, not knowing where he was going, not wanting to wake me, that touch was so erotic. No pulling, no squeezing, no grabbing. My breasts were the destination. My nipples were of interest. Every reaction was of interest to his blind fingertips.

I was lying on my back. He was next to me on his side. I could feel the throb of his erection as it tapped against my thigh. I pretended to remain asleep. His hand roamed down to my wetness. At first, I thought he'd know I was awake because I was so wet. But I went on pretending I was asleep, and he went on exploring as if not to wake me.

He moved carefully, trying not to move the bed. He moved my thighs apart in slow motion. He kneeled between my legs. With the lightest touch, he moved my pubic hair apart, and his finger, like breath, touched upon my clit. I felt I was going to explode. I wanted to "wake up," to grab his fingers and run them in circles on my clit, on my labia, the way that I did. I want to take his cock inside me right then.

"Now. Now. Now," was screaming in my head. "Put it in me, now!" But I continued to pretend to be asleep. He began to rub the very tip of the head of his cock, almost not even touching, on my clit, my labia, near my begging opening. I forced myself not to make a sound. I forced my hips to stay still. I tried to focus on his cock instead of the feeling of almost uncontrollable yearning. I wondered if all girls feel this good during sex. Do most women feel like I feel? Why is it so bad if women like sex as much as men do? Why does it have to be that a man "gets something" from the girl? That a man can use her for sex? Can't we both just love it? When I was little, I thought it was a gift from God. Now, I definitely think it is.

He puts in the tip. The weird logic of my brain said, "If you were actually asleep, a cock entering you would wake you, so it's ok to pretend to wake up."

I pretended to wake, but acted very groggy. I wanted it to stay slow like this. I didn't want him to feel sudden free rein to do what guys do and just drive it in any way he likes it, forgetting me as part of the equation.

I moaned and turned my head and pretended to discover what was happening. He halted for a second, and I re-closed my eyes and let my hips roll in circles around his unmoving shaft inside me. We started to move together, and I thought if I could get him to keep moving just like this, but then he could put his weight on me where his pubic bone was, and stroke at my clit and vagina as he moved, we could cum together. I reached forward to pull him toward me, but it was too much. The foreplay for him, too, was overwhelming, and he pulled out fast and came on my tummy.

Neither of us spoke. I was so close to cumming and so wanted to. But I knew it wouldn't happen.

Without acknowledging, without a word, he grabbed the bedside Kleenex box, pulling out tissue after tissue after tissue. When he stopped pulling, I started pulling tissue after tissue after tissue while he wiped his penis, my stomach, his balls, my thighs. Then, I wiped, and he pulled tissue after tissue after tissue until we were sticky but dry. And awkward.

It shouldn't have been. It was amazing. For both of us. It should have been a kiss and a cuddle. Maybe we would ask each other's names. That was the thing about these dry humpings. We never really knew each other's names. Sometimes a first name. It didn't matter. It was the first time I didn't take offense anymore at that Bob Seger lyric, the one that went, "She used me, I used her, but neither one cared."

That's what it was.

But then I said it. I should have said something lovely.

But I said, "do you think that was rape?"

I didn't think he raped me. He didn't. Even though I was technically asleep, and he was having his way with a sleeping girl, I knew I was awake and maybe he even knew and we were both playing this game. I wasn't accusing him. I don't know why I said it. It just came out. But the look on his face. All the blood drained. I saw him gulp. Once. Twice. He got up and got dressed fast. I sat up and wrapped the robe around me.

"I'm not saying you raped me," I said, trying to hold onto his wrist. But he was frantic. Pulling on pants, zipping. Cramming socks in his pocket. Twisting his head around the room looking for shoes.

"You didn't rape me," I say, deliberate, assertive. "I was just asking. I think I've been raped before but not even just in a violent way. I was just wondering what the line is. When it's rape."

"You didn't rape me," I say toward my bedroom door as he runs out and out of sight. I hear the front door open and pull shut behind him. I tiptoe to the front door and lock it.

I sit up through the night thinking of him. Of that experience. Trying to remember his name. Where I met him in the first place. I was thinking maybe I could find him and apologize. Maybe he would understand how confused I was and why something so thoughtless would come out of my mouth and then we could play again together. But really, you can only play the sleeping game with authenticity the first time. After that, it's just agreeing to suspend belief. It's just acting.

***

Two nights till Fame comes home. Again, I sleep the day away. I check the glasses on the windowsills. I turn on all the lights. The TV is on low volume. I wait for the night and stare at the application on the table. My hair is up in a ponytail. No makeup. I'm relaxing a little more than I did the previous nights. I let myself lay my head on the sofa pillow, and I cover myself with the afghan my mom hand crocheted.

There's a knock on the door. All my senses are on sudden high alert. My heart is pounding too hard. My skin is too hot. My throat, cement. My stomach, clutching. A shadow. A man's shadow is at the front door; I can see him through the window of the front door. I make myself into a pancake on the couch as if I'm part of the furniture. There's another *rat tap tap* with light knuckles on the window of the door. I'm so scared, I start to cry into the pillow, forcing the tip of the pillow into my mouth so no sound escapes.

One more *rat tap tap*. He stands there. I see his body shift. What if he thinks I'm not home and then, thinking the coast is clear, he comes around to crawl in the window? Or what if he knows I'm home and faking, and he comes around to crawl in the window? Did I lock the door? Yes. Yes. The door has been locked. Maybe he knows how to pick the lock? Maybe this is a test. I roll down to the floor and crawl on my belly to the kitchen area and lay under the phone. I can just jump up, grab the phone, and dial the operator.

The shadow fades. I listen for the window. I don't dare move.

The phone rings loudly. I jump. My heart races. Staying low, I lift the handle off the receiver.

394

I whisper, "Hello?"

"Hey. It's Mitch. All your lights were on. I knocked."

My heart is still pounding fast.

"You did? I must've been in the bathroom," I say, trying to sound super casual.

"Can I come over? You wanna come over?" he asks. It sounds like regular life. Life before the bunker. Life the way it was before.

"Um," I say. Because I'm still in the bunker, in hiding, and he's still out there, and Fame isn't home, and I'm not sure.

"I'm coming back. Be right there." He hangs up the phone. I run into the bathroom and quickly brush my teeth. Oh my god. I look stupid. He's never seen me without makeup. I grab my makeup bag but he's already at the door.

We chest to chest, no pelvis hug. He surveys the living room and kitchen as he walks in.

"Brought'cha a beer," he says, putting one on the coffee table and cracking his open.

"Thanks," I say even though I don't drink beer, walking behind him to turn the latch to lock on the door.

We talk about I don't know what as we sit on the sofa. I'm giggly and shy. Which I'm not usually with Mitch. I can see him looking twice at me because he's never seen me without makeup. He finishes his beer. I've only had a sip of mine.

"Are you gonna have it?" he asks.

I shake my head.

"Want to come to my place?" he asks. The waterbed is on eighty-two. Hehe."

Eighty-two is my favorite temperature.

"I can't," I'm crushing my palms together between my knees trying not to speak about it, but it comes tumbling out. I tell him about the mini rape that didn't quite happen so it was un-reportable, about Fame being away, and Kittie moving out. Being alone and afraid the man will come back. That I can't go to his apartment because if I come back here by myself maybe the man will be here waiting for me.

"The cops didn't do anything?" he asks.

"No," I say.

"But the guy broke in. He nearly raped you," he says.

"But it was my fault for not locking the door so technically he didn't break in—"

"Technicality," Mitch says. "Trespassing, for sure."

"He didn't rape me. He tried, but—"

I start to laugh. So weird of me. Mitch is looking at me like "what's so funny?" It strikes me as so funny.

"These fucking dance clothes!" I say. "I'm wearing ballerina shoes and ballerina clothes and if I have to pee, *I* can't even get them off in time. I can never get them off," I say, catching my breath. "He spent most of the time struggling with leotards and tights. Now, he knows my pain," I choke out the words, my eyes watering. Mitch is laughing because I'm laughing. We both catch our breath and calm down.

"I can't believe they wouldn't even be looking for the guy. What if he comes back?" he asks.

I start laughing again. "I know!" I say. "That's the whole point. What if he comes back? That's what I'm afraid of."

"You should have called me," he says, hugging me.

"What would you do?" I say.

"I would have come over."

I wipe my face.

"Let's go," he says, standing.

"I can't," I say.

"In the morning, I'll check everywhere," he says.

I leave all the lights on, and we lock the door behind us.

***

Being at Mitch's, I almost forget. We talk about the scene I directed him in. We play gin rummy. We make out on the waterbed. Because my back still has scabs and bruises from the bottom platform of the waterbed, I'm on my knees with my hands on the bed frame. Mitch is behind me. Another nice thing about Mitch is we always use condoms. A relief because, if not, it's always torture to be afraid after.

We're making love and laughing, and the bed is in surfable waves. He's behind me and then finishes, collapsing his torso on mine, and we breathe together for a few moments. When he pushes himself upright, I hear, "Uh oh."

I reach behind me, holding his slipping cock. I feel flesh. Where's the condom? He's not moving, either. Something happened. I feel the torn rubber, the harder rim at the bottom of his cock with nothing in-between. We stay in that moment of alarm.

"It's ok. I got it," I say, fishing the remaining condom from deep inside, giggling it off so the moment isn't heavy, so we could still be in "this was so hot, you're so hot, we're so fucking hot."

The next morning, we've forgotten about the condom. He has. Me mostly. Not. Sort of. For now. We walk back to my apartment, lights blazing, TV on.

He walks into each room. He opens my closet door and surveys. He looks under my bed, under the desk. He checks Fame's room and looks under the two twin beds. He checks the window locks. He checks in the broom closet. He checks under the sofa. He sits on the daybed in the living room and looks at me.

"No one's here," he says.

"Thank you for checking," I say.

***

Even though I slept, I still don't go to classes, and I still don't go to work. I will. As soon as Fame gets back, everything will go back to normal.

I take out the application. It wasn't difficult to explain to them in the application why a program devoted to the art of emotion and expression would be everything I needed.

It was getting my imagination to imagine myself, my life in ten years. I didn't know what I had permission to hope for.

It was so difficult to feel that I would be the one granted dreams. If I dared to write down the dreams I thought could actually happen to me, for me, wouldn't that jinx them? Wouldn't the Universe laugh in my face? What if someone else saw it? Read it? Would they be like, "Who do you think you are? You think you're that special? Please. Give me a break."

So, it's hard to get it out and on paper.

Every light is on, but I light a candle and open my journal.

I write:

I hope it is ok to reimagine the question. Pretending there are no boundaries of money and pretending there's no such thing as being tired, I'm imagining my perfect twenty-four hours in my perfect life ten years from now. It's clearer imagining a slice of a perfect life than an endless tenth year from now. I'll start ten years from now at twenty-seven. Yikes. I'll work my way back to me now."

"In ten years, I'm in demand as an actress worldwide for film, TV, and stage work. I use my money and fame to change paradigms of thought, especially for women. Expanding their safety and possibilities. Hope."

"Ten years from now, I'm married to my soul mate. My true love. We're partners. Like Burns and Allen. Like Nichols and May. Like the Lunts. Lucy and Desi. He is my perfect partner in life and in acting. He's meant to be my partner, and I, his.

"I have children. Many children. Children of my own and children I adopt from other countries. I travel the world. I speak many languages. I live in a vast place, so I'm able to have many animals in my life. My home is by the sea. I have been blessed to know hundreds, thousands of people intimately. Naked, emotionally naked. For it is this connection that gives meaning to our lives. Earlier in my acting life, I study in an intense theater program, like Yale or Juilliard or like yours, that will be the springboard to all the dreams I dare to dream."

As I write, I feel the dark claustrophobia of desperation loosen.

There was a time when what I hoped for could become real. My dreams weren't dependent on fate. My dreams were dependent on me. If there was a will, there was a way. My world was bigger when I was little, but the whole world isn't just what happened here at WIU. In the WIU theater department, with the boys here. Just like in high school, when I went to Germany, the whole world wasn't there. Maybe I will make it to twenty-seven. Maybe some of these things will come true.

I rewrite from my journal onto the application form, address it, lick the envelope and the stamp and, as I'm hiding my journal with these embarrassing fantasies I dare admit, the handle to the front door jiggles.

I stop. Freeze. The door opens. I scream. She does too. It's Fame!

- 39 -
UNPLANNED

I'm exhausted every day. I think of Mitch, the waterbed, and the condom. A rush of fear runs head to toe. It's too early to know. In classes, I'll suddenly remember I don't know, and a rush of panic will fill me.

I pray to my period, "Please come."

But it doesn't. Not the day it was supposed to. Not the day after. Or the day after that. If I feel a trickle of warmth leak out from below, I rush to the bathroom to peer at the crotch of my panties, hoping for that dark-red slash. Nothing. Just clear discharge.

What if I'm pregnant? Right now? Impossible. I have no money for a doctor *to even find out* if I'm pregnant. How would I have enough money *to be* pregnant? How would I have enough money to give birth? How would I have money to raise a child?

But I never ever want an abortion again. In some way, having a child would be better than being alive as I am. A wanna-be actress who can't even act yet. A failure. I'm trying so many things to finally be something, but nothing ever happens. Any talents I have are not developed yet, if they even exist. Any destiny that might be mine has not revealed itself. I don't mean much to anyone except my dad and my mom. And she doesn't think I'm funny or interesting or fated for the future, I imagine, just dramatic, oversensitive, and emotional. Just the daughter that she loves who is smart and wasting her life and hopefully will find Mr. Right after college.

Being pregnant is impossible. Being a mother at seventeen and broke? Impossible. But being a mother is one thing I wouldn't fail at. I could be special to someone. To my child.

Fame says there's a place just off campus called the CPC. The Crisis Pregnancy Center. They give pregnancy tests.

"How much are they?" I ask.

"It's free."

"It's *free?*"

"It's like a charity to help women," she says.

Wow.

I didn't know there was anyone that helped us.

***

At the Crisis Pregnancy Center, they give me a pee in a cup test.

I wait. She tells me I must come back in a few days. I think of nothing else. I go back.

A woman with pitying eyes calls my name. Her office is a bare room with linoleum floors, and a large color picture of what looks like undersea life takes up one of the walls. I sit in the single chair next to her desk and tuck my hands, palms together, between my thighs.

"It's positive," she says. "You're pregnant."

My bones tremble. I can neither think nor feel.

"You have choices," she says, wrapping her hand for a moment around my forearm.

"I can't afford to have a baby," I say. "I want a baby. I want to be a mother so bad, but I'm not old enough."

"There are options, like I said. If you want an abortion, you have about two weeks before it's too late. Do you understand what an abortion does?" she asks.

I nod. A tear rolls out one eye. I swipe it away at my chin.

"An abortion can damage your uterus. It can make you sterile."

I didn't know any of this. I want children.

"It can leave you scarred. It can provoke miscarriage," she says.

Oh my god. She slides the Kleenex box to me. I'm glad she's telling me. They didn't tell me this the first time.

"And many women never get over the grief of what they've done," she says, putting a stack of pamphlets and brochures on the desk. "This is a list of adoption agencies. You could make a family very happy," she says.

The Baby Fold, the brochure reads. I could. I never thought of adoption.

"But I can't work when I'm pregnant," I say. "Once I start showing, that would be it."

"Well, legally, they can't fire you. A law was passed two years ago," she says. "And, legally, you can still remain in school."

Is this true? We always knew once you got pregnant, that was it. No one hired pregnant women. When I was growing up, pregnant moms in our neighborhood, if they weren't just housewives, either quit or got fired as soon as they got the belly. When my babysitter went to college, got married, and got pregnant, the college made her leave until after she had the baby.

"Are you sure?" I ask.

She pulls out a flyer. Just black type on white paper. A copy of a law. The Pregnancy Discrimination Act. 1978. I don't read it. I'll take it home.

"But who's going to hire a pregnant girl to waitress?" I ask, trying to feel out this option.

"If you get a job first, the law says they can't fire women for being pregnant. But don't worry. If you choose to place your baby for adoption, couples will take care of your expenses during your pregnancy right through the birth."

The flyer says the adoption agency is for Christians.

"Do you have an adoption agency for Jewish families? I'm Jewish, so I'd want my child to go to a Jewish family," I say.

"I believe so. I'll be right back," she says, leaving me with my positive result and a desk full of brochures. I can't even look at them right now. I wait. The large glossy colored poster that takes up much of the wall is not of sea life like I thought but of yet-to-be-born babies in bellies. I look back at her empty chair. She returns with a small Xerox copy of names and contact information of couples.

"Here you go," she says. "These are the couples registered with the Jewish agency. Once you decide, I can help you contact any of these agencies." She smiles, placing her hand on mine.

"Do I also make an appointment for abortion here?" I say.

"These are abortion clinics," she says, taking her hand off mine, moving another small Xerox to me. "We don't have abortion services here. The closest is Peoria. You'll need a ride there and back. Abortion costs range from two hundred and fifty dollars to three hundred and fifty dollars. Not all clinics are reputable. You'll need to call for an appointment if this is your choice."

"I'm not sure what my choice is," I say, wanting her not to be curt with me, wanting her to be kind, to like me.

She organizes all the papers facing the same way, and taps them on the desk to even them out into a carriable pile. She places a thick full color pamphlet that seems large enough to fold out into a map on top of my to-go bundle. It might be the smaller version of the poster on the wall.

"If you need to talk, just come back," she says.

I take the pile in my hand. I think I say thank you. I don't remember if I say thank you. I leave. I trudge into the winter dusk and make my way back to my apartment.

I am numb.

I will call Mitch.

We can decide together.

I know he will probably want us to get an abortion, but he can say it, and that'll make it final. We can split the cost, and he can go with me. It won't be as bad as the first time. The first time was just a year or two after *Roe v Wade* was passed. There was no anesthetic. Just a hand holder. I think of that doctor's bloody coat. I cry walking home, thinking I'll have to do that again.

I walk in a daze. I went the wrong way. Now I'm lost. It's cold, and it's getting dark.

I won't tell anyone.

I'll just call Mitch, and we can make an appointment and go.

This is not like the first time. The first time, I didn't know there were choices. I was only a child. I didn't know it was dangerous in so many ways.

What am I doing? *What am I doing?*

I have been living as a child, just reacting. Living unconsciously.

I am awake.

I am conscious now.

***

I could just go over, but it's early. I'll call. I dial his number. A girl answers. A girl? There's no girl living with him and his roommate. Maybe it's his roommate's friend?

"Is Mitch there?" I ask.

"Who's this?" the girl asks, very snippy.

"Who are you?" I ask back.

"Debbie."

We're both silent.

"Mitch's girlfriend. Who are you?" she asks.

"I'm Mitch's... girlfriend," I say.

"Oh, fuck you," she says. "I've been his girlfriend since high school."

I am quiet, blindsided. "But can I talk to him? It's important."

"No," she says, adamant.

There is only silence.

"Tell him..." I say into her silence. "Tell him I am pregnant!" I say, yelling, my voice quavering.

More silence.

The phone is dropped but not hung up. I hear yelling between Mitch and the girlfriend I didn't know he had. I can only make out pieces, the expected pieces. "Who is she?" Things like that.

Then, her voice, regulated, sounds at the end of the line, "He doesn't want to talk to you."

I can't believe that's true.

"Tell him an abortion is three hundred dollars. If not, tell him I might have the baby and child support is a lot more than three hundred. Tell him to call me."

She hangs up on me.

I stand by the phone, unmovable. I just stand there still holding the hung-up receiver.

Suddenly, the phone rings, startling me. I put it to my ear.

"Why are you talking bullshit to my girlfriend?" Mitch is pissed.

"You never told me you had a girlfriend," I say.

"Are you trying to fuck things up for me?"

"I'm pregnant," I say.

"How do I know it's mine?" he asks.

"Well, it is."

More silence.

"You didn't tell me you had a girlfriend," I say.

"I do," he says.

"Hard to tell," I say.

"What do you want?" he asks.

"I need you to help with the abortion."

"I don't have any money."

"I don't have any money, either," I say.

"I don't even know if it's mine," he says.

The silence draws out. I'm starting to cry.

"Don't call here again," he says. The line goes dead.

I'm shaking. I'm confused. I'm heartbroken. I'm scared.

I'm disposable.

Shut up! Fuck you. I hate myself. Such a fucking victim.

– 40 –
The Pamphlets

I am alone in our apartment. I take out the pamphlets and separate them onto the coffee table. All these words, all these pictures telling me. Telling me. Why are you telling me all this? All this. Why are you forcing me to know all this? All this. Telling me what I'm supposed to do. What am I supposed to do?

There is really no choice. I'm too young. I'm alone. I have no money. But I'm terrified to go through another abortion. I remember every sound, every tear of flesh, every needle. I remember my insides being torn out. I remember the grief. The anger at Jett.

But it wasn't a baby. It was a cell. Cells. Like a seed that wasn't a plant yet. But I ripped the possibility out of my body.

410

I was too young. High school. My parents would have killed me. You can't be pregnant in high school. You'd have to drop out. If a girl got pregnant in high school, she was sent away until it was sorted out. Even then, they didn't go back to school. Her reputation was done. She was in for a life of daycares and waitress jobs, maybe forever.

You can't be pregnant in college, either. Would I take classes until I was showing and then take a break and hope to come back? How would I afford daycare? How do you come back when you're breastfeeding a baby? How do you go to classes with a baby? I'd have to drop out, too. Even if there was a new law now.

Then what? Where would I live? I couldn't go home. My parents would kill me. How could I stay in this apartment if I couldn't work when I was pregnant? How would I pay rent? Who would hire me with a big belly? Who would hire me if I had to throw up all day?

Would the father have to help pay? How do women do this? What can I do? What do I do? What should I do?

I page through the flyers of adoption agencies. The Jewish one. The Christian one. *The Baby Fold.* I skim, trying to see through the blur. I blink. A tear drops on the page. I hold it up so the water slides off. Names. Mr. and Mrs. A–Z. So many couples wanting a baby. Each making their plea. Offering up hope and help. Thanking you ahead of time.

I go to my closet and pull down the tiny wooden box hidden under piles of second-hand clothes that come tumbling down on my head from way in the back. I dump out all the change and bills on my bed. My tips from Kuli's. Kids don't tip much and neither do the locals. Sometimes nothing at all. Quarters. Sometimes a dollar bill. I try to save some every week.

I have $126.89. More than I thought.

If I have the abortion, and it's $250, and Mitch pays half—

Yes. That's the only way. I might need money to take the train there and back. I don't know where Peoria is, but if Mitch pays half—

I think you have to take time off after. To recover.

I lay in a curl on my bed, the money falling into the curve of my body. I put the soft edge of my flannel blanket in my mouth, close my eyes and stay still. I listen to my heart. I feel the tears rolling over my face onto the pillow. I feel my body rise and fall.

I stay still, feeling safe for one moment like a snail in a shell. If I don't move, it will all stop. It won't be real. It'll be over there. There will be nothing for me to decide whether I stay right here.

I do. With the blanket in my mouth, sucking it till I can hear it squish like I'm slurping through a straw. I have to get up. I know that. I tell myself that. Come on. Get up. Push up. I do. I push myself up, still in a ball, and unfurl at the side of the bed. I move myself back into the living room.

The color brochure. It's a big square that unfolds into three other squares to make a poster-size brochure. Yes, this one was a portion of the one on her wall. There are bright pictures in squares starting at the top of the poster. Each one is a full color glossy photo journey with text underneath that reads "of your baby." From conception, one week at a time, to birth.

"Forty weeks of."

"Right now, your baby is developing toes…"

"Now, your baby's hands and lungs are forming…"

"Now, your baby can sense and hear…"

Oh my god. *Oh my god.* I have to bury my face and sob before taking a breath, starting at the beginning, the first square. The one I'm at right now.

Ok. Ok. Breathe.

Two weeks. I'm further than two weeks. Two weeks, the brochure says, is fertilization. The picture shows what looks like a pearl surrounded by baby pearls on top of red fingers of seaweed. This is when the egg was fertilized. This is when the condom broke. This is when Mitch's sperm was involved.

But now? Where are we now?

Four weeks. When your period is due but doesn't come.

"Your baby," it says. It doesn't say cells. But the picture shows a cell that looks like an apple the size of a poppy seed.

Why are they saying "your baby"? It's not. It's not yet.

Five weeks. I think that's where I am.

413

"Your baby," it says again, and the picture looks more like a see-through squid or a fetal tadpole. It's still just cells. But then it says, "The tiny 'heart' will start to beat this week."

Why is "heart" in quotations? Is it a heart or is it just something pumping? I don't understand. Then it says, "Your baby is the size of a sesame seed."

Six weeks, seven weeks, eight weeks.

They keep saying "your baby," but the pictures keep showing a translucent amoeba-looking sea creature starting to take a shape. I don't see a baby, but then I read the words below, and I'm being torn between what I'm seeing and what they're saying.

"The nose, mouth, and ears are starting to take shape, and their intestines and brain are beginning to develop. Your baby is the size of a lentil. A blueberry. A kidney bean."

Six, seven, eight weeks would be the termination date. Somewhere in there. Between lentil and kidney bean. Between pearl and tadpole.

I want to make myself stop reading there. I know what comes next. At some point, the cells become a baby. But not yet. Not yet. I fold up the poster.

For the first time in my sexual life, I am aware of my responsibility. Of consequences. I am a child. I have been a child. No one taught us this. No one talked to us about this. They said don't have sex. Or don't get pregnant. I didn't know babies went through stages this intricate that changes could be seen every week. I just thought, there was a time that it is cells and a time it's becoming human. I don't know anything. The choice is not as simple.

I'm aware, not so long ago, there was no choice. You risked your fertility and your life. The weight of what I need to decide hits me full force. I open the color brochure all the way and read through. From conception to birth.

"Their embryonic tail has disappeared, and they weigh just a fraction of an ounce, but they are about to start gaining weight fast. They are the size of a grape."

"Your embryo's skin is still translucent, but their tiny limbs can bend, and fine details, like nails, are starting to form."

"Your baby is the size of a kumquat."

I collapse to the floor with the brochure, breathless, on my knees, pressing my forehead into the carpet. I'm overtaken.

I thought this place was supposed to be *for* women. Not a place to make you feel terrible for the rest of your life if you have to have an abortion. How cruel to give out this brochure! Give it to someone who knows they are going to have the baby, but don't give it to girls who can't or shouldn't.

Oh my god. *Oh my god.*

What am I supposed to do?

I can't have the baby, but I can't have an abortion.

Not after seeing this.

I cry into the carpet. I pull up on the shag, slicing my fingers. I cry up to the ceiling.

415

"Please, God, help me know what to do."

I hate myself.

I hate my neediness that caused this.

It's all my fault.

I hate that I have to make this choice.

I hate my desperation. I hate my fear. I deserve my aloneness.

"Please. Give me a sign, and I'll do it. God? I'm so sorry."

I lay on the patch of shag carpet, now wet and torn. My breath catches in my throat, I hiccup, and I sob. My forehead is smashed on the shag carpet, rocking side to side.

I reach for the color brochure. Five weeks, six weeks, seven weeks, there is no consciousness. My baby, my fetus, my embryo, still just cells. But they are cells that will have life soon.

It's a terrible choice. I am still a child. I approached sex like Russian roulette. I didn't mean to. So many push me-pull you factors. So lost. So needy.

Ever since I had the body of a woman, the only time, the only way I've felt valued by men is sexually. I wanted to be valued. I want to be desired. I want to feel that power my sexuality has. I want to feel pleasure of men. I hoped after the sex, they would finally see me.

It was hard to say no. Sometimes, they didn't let me say no. There was punishment in saying no. I wanted to please them. To have meaning to them. To be cherished by them. I had so little say over my own body sometimes.

That's the past. A choice is in front of me. I did this. Me and him. But it is in *me*. He will have to help. I will sue him. I will sue him, and he will help me pay for this abortion, the killing of these cells. And I will take the pain of the suction as they rip my insides out, and I will do the bleeding and the cramps, and I will do the regret and the guilt and the sadness and the shame. And I will think about how old this child would be, every year, for the rest of my life.

Oh my god, I can't get an abortion. I will sue him, and he can help pay for me and his baby during this pregnancy so I can have this baby.

I *will* have this baby.

I spend the night on the shag carpet with the brochure and a last plea at the ceiling for an answer.

– 41 –
LEGAL AID

Student Legal Services. A small office with blue carpeting, plush chairs, and a full bookcase on two sides of the wall. I stand in front of a young man. He's older than most students. I don't know if he's a student lawyer-to-be or a lawyer for students. He motions for me to sit. I get one arm out of my winter coat and sit anyway, one arm in, one arm out.

I'm determined not to cry. I'm determined to present the facts and get legal advice. I tell him I'm pregnant, that I need the man to be responsible either for half the cost of the abortion or to start paying for the pregnancy so I can have the baby. I can't work while I'm showing with a pregnancy, and I'm willing to have the baby if he doesn't want to help with abortion costs. Either way, I want him to pay half.

Without opening a legal book, without moving his clasped hands he says, "It's not possible."

This answer never entered my mind.

"What do you mean? Why? What does that mean?"

"Until the child is born, and paternity can be proven—"

"I know he's the father. *He* knows he's the father. We were both there when the condom broke," I interrupt, getting frustrated faster than I thought.

He just looks at me.

"So, now what?" I ask. "He gets out of everything? I have to make the choice? He can just pretend he's not involved?" My nose is starting to run. I'm determined, no tears. Still, the hot lump in my throat throbs. "So, I have to find the money to pay for the entire abortion if that's what I choose? He doesn't even have to think about it? Is that the law?" I lean back, eyes wide, waiting for him to acknowledge the unfairness.

"It's a matter of proving paternity," he says.

"Ok," I say in a calmer voice, switching tactics on my argument. "Let's say I decide to have the baby. Can they stick a needle in me and him while I'm pregnant so we can *prove* he's the father? Then will I be able to sue him to help me pay for my life while I'm pregnant?"

"That's not the way the law works," he says, and it seems like he's getting impatient.

"So, what do they do? How do they prove it?" I ask.

I cannot comprehend why he can't be sued. Why he is not held half responsible. Why are we both not held accountable for this decision and for the financial burden? My argument is solid.

"After the baby is born, you can sue him for paternity—"

"Oh, like a new mother who is completely broke is going to have the time and money to sue," I interrupt.

"They can then administer a paternity test," he says.

"I *know* he is the father," I say.

He starts to stand. "I'm sorry, I can't—"

I stand, too, interrupting him, one arm still outside of my coat. I let the tears come; I don't care.

"He should have to be part of this," I say, wiping my runny nose with the one coat sleeve.

He wants to walk away from his desk.

My words come out in clumps over the cement filling my throat. The injustice is too nonsensical. "Why is it only the woman who has to go through the pain and he doesn't even have to be there? How is this fair? How is this justice? The man should have some responsibility."

He doesn't answer me. I'm waiting for him to answer me. I'm breathing like I ran a mile.

"I know it seems unfortunate," he says.

"Unfortunate?" I ask, almost laughing, thrown off by the stupid choice of word. "I *know* he's the father. Tell me…" I say in a low voice, trying again to speak rationally, "…how is this fair? How is this helpful to society? How is this helpful to mothers? Isn't this too stressful? If this is stressful to the mother, won't that make her not a good mother because she's too stressed? Why would we want that? Wouldn't we want mothers who feel calm and are able to focus on their baby and give them love? It all starts with the mother."

He is standing, his hands now clasped in front of him, his eyes not looking at mine. He walks toward the opening of the doorway, signaling it's time for me to go.

I'm defeated. I walk to the doorway. "Is that really the law? Of the United States of America? A fair and free country? That's really the law? That men have no responsibility until you can prove it?"

"I'm very sorry," he says.

I walk past him, putting my other arm in my hanging coat sleeve, saying under my breath, but loud enough, "Why would I lie about who the father was? Jeez!"

I talk to myself, watching my feet on the sidewalk, a thought with every step. How did this happen? Surely, when the higher-ups realize the burden this puts on women—women who are gifts to this world, women who are lovely to look at and touch, women whose nurturing and loving natures bless men's lives, women who have to suffer with blood and cramps every month for the sake of mankind, women who have to pay more to live than men do just for period supplies and birth control and dry cleaning—surely when the higher-ups hear the burden this was causing their beloved soul mates, they would change this absurd, burdensome law.

I'm burning with frustration, confusion, and anger.

I open my front door with fear. I'm back to where I was. Alone with an impossible choice and no way to pay for either.

– 42 –
HAZELNUTS

I watch Mitch's apartment but don't see him or his Debbie come or go. It's Christmas break, so a lot of kids have gone home. I still have a few days to schedule the procedure. To decide. To earn. I work every night at Kuli's, trying to raise as much as I can. I go to the library in the day, so I'm not home alone with my pamphlets and thoughts.

There was a boy in one of my regular classes that I used to see in The Union that I know liked me, but he wasn't really my type. Not even for kissing. He was too tall. Almost seven feet tall. I asked him and he said six feet, seven inches then he changed it to six feet, nine inches when he hit his head on the ceiling lamp.

His name was Neil. He had sensitive features. He had eyes that always looked down and a mouth waiting to be shown whether it would turn into a smile or a frown. He was shy. A follower. Soft, fine light-brown hair. His neck was permanently cocked to one side. As if he was used to ducking through doorways and dodging hanging lamps. Whenever we talked, he smiled. He seemed surprised by it, and he would lick his lips and move his expression back to neutral. But then I'd say something, who knows what, and there he'd be, smiling again.

Here he is at the library, sitting at a table for six by himself, his long legs outstretched under the table, his feet a foot out on the other side. In his hand, he holds the tiniest book I've ever seen; it's palm-sized for him.

"That's a teeny-tiny book," I say.

"Hi," he says, standing fast, his chair falling backward onto the floor.

"Aw. You don't have to get up. Didn't go home for Christmas, I guess?" I ask.

He shakes his head and looks at me from under shy lids, his head bent to one side.

"Me either," I say. I sit and turn my head to see the title.

"I'm thinking of going vegetarian," he says, tipping the book toward me.

"My dad's a vegetarian," I say. He hands me the book. I read the description. The book seems to be about health food and a woman who was pregnant. Coincidence? During her pregnancy, she only ate what her body told her it wanted. And her body, for the first six months of her pregnancy, only wanted hazelnuts.

"What are hazelnuts?" I ask Neil.

He shrugs.

"Did you read this already?"

He nods. "I was almost done," he says. "And then she ate hazelnuts and grapefruit. Only."

My eyebrows rise.

"Hazelnuts and grapefruit for the whole nine months till she gave birth," he says. "She had no morning sickness."

I look at him then page through the book, reading a sentence here, a paragraph there. I stop on one and read it to Neil.

"And the baby came out with a full head of hair and, I quote, 'A loud, squawking healthy plump baby boy!'" We both seem delighted by this odd conclusion.

"Can I borrow this book from you? Or is it the library's?" I ask.

"You can have it. It's mine," Neil says. His long arm reaches over to a small pile of books at the end of the table. "I was just getting these."

Neil walks me home.

He says, "Well, bye. You seemed sad when you came in the library, but now you seem really happy." His eyes brighten.

"Well. I was glad to see you again," I say and watch his smile widen and his teeth fight to neutralize his lips to no avail.

He's very sweet.

We agree to get together over the break especially since we're among the few still on campus. I don't know if we will. I might have an abortion next week. I don't tell him that.

I am happier. Excited. Neil's book inspired me. I could do that. I could eat all health food. Or just hazelnuts. And grapefruits. I could do this. I could have this baby. I have a baby inside me! This is the first moment of my life that is truly important and meaningful.

Right now, these cells are probably the size of a hazelnut. They should say that on the brochure. I have something bigger than me. Something of me that is of God. I have something to care about that is bigger than just me. I have a purpose: to give this baby a healthy life. I can be a gift to a family that is aching for a baby.

I feel special. I feel purpose like I've never felt purpose before. Being a mother is something I can be, not someday, but now.

Neil goes with me to the local health food store where I buy bags of hazelnuts and dozens of grapefruits. We sit on a park bench and start eating them as if the more I eat, the healthier my baby will be.

Neil's eyebrow stays raised with each hazelnut I pop in my mouth. I offer some to him, but he shakes his head. He rests his forearms on his long thighs, his head fallen, and looks up at me.

"Are you pregnant?" he asks after I've eaten a small bag of hazelnuts and two grapefruits.

My mouth is still full of grapefruit wedge so I mezza-mezza my hand and put up a finger to mean "one minute." I swallow and say, "I'm going to give it up for adoption."

"What's the father say?" he asks.

"Nothing. He doesn't care," I say.

He carries both brown paper grocery bags home for me. I do most of the talking because he's so shy.

"After he hung up on me, I went to legal aid. Did you know that the man has no responsibility at all? None. Not until after the baby is born. And even then, you have to sue him," I say, still astonished.

Neil ducks his head to the side to go through my front door. We unload the groceries, filling two shelves of the refrigerator with grapefruit.

"Your roommate is going to think you went crazy," he says.

"At first, she'll think it's a diet," I say. "But I'm gonna have to tell her because she'll see me getting pregnant-er, and I'll still be living here."

"Are you allowed to stay in school?" he asks.

"I don't know," I say. "I thought about getting an abortion, but I had one when I was really young, and it was the worst thing I ever went through. And I only have about half the money for an abortion. The guy doesn't have to help. But I think this is a good plan, too. I feel like I have a purpose."

Neil sits at the kitchen table, moving the salt and pepper shakers around each other.

"I think you had a good purpose before. Weren't you trying to be a comedian or something? I remember the play you were in. I laughed so hard."

"Really? Thank you," I say. "Not a comedian. More an actress. Do you think it makes me a self-centered person?"

He shakes his head, but I don't know if it's what he's really thinking.

"Most people think it's being shallow and self-absorbed. Plus, I'm not good yet. And I don't know if I'll ever make it as an actress, so I could be wasting all this time."

"What are you doing tomorrow?" he asks.

"I'm shopping for maternity clothes. Weeee!"

"I'll go," he says.

Oh. Ok.

***

At the second-hand store, the maternity section is all stuff my mother wore in the 60's when she was pregnant with me. I try on different tops and model in the mirror for Neil. I pick out one to buy and one to wear home. I'll grow into them, but at least I have something on the ready. I don't really know the timing of it. Do you one day wake up and your belly is sticking out?

"Seems like you got it planned out," Neil says.

"Here's what I hope," I say, swinging my bag and swishing the top like a loose sail. "I'll be a glowing mother just like the one that ate the hazelnuts. I'll have a beautiful boy that comes out squawking with a full head of hair without any labor pains, like in the book, and I place him with love in the adoptive family. I'm going to ask the family if they'll take my number and send me secret photos so I can see my boy growing up. And, when he's old enough, if he wants to meet me, I'll tell him why I couldn't keep him and how I wanted him not to suffer and be poor. That I was too young and had no career yet and no way for us to live, so I chose the perfect loving family to take care of him and give him everything I couldn't. If he wanted, he could see who he looked like in my family, and I'll tell him family stories and tell him his biological history, and he will forgive me. And I can forgive myself knowing I did the right thing."

We get to the apartment and open our lunches we picked up from the health food store. Salads with sprouts. We're both going vegetarian. Neil, for health sake. Me, for the baby. I'm going to go exclusive on hazelnuts and grapefruits starting tomorrow.

We both take a forkful of alfalfa sprouts and chew. Then Neil takes another forkful, and I run. I miss the full toilet and vomit half in the bowl and half down the sides and on the tile. I throw up again. Hard. I throw up as if I ate Thanksgiving dinner instead of a few sprouts.

"Are you ok?" Neil peeks his head around the bathroom door.

"I'm so pregnant!" I say, laughing, spitting. "I'm going to be a mom. Even if only for a few minutes!" I say, wiping my mouth with toilet paper.

This is going to be great.

– 43 –
PARENTS

By the end of the week, I knew, if this is what I was going to do, I needed to tell my parents. But since I had made the hard decisions, all I had to do was tell them and tell them exactly what was going to happen so they didn't have to be angry or upset or worried or not know what to do. I would have done all that. Made the choice. Found an adoption agency that would take care of me until the birth. Decide if I was going to stay in school. I was. I was going to stay in school until the birth and be taken care of by the adoptive family. This was a good choice. The best choice for everyone. My mother would be upset at first, but once she heard how deeply, how thoroughly I thought it out, she'd be ok.

I call when I know they'll both be home. After dinner. Around seven.

My heart is crashing against my ribs. I exhale and listen to the ring. It's ok. It's ok. I know everything to say. It's done. It's decided.

My mom answers. Before she can talk or ask or say anything, I say, "Mom, I have to tell you something."

That's all I say. She says nothing. I wait. Then, suddenly, she says, "Oh my god! You're pregnant!"

There is a long silence.

"Just listen and don't say anything, please," I say. "I'm pregnant, and I decided to have the baby. I have a Jewish adoption agency I'm going to give the baby to, and they are going to help me while I'm pregnant to have the baby. You don't have to worry about anything."

More silence.

"I want you to come home. Now."

I didn't expect her to say that.

"I want you to come home. We need to talk about this." She's speaking in a whisper.

"No, I don't need to come home. I'm fine. I'm happy about this. It's what I decided. It's ok."

"No. I want you to come home. When is the next train? I'll send you money for the train."

"I don't want to come home. I'm fine. It's what I decided," I say.

"Do you want to kill your father? This will kill him. Do you want to kill me?" she asks.

I didn't want to kill anyone. That was the whole problem. Any choice I made was killing someone.

"This is not the right decision. This is not a *good* decision." She is hissing through clenched teeth. She's upset. She's furious.

I am all tears; no sound escapes my lips.

"Find out what the train schedule is and call me back," she says.

And the call is over.

***

I go home on the train. It takes two and a half hours. I take a taxi to our house, the one we'd been living at since we moved when I was in the eighth grade. The one Mick and I used to lay around in and make love in after my parents went to sleep. My brothers are in high school and junior high now. They're not home. My dad is not home, which is what my mother wants because she is crying and all covert. She sneaks me into our house which is weird because, technically, if I weren't away at school, I would live there. We go into her bedroom which we rarely do. We sit on the edge of her bed up by her pillow on her side of the nightstand. She takes out an envelope. She hands me $250. She tells me to get an abortion. I hand it back to her.

I start the argument. All the plans I told her on the phone. The way it will go when I told Neil. All of it plus, "A baby is a blessing. This is a blessing, and the only thing wrong with this is that it's not good timing. It's not a terrible thing. Why are you so upset?"

"I saved this money," she says. She's shaking. Her whole body is shaking. "Your father doesn't know about it. It's my secret money. Get an abortion. That's it." She puts the envelope in my palm.

"No," I say, laying the envelope on the bedspread. "Nothing is wrong. Being pregnant is a good thing. I will make a couple very happy. Sometimes life isn't a perfect pattern, Mom."

How dare she not trust me to make this decision?

"Your aunt, Barbara, is here." Her hand trembles as she again takes up the envelope.

"Why?" I ask. I can figure out why. Barbara is my mother's youngest sister. She's cool. She's divorced. She's a single mother. She used to smoke pot. I think my mother felt I would listen to my aunt. She must have called her just for this secret meeting. As if my aunt could get through to me.

My aunt peeks around the bedroom corner. She hugs me and sits next to me on the other side. All three of us are sitting on the edge of my mother's bed. I'm hearing washes of what they're saying.

Aunt Barbara is saying how hard it is to be a single parent.

My mother is weeping, saying, "You don't know how painful it will be to carry a child and give birth and then have to give it up. It will kill you. It will kill us. You don't know what it is to carry a child in your body and then to have it taken away. You will never recover from that. It's too much. You are too young to have a child."

I keep my eyes set. I won't look at theirs. They're not going to convince me. I'm not going to let them convince me. Because what she says sounds true. What she says hurts. I know she's probably right, but I made the choice. She doesn't know how hard it was to make the choice. Then, to get behind my choice? No. No. No. I won't change my mind.

"Right now, it's not a child. It's not a boy. It's cells," my aunt is saying.

"You will get pregnant when you're older," my mother says. "Someday, you'll be married, and you and your husband will welcome your baby. You'll be able to give it a good home and love, and the time will be right. You will experience being a mother. Now is not that time."

She puts the envelope with the money back in my hand.

– 44 –
The Choice

On the train back to campus, I stare out the window, watching the cornfields go by. I grit my teeth. I'm furious with her. I went through the hard part. I tore up the shag carpet. I had the talk with God. I had decided. I made the choice and making the choice was the hardest part. And now, I was back to the choice again.

The closest clinic is in Peoria. I make an appointment. They won't let you take the train. It has to be a ride from a friend. I tell the adoption place I changed my mind. I tell Fame I'm pregnant and the date of my appointment. Mitch left an envelope with sixty dollars in my mailbox. No note. I hate him. I ask Neil if he wants the grapefruits and hazelnuts. He doesn't, but he comes over.

He ducks at the transom as we go into my room. He sits on the edge of my bed. Neither of us say anything. Our fingers play with the yarn on my mom's crocheted afghan. He clears his throat. I look up, but he's focused on the afghan.

"We could get married," he says.

My eyes well. I know he just wants to be with someone. He's shy and doesn't know how to date. I'll do. Instant wife, instant family. He's a good friend, but there's no chemistry between us. Still, for a moment, I consider it.

"You could keep the baby. I could work," he says. He takes my hand. It feels awkward. We've never been romantic. I can't even answer. It's just so... nice. But also, not what I want. We'd be divorced so fast. What is wrong with me?

"I would," he says.

"I know," I say. I put my hand on his. "Do you think you can give me a ride there? If you're not busy Thursday?"

Neil agrees.

***

His car is old. The seats are hard. The heater doesn't work. The stick shift tugs. But he has a car. And he's been my friend through this. How is that?

We leave early because it's a long drive. About two hours with traffic, less without, but we leave at nine for my 11 a.m. appointment. Instructions are to wear loose clothing. Bring an extra pair of underwear, a sanitary napkin, and a paper grocery bag.

It's freezing in his car in the early morning on the drive. Neil drives with his gloves on the whole way. I have my wool winter coat that goes to my ankles. I hold the collar closed under my chin with my mittened hand. We don't talk. Only our breath in white silent huffs fill the space. I'm scared. What if it's like last time? I asked them when I made the appointment. Do they use anesthesia? Yes. They said they numb you.

"They say they have anesthesia," I say.

Neil nods.

We're running close to check-in time, almost late. He lets me off at the front door and goes to park.

"I'll be in the waiting room," he says.

"Thank you," I say, closing the car door.

Inside, there is a small sign-in room with a desk. The woman at the desk asks if I brought the extra underwear, sanitary napkins, and my paper bag. She puts my name on the list. I'm told to go change into the gown they give me, to put my clothes in the paper bag with the panties on top and the sanitary napkin on top of that.

I do, and I sit in yet another room off the first room lined with folding chairs, every single one filled with girls in the same gown with their paper bags by their side, waiting. I'm called. I think this is it. But a nurse takes my blood pressure and my blood. And I wait. And I wonder where Neil is. There's nowhere to wait inside.

Girls get called. Some go in a room and come right back out like me. Blood pressure and blood work. Some go in and some take their places. There are several different small waiting rooms with what seems like an endless stream of sad faces. No one talks. No one. Not one conversation. Our ears are wide open. We're listening for screams. For a machine. For pain. Most girls sit and stare. No one reads the magazines. Some girls have quiet tears streaming down their cheeks.

They call my name.

"Leave your bag," I'm told. And I follow the nurse.

"You're RH negative," she says. And they give me a pill and a thimble cup of water. I don't know what that is. I don't ask. I feel as if I've had to abandon my body today. Let them do what they want with it. Drug it. Poke it. Needle it. It's no longer only mine as if I've given up my right to care. As if I deserve any pain I get.

I go back and sit. The clock on the pink wall says one. One? It's been two hours and still not brought in? I wonder where Neil is again, if he's ok. Is there a room up front to the other side where the rides sit? From the outside the building is small. Mostly brick. There are windows up near the roof. It's only one story, a maze of little rooms inside. Only the address is on the front of the building. No clinic name. There's a big parking lot that might be shared. Maybe he went to a Hardee's to sit? He wouldn't. Because how would he know if I was done? He'd have to be close.

I go to the desk.

"Do you know when I might go in?" I ask. "I have a ride waiting."

She asks for my name and runs her finger down a long handwritten sign-in sheet.

"RH negative," she says. "You have to wait for the pill to work. About an hour."

I thank her and return to my bag and chair. I look at the other girls. I listen for pain. I'm sad. So sad. And angry. And defeated. I don't have my journal. I should have brought my journal. It would have taken the pain for me. It would have eaten the hours. Helped me forget.

I think about Mitch. I wonder what he's doing today. I could never do to him what he did to me. I never would think that of him. I wonder if he thought about it after Debbie went home.

The room is clearing out. Girls are going in and their chairs are remaining empty. There's just three of us now after a day of all chairs being full. The clock on the wall reads five minutes to four. Five hours since we arrived. Seven hours since we left this morning. Poor Neil has been out there all day.

They call my name. "Ready?" she asks. I'm surprised I have no voice.

She walks in front of me as I follow her with my bag, remembering the first time. The first time walking to the room, this "dead man walking" walk was easier because I didn't know what was coming. It was a shock how terrifying the pain was. There was no warning.

I'm remembering that Mitch did what Jett did. Disappeared, leaving it all to me. Remembering Sue and I driving to Rockford, singing all of Stevie Nicks songs, not knowing what to be afraid of.

It's a small room with faded pink walls and a low ceiling. She tells me to leave my bag on the side. She checks for the underwear and the pad. The room is empty but for me and the nurse now setting things up. I see the machine. The machine that was by the doctor the first time.

"They said they give anesthetic?" I ask, checking once again.

"Laughing gas," she says. "Like at the dentist."

That doesn't make me feel reassured. I thought they knocked you out. I thought I wouldn't have to be awake.

She has me crawl onto the table, my sock-covered feet in the stirrups. "Scoot your bum all the way to the edge," she says. "Are you ok?"

I nod. I'm hardly in my body. I'm surrendering myself to whatever happens. I feel floppy, like I'm taking a break from me right now.

There is a kitten poster on the ceiling above my head. White and fluffy with a pink bow and doe eyes. Somehow that's what makes tears roll into my hair and onto the crispy white paper.

"Ok," the doctor says, pulling his stool between my open knees. "So, it'll be quick. A ten-minute procedure," he says.

They said that last time and on the phone. A quick, painless procedure. Ten minutes. I don't think it is. It wasn't.

I'm hoping this time is different. It's been years since the first time. Maybe things have progressed.

The nurse is by my head. I hear her turn on the gas.

"It won't take away the pain, but it will help to relax you," she says. I'm trembling, but it's better than the first time where they had nothing.

The doctor says he will explain as we go. Just relax. The nurse says she's going to put the gas mask on, and she'll be right there holding my hand.

My eyelids close as I let the gas relax me. I feel both her hands enclose my right hand. This is better. This is ok.

I'm aware of the doctor as if from a great distance, like he's on the far side of a telescope. Cold metal enters my body. I try not to concentrate on it. I stare at the kitten with the pink bow. It's too sweet. Incongruous. I close my eyes.

"We are going to wash the area."

Inside me, something swabs. It stings, but I know the worst will come.

"We are going to dilate the cervix."

My insides quake, but, outside, nothing moves.

A needle pierces me. I feel a tube being forced into the middle of my cervix. I rear up. I hear myself in the mask. My quiet tears become loud sobbing. The pain, *the pain*—can I last through it? Will I make it? Ok, relax, relax—relax!

"Put your hips back on the table," I hear a frustrated order from a distance. The nurse moves down and lowers my hips with her hands. I am a bad patient. The noise of the suction machine winds around my brain—

"Relax!" they yell at me.

The machine enters my uterus.

The pain, *the pain*—don't concentrate on it!

My outside is sobbing. I can feel the monster pulling, ripping out my insides—

Breathe! Don't forget to breathe.

It's tearing inside me like a whirring drill, hundreds of rats eating my insides.

I am murdering—oh, God, please forgive me—I'm sorry, I'm sorry, please let it be over—!

Breathe! Relax!

I can't!

I am so filled with hate and emptied of love. In the now bare cavern where love once existed, the breath of hate swoops in and fills all the spaces. I cannot stop the trembling. I cannot stop my body from bucking up. I cannot stop my screams under the clear gas cone.

The machine dies down and the hand holder wipes the tears from my face. The doctor and the helper go out without a word. Now they can go home, grab some dinner, and watch TV. I am left to catch my breath on the table.

The hand holder returns and helps me sit. She moves me forward and waits for me, going at my pace. She hands me my panties and pad. I put them on over my trembling legs and pelvis, she helps me off the table, and we walk.

She holds my arm, moving me to a large recovery room. The largest room I've been in. There are a dozen La-Z-Boy recliners, all filled with girls. Next to each is a small table and next to that, the girl's bag.

I'm placed in a recliner. There are rooms in women's lives that men never see.

They hand me a small glass of orange juice and tell me I must drink it. They offer me cookies. I'm too nauseous. I am still in so much pain. I wasn't in this much pain before, not after the last time I went through this. My uterus is pulling in and up, cramping. There is no way to sit without causing more pain. Drops of blood slip onto the sanitary napkin. I close my eyes and wait for the dizziness from the gas to pass. I am weak and torn. I wonder if the doctor didn't make a mistake and suction a piece of my heart out.

Her hand is on my shoulder. It's too soon. I don't know how much time has passed, but the exit lady is asking, "Can you get up and put your street clothes on?"

I say yes when I mean no because I don't want to be impolite. I am the last to leave.

I struggle an inch at a time to move forward up off the chair. It wasn't this bad the first time, trying to get up.

I shuffle, holding the wall, to the changing room. I follow the instructions typed and posted to the wall: robes and ties in this hamper, bags hung outside the wall, shoes in containers.

One hundred robes, on hundred slippers, one hundred bags. One hundred bodies ripped open. One hundred hearts torn apart. One hundred women having to make one of the hardest choices.

***

Somehow, there's Neil. His eyes hurt for me. I can see his helplessness. The woman is giving me, us, instructions on birth control pills I must take to regulate my period, as if Neil is my partner, then final exit instructions I nod to.

It's rush hour. What should be an hour and a half to two hours is stretching into three. Peoria to Macomb. The seat in his car has no cushion left. Just vinyl on metal. I cannot find a way to sit. Excruciating pain like this is not normal.

Neil tells me he had been waiting in his car the whole time.

"I'm so sorry," my voice eeks out.

"No, no," he says. "I finished reading a whole novel."

"War and Peace?" I whisper, attempting a joke.

He half-smiles, his eyes on the road.

After that, we don't speak. It's a long, long drive home. On the unpadded seats, every bump blackens my brain. I try not to make noises, but I do. I see the fear in Neil's eyes as he tries to slow for each bump. A thousand. There are at least one thousand. I am sure of this.

Neil parks. Fame rushes out to get me. She has my bed ready. I lay under my covers, stiff on my back, hands on my cramps. I am like a corpse who has felt its own autopsy.

Neil returns from the store bringing my request: three cans of Betty Crocker chocolate frosting. Because raw icing is medicine.

– 45 –
HOSPITAL

Three days after the procedure, I'm back to classes. Catching up on the last month lost. Something about the way things happened feels like an end, a period, an exclamation point. Time to reclaim. I'm just gonna be like everyone else and not think so much. Ha-ha. I've got lots to do, and I'm not letting things drag me down anymore.

I miss Mick, but I talk to him in my journals. He's my spirit best friend instead of the man who completed me and the loss I've been trying to fill with poor substitutes. I haven't seen Mitch since I came back to life. Maybe he's avoiding me. Frankly, Scarlett, I don't give a damn.

I am not so terrible an actress. I'm funny and intense, and I'm learning. Auditions are coming up for the last plays of the year. I'm getting all the scripts and practicing on my own. I may be invisible now, but one day, I won't be. One day, I'll have the tools to use everything inside me. One day, I will be someone to want.

***

Our kitchen table is papered with copies of pages of the scripts, all of them highlighted, scribbled on, or stapled. Fame will be auditioning, too. We walk around our apartment, underlining, reading aloud, and memorizing.

I take a break to lay out on the grassy green in the sun, taking advantage of the rare early-spring cloudless day. I spend a few hours outside, a few inside. I'm leading a balanced life now. Doze. Wake. Doze.

By two o'clock, the clouds are taking over. I peek under my bikini bottom. Yes! Tan lines. I look sexy with a tan. And I mean to look sexy. Gone are the freshman pounds. Gone is my "trample on me" attitude. I can't wait to put on something sexy, walk the campus, and not want any guy. Not unless he really wants me. A relationship.

Back to work on the scripts. I try to take a shower but, oh my god, am I sunburned. Opening my mouth, my face feels like it's cracking. I am walking stiff. I can't sit. I feel sick, and my skin is aflame, and I'm teeth-chattering freezing. I lay down naked. Sharp zaps are snapping at my legs, my belly. I make it to the toilet, sit, and feel something pour out of me. In the bowl, there is black blood. My ears deafen with a long, loud ringing sound. Nothing else is audible. A cold sweat beads on my burning skin. I call out to Fame, wipe, and insert a tampon. I hold onto the sink. Fame grabs me before I topple.

What's happening? Why am I fainting? I hear Fame calling the paramedics. She comes back and dresses me in her gingham dress. She doesn't want me to be naked for the ambulance. The paramedics rush in. Several men. They move my thighs apart, pull out the tampon, and catch the hemorrhaging. The pace of their voices quickens. Orders. Urgency. They administer the IV while I'm still in my bed. They lift me onto a board and carry me out. I am losing consciousness when I hear Fame yell, "Think of this for the theater! Remember it! You can use it as an actress!"

And I will. I will. I'm thankful, because I'm an artist, someday even the worst of my life will matter. At least to my art.

***

I don't remember the night in the hospital, only pieces. I had an infection from the abortion, so I have an antibiotics IV. I sleep-wake-sleep-wake most the next day. No food. My bedside phone rings. Fame wants to know if I need anything. No. Nothing.

"Your journal?" she asks. I think about it. It's my friend, my confidant. It accompanies me everywhere. No journal. I am nowhere. The dusky fog of sadness is impenetrable.

"Your mom called. I told her you were in the hospital," she says. "I hope that was ok. I gave her the number."

"It's ok," I say.

"Do you want me to visit?" she asks. "Or Neil? He asked, too."

"No," I say. "Thank you, though. Tell him thank you, though."

I close my eyes and sleep through the day and the night.

The doctor comes.

"You're ready to be released," he says, expecting me to thank him.

I keep my face turned to the wall.

"Are you in pain?" he asks.

I face the wall.

He writes something on my chart and says he'll check back before he leaves.

The phone rings. I let it.

The nurse comes in.

The phone rings again. I let it.

The nurse answers it.

"It's your mother," she says, holding out the receiver.

I stay facing the wall.

She tells my mother I'm asleep.

I can't move from this fetal position. I'm cement. Turned to stone. I can't open my eyes. I've been buried alive. There's no time. No "where." No feeling. I'm numb. Shallow breath. Just breath. Darkness. Is the darkness in me or around me?

Both.

An image, as if lit by a flash, opens in the blackout of my mind.

Mick's face. He's smiling, dressed as Bo Peep.

The image brightens then dissolves, the same way Mick's light did the night he died.

Blackness.

Like slides from a projector, moments illuminate:

Holding Jett's hand on the plane to Germany.

Watching Jett walk by me as if I'm invisible.

The sheet with tomato soup that had been pushed into the garbage

My pink prom dress lifting like wings in the breeze

Mick's gentle hand on my upper back.

Memory fireworks burst and zip open like Polaroids.

His front teeth clicking, forward and back.

His waterbed.

His girlfriend.

Rick's Hallmark cards. *Siempre.*

Men are wolves.

Some women, too.

Bathroom stalls, black markers.

Stuffed pajamas hanging.

Mim's beige eyelashes under fluorescent bathroom lights.

451

Flores para los muertos.

Get her off, get her out. Brick shithouse.

His shark eyes.

His Adam's apple.

His bouncy hair.

His Bible.

His.

His, His.

My worth is less than the whim of His penis.

How do I love them without being devoured?

***

What day? What night? How many? I don't know.

In the distance, the phone rings.

In the distance, the nurse talks into the phone.

In the distance, I hear, "It's your mother."

The nurse comes into focus. She motors the bed to a sitting position. I open my eyes. It's bright in the room. I thought it was dark. My arm is taped to a board. She puts her hand on my forehead with a touch that says "shhhh, it's ok. You are safe and you are loved, and it's ok to close your eyes."

And my eyes do.

"We didn't want you to break the IV." Was that why my arm was taped to the board?

What had I been doing?

Her hand leaves my head. I open my eyes. She's holding my chart.

"The doctor wrote you may have depression." She looks at me as if it's a question.

I don't know what I'm feeling. Underground, underneath, underwater, underearth, under, under, under, down below, as if the world is at a far, far, far away distance.

"Do you think you have depression?" she asks.

Depression or depressed? One is because of something. The other just is. One is reasonable. The other is a mental illness.

I know which one. I shrug my shoulders.

"I'm going to get you ready to go home in the morning," she says.

She pets my hair as if I'm a bird. Someone to care for. Someone to be tender with. As if I matter.

"Your mother keeps calling," she says.

I shake my head.

I am unable to be vulnerable with my mother right now, ashamed of my new body parts that suggest sex. I'm hurting her by growing into a woman. My mother is too fragile to feel anything that hurts. With me just being me, I can hurt her. It's my job to protect her. To protect me from her reaction.

"I'll come back to help you dial, ok?" the nurse asks, her hand, like gravity on my helium self.

My mother cannot know any of this past year. Her knowing would make it worse. In her knowing, my failures would stay alive, like malevolent ghosts refusing to be buried.

453

"I'll come back." The nurse's warm palm leaves my forehead. It's cold where her hand lifts off. I press the back of my head into the flat plastic-wrapped pillow to keep from drifting away. I watch her slip out to the hallway.

I think of my mother's touch when I was little. My mother wants the world for me. Yet, to her, I am too much. Too sensitive. Too curious. Too emotional. Too dramatic. Why can't I do things the way others do?

The phone rings.

I answer.

My mom says my name.

"Hi, Mom." I sound chalky. It's been so long since I spoke.

"I'm worried about you, honey," she says.

My face squinches, turns red. I hold my breath to keep my sobs in.

"Do you want me to come down?" she asks.

I know she doesn't want to come down. I don't want her to come down. She needs me to be ok so she can be ok, but I'm not ok.

She says my name.

"When do you leave the hospital? Did they tell you?"

"Tomorrow," I say.

"Did they say what's wrong with you?" she asks.

"Infection," I say.

"I should come down," she says.

I am embarrassed to be me in front of her. I want to believe I am destined, charmed. When I'm with her, I feel like plain me. My mother's daughter. A someday nobody.

"No," I say.

I want to be what she wants, but I'm not. She would love for me to "make it" as an actress, but expects my eventual failure. People like us don't dance in the stars.

"I'll call you tomorrow afternoon when you get home," she says.

I look at the creases the tape around the board is making on my arm.

"Ok," I say.

"Good night, sweetheart. Talk to you tomorrow," she says.

I need to be away from her for now. To let myself become. To solidify. To believe there's magic in me so I can believe it's possible to someday be an actress extraordinaire.

"Mom?" I say, to the dial tone.

- 46 -
TIRA

In the university library, I discover there are whole rows of theater plays that take up entire sections of shelves. I pull a bunch off a shelf, make two huge stacks on a nearby table, then page through to find large chunk paragraphs in-between dialogue. Monologues. I need a monologue.

Apparently, there was this thing actors did. They went off to summer stock theaters and got paid to act. Like a real job. Theater students traveled to audition for Artistic Directors for their summer productions. Our school was going. All of us. Even me. I missed this news, being in the hospital. For the audition, each actor has to present a two-minute monologue.

I'm in search of the perfect one. The only way I can imagine that a monologue will be right is if it's something I can feel myself saying. I read the first few lines of each one to feel it in my mouth. A few possibilities, but I don't know.

How do you know how a character is supposed to look or sound, and how do you make them fascinating enough? Nothing stands out. I've never performed a monologue. I'm not sure what to look for. Do they actually time you to exactly two minutes? This will be my first professional audition. Thinking that makes my heart pound, so I stop.

Another shelf holds single plays, each a booklet unto itself. I grab one, page through, and put it back. I grab another. Page through. Put it back. These are easier to skim. I grab another. This one's good.

I read the beginning. There are stage directions and a few first lines.

Bare stage. Tira sits, knitting. She notices the audience.

"Oh. Hello. Tira. My name…."

Only five words but I know exactly what she's feeling. The character's caught in a private moment. She's startled. Suddenly, there are people, an entire audience waiting for her. There's fear, embarrassment, and self-consciousness, as if she's recovering from a clumsy trip and sprawl in public. Other people are gawking, covering the mortification by laughing, "Oh my god, I'm so clumsy. Ugh! I'm fine."

I turn to the cover for the title.

Tira Tells Everything There is to Know About Herself. By Michael Weller.

The real monologue is churning beneath those words. I feel this. I could say this. My hands tingle. Something about this girl—this play—I feel like I know everything about her.

The words could fall out of my mouth. I need to be entertaining. I understand this.

Never show your distressed, sad, needy self. That's such a downer. Do something. Liven the place up. Please, me. Isn't that what you do? Isn't that why we keep you around? Fill the space. Make the conversation. Tell a joke. Make them laugh. Tell a story. Confess my life so you, they, the people, the audience of my life, won't be bored and think, "Ho hum."

So they won't leave.

I sit cross-legged on the carpet in the aisle back against the metal shelves. I read the rest of the opening monologue.

Tira says she's waiting for a man. "Ho hum," she says. Ho hum because he, the man, is not right for her.

I read the scene. The man she was waiting for enters. It's evident he's in love with himself being in love. Not her. She's exchangeable. But she stays, she tries, she wants it to work because to Tira, any man is better than no man. Her value is how men feel about her.

Tira, who is sweet and funny and a bit naughty, desperately, yes, *desperately* wants to be loved and cherished by a man. Men are her mirror, so even if the mirror is cruel, it's better than no mirror at all. No mirror means she doesn't exist, she's invisible.

I read the whole play. I can't stop. My eyes zip across the words, propelled. As if I'm seeking some clue to solve the problem of me.

The men are stereotypes, hilarious horrors. Yet, through Tira's perception, no matter what, men are never wrong. They're the authority because they're men. They are possibility. If you want the job, you must please the boss. So, she chameleons herself to fit each man's peculiar needs. Still, after each brief but intense encounter, each man disposes of her.

Between encounters, she comes back to the audience to laugh it off, but she sinks deeper into confusion until, at last, she's alone with just the audience, and, in real tears, she says she's decided to commit suicide by holding her breath. So, she holds her breath. We know it won't work. Of course it doesn't work. She fails at everything. Even this.

"Woops," she says. "Well, anyway, that's one thing about me. I'm consistent."

I feel like she says it with a sort of wink. There's something about the way she means this. I'm not sure what it is, but it feels conquering.

In all other plays so far, even this one, I don't know if the way I see the character is the way the playwright intended. But at this moment, for this monologue, it wouldn't matter. I can piece together all her monologues into one two-minute piece and as long as it's true to her emotional journey in the play, it will be a true interpretation. The lines on the page are just the tip of the iceberg. I'm living in the beating heart of her. I'm playing her true.

I feel I'm having an acting epiphany. My first. I'm understanding something I never understood before. I think back to Gay Wellington in Mim's production. I did it organically but didn't know why it worked. Is it that I've found the voice and thoughts and language of me through this play?

Sitting on this natty library carpet between the rows of books, I'm sure I look silly and dramatic, clutching this play to my chest like a meant to be talisman. This meant to be play that's causing me a rush of recognition that I'm exactly where I'm supposed to be. As if in discovering this play, this Tira, I'm unearthing something that is about to shift everything. Maybe everything I didn't understand about acting?

If I check it out of the library, I know I'll want to keep it, and there's nowhere to buy plays like these that I know of, so I take it to the Xerox machine. My hands vibrate with anticipation as I lay open the pages on the glass of the machine. It's twenty-four pages, only twelve laid open and flat. A dollar twenty.

I remove the other Xeroxes from my bag and leave them for someone else, anyone else, on the library table. Tira is the only play I take home with me.

I rehearse, thought by thought, feeling by feeling, making certain the lines come out only if it's impossible not to say them. A necessity of feeling.

I've never felt this before. Everything I thought you had to do to be "acting" was incomplete, even incorrect. I thought the point was the lines. Memorizing the lines. Waiting for your cue. Trying to figure out how you should be moving about the stage. Hand gestures, facial expressions.

Being Tira, the lines are secondary. The lines need to be memorized, yes, but they are the last piece, not the first. First is understanding the conflict the character is in. First is the feeling, the thoughts under the lines. The words are the last reaction on the triangle of feeling-thought-word. Because with Tira, I am her, she is me, I understand this not just intellectually but in my bones, my flesh. It's a gift.

I decide instead of Tira knitting, as it says in the stage directions, her first moment alone on stage should be her practicing holding her breath. Already contemplating suicide.

I memorize it. I walk to and from classes speaking it. I work out the staging in our living room and get it ready to present in acting class. I rehearse until it feels exactly how the performance would come out of my thoughts, my heart, my mouth.

Then, it's presentation day in acting class. Each actor will perform their piece in front of the class so the teacher can give notes and prepare us for our auditions in Madison.

Every acting student in the department who's going to audition is there. The room has never been this full. I know the people in my acting class, but there are many more

461

people auditioning. Many of them I've just seen in the halls or in productions. My stomach rolls over.

Some kids wear outfits that probably go with their character. Some are just wearing regular clothes. I'm wearing what I think is Tira. Tira seems like an open flower hoping for bees, so I wear my black skirt with flowers and a pink top with flowers and my pink ballet slippers with purple tights to keep me warm. And colorful.

Our school chairs with built-in wooden desk tops crowd the room, leaving only a small section up front that has been set aside as the stage. There's much scraping of metal on linoleum, as well as the creaking and quieting of voices and bodies as everyone settles in.

Fame was already asked back to her summer acting job last year, so she's not here. I only have one other friend in acting class. Cosmo.

I sit next to her and smile. She wiggles her eyebrows at me. We both go back to studying words we already know. I'm all nerves. Everyone is jittery, looking at their well-worn pages, muttering their lines. There are lots of closed eyes and exhaling. I'm not alone.

Our teacher is newly officious. He has a stopwatch in his fist. He's really timing us? This is serious. I'm fine, though. I'm fine. I wrote and rehearsed it to be two minutes. The teacher stands. The room hushes. He announces the order as if it's a real audition. I'm almost last. I don't know if It's because he doesn't think highly of me or because he realized I was actually here and stuck me in.

I wanted to like him. I wanted him to see something in me. But that's not the way it's gone since I started here. Then with all my personal debacles that became absences, I must have seemed more and more flaky and uncommitted in his eyes. A space cadet. I think he wrote me off.

We begin. Each person goes to the stage area in the front of the room, says their name, says their piece, title and author. I didn't know that we had to introduce ourselves like that. Most everyone is pretty good.

It's my turn. My chest is thudding. God, it would be humiliating to fall on my face in front of these people who already think I'm worthless. The room has low expectations when I get up. I can feel it. People are fidgeting or resuming whisper conversations. I don't care. I love Tira. I *am* Tira. I want to express her. I want to tell her story.

I sit on the chair and close my eyes.

No! I forgot to say my name, say the piece! No! Too late. Stay in it. Move on. I pull in the remaining oxygen through my nose and hold my breath. I gasp for air. Surprise! What seems like hundreds of strangers are staring at me. I ride the sensation of that fear adrenaline. Do what Tira does, says, rolling down that wave of self-preservation.

"Oh! Hello! Tira! That's my name. I'm going to tell you something about me. In fact, I'm going to tell you everything there is to know. Ho hum..."

I go on and on, surfing the tsunami of feelings, entertaining in that self-deprecating way of deflection. Hey look over here, not within me. Gotta please 'em. I'd rather hurt me than you.

They laugh. Their laughter rises. I let it. I hold for it. They don't know what's coming. It's my ball. It's effortless. I don't have to be afraid of missing a line or where or how to move. It takes care of itself. It's as if all I have to do is be in the absolute moment, Being.

I finish. Exactly two minutes. It feels like cheerleading when I stick the landing. My class applauds like we always do for each other, but it's exhilarating. A clap like I made them happy. The teacher looks stunned. My class looks at me as if they've never seen me before. The way the step sisters see Cinderella as she stepped into the slipper that fit.

***

The morning of the auditions, I carpool with Cosmo, my only pal from acting class. We leave when it's still dark. We drove up from Macomb to Chicago last night and from Chicago to Madison this morning; it's a two-and-a-half-hour ride. I'm super nervous and super cold, dressed in my Tira outfit, buried under a thick winter coat, mittens, and hat. Cosmo wears a sweatshirt, white jeans, and her raspberry beret. Even though it's early and freezing, she's very chatty. I have no idea what we're talking about. I keep laughing when I know I should, and say, uh huh, when I should, and my cheeks hurt from fake smiling. I don't want to not be sociable. So, my outsides are participating, but my mind is running a film in my head, of every moment Tira goes through. If I don't, I'll vomit with nerves.

Every time I think of doing this in front of actual Artistic Directors, my stomach rolls, making me vomitus. I'm not ready for this. I'm not ready to audition in front of professionals. What if I forget my lines? I mean, I know them. *I know them.* But what if I get so panicked that my mind *zzzts* out and I'm standing there, in front of a theater of professionals, blank? No one can help. Other actors don't know each other's monologues, so they aren't able to call out a forgotten line. I clutch the armrest on the car door as if it'll keep me from falling out of the sky.

"Are you nervous?" I ask her.

"Mezza-mezza," she says.

We arrive before our teacher. Before almost anyone. I'm happy to be in the warm theater building. The University of Wisconsin in Madison. Yes, it's becoming spring in southern Illinois, but in Chicago and Wisconsin, winter is holding on. People are just setting up the welcome table. We tell them our names. They say we're the first to check in. They scan their sheets, paging through to find us. Cosmo is number six. Eek! That's almost first. She's unfazed.

"Groovy," she says. She swishes her long brunette mane over one shoulder. I'm number forty-four. Phew, ok. Ok. Not first. Right in the middle, I think?

Cosmo says we should check out the theater. We walk to the entrance, but the doors are locked. Cosmo leans against the wall and sinks to the floor.

"I'm gonna chillax here," she says, sitting with her knees up, digging through her backpack at her feet.

I try to sit next to her, but my insides are rolling. I have to walk, to rehearse, to run the lines, or I'll implode.

"I'll be back to watch you. I'm freaking out a little," I say. She gives me a peace sign.

I find a bathroom and check my hair and makeup. I seek an empty space where I can run my piece. I roam the halls until I see an open door, lights on, that leads into a costume department. There are period costumes and other costumes currently being built on mannequins and costumes on racks and hats from every century as well as gloves and stockings coming out of every drawer, and, oh, God, I love the theater. It's history coming alive.

I love the people who love the theater. It's a private club with its own language. A secret feeling shared without naming it. I want to be a good enough actress that I will be allowed in. Acting, theater, writing, or anything artistic feels like what it means to live a life, and I want to do this thing forever in my life.

Suddenly, there's someone else. A boy. A man. Around my age but a little older, standing casually, leaning on one hip, checking things off on a clipboard. I didn't realize he was there and, as he sees me, I can see in his expression he just realized I was there. But he's not startled, he just smiles as if he's used to people walking in and out.

He looks handsome in a funny way because he's surrounded by a rack of pink, flouncy layered lace petticoats that make it look like he's lost in a bouquet of peonies. His hair is dark brown, shaggy cut with bangs and soft feathering at the nape of his neck. He's wearing a white t-shirt tucked into white carpenter pants with a belt accentuating his waist. He looks like he's used to being backstage, behind the scenes, where being cool doesn't matter.

He says he's on work-study to help with the auditions. A theater student, too, but getting his MFA in Directing. That means he's probably twenty-two, twenty-three, or even twenty-four.

I admit to him that I'm petrified. That I never auditioned before. That I was just looking for a place to myself to run my piece. I'm so nervous about this, my first real audition, I forget to ask his name.

He says, "You'll be fine." Then, he realizes I'm not. I'm shaking.

"Do you want to rehearse it for me?" he asks.

"It's only two minutes," I say, grateful.

He leads me to the back of the costume shop where he sits on a ruffled sofa covered with different flower patterns of tossed material. It's like everywhere he goes he has his own backdrop.

"What's the piece about?" he asks.

"Oh. Do I have to tell them that?" I ask.

"No, no, for me," he says.

"It's about Tira, this wacky girl, who thinks she has boyfriends she wants to be loved by, but all of them dump her, and she doesn't know why. So, at the end, she's going to commit suicide in front of the audience by holding her breath, to keep even her suicide light, because nobody loves a downer," I say. "So, I related to that. A lot."

He laughs. "You're funny," he says, thinking I'm joking.

I place a chair a few feet away from him. We have only a tiny space between all the costumes. I look down and refocus. I look up and introduce myself. Introduce the piece. Sit on the chair. Close my eyes. Hold my breath. Gasp for air. Open my eyes. Surprise! I go on the roll.

He leans forward. He laughs. He doesn't know what's coming. I look in his eyes as if he's the other actor. I lasso him with my words. I tease him, play with him, listening to what he's not saying, as if he's part of this dialogue, not monologue. Needing him as the audience to love me, Tira.

"Do it again," he says, leaning forward in full attention. I do. It's spontaneous now, just playing off what I'm intuiting from his reactions. He laughs in different places this time.

"Actors on deck," we hear over the PA system.

"What's your number?" he asks.

"Forty-four," I say, wondering if I should get "on deck." "On deck' is a new word for me in theater language.

468

"Plenty of time," he says. "Unless you want to wait back-stage now?"

"I don't want to stand there. It'll make me lose my focus, but my friend is number six, so I should watch her."

"Right on," he says, reaching for his clipboard.

"Thank you for this," I say. I sling my backpack over one shoulder. "If I come back, are you gonna be here?"

"Should be. Not sure," he says. "You're gonna kill it."

"I'll be back," I say.

Half of my class is performing much earlier than me. I get backstage in time to squeeze Cosmo's arm. We peek at the stage. It's not the main stage so phew. It must be their black box stage, but still. The lights are up, both on the playing space and the audience. Every seat is filled with directors taking notes. I pictured auditioning in classrooms, my living room, the costume shop. Not this. This never entered my imagination. My hands and feet are pins and needles.

"Number six," blares the PA.

Cosmo exhales and strides on stage. Oh my god, she's so brave. That's all I can think as she's doing her monologue. She does great. Just like in class. She strides off stage and bursts into a giant smile coming through the backstage curtain. We stay side by side to watch the next ones. Cosmo whispers she needs a cig, that she'll be back in time for mine. I stay. I watch. I become vomitous. I have to not watch.

I know I'll hear the numbers being called on the PA system in the hallway. I head back to the costume shop.

He's there again with a backdrop, because he's taking notes, maybe inventory, of the men's suits that are stacked three racks high in lines of gray and black slashes. Like he's standing against a painting of sooty city buildings.

I feel so bad not knowing his name, but it's too embarrassing now to ask.

"Your name should be Angel," I say. I mean that but, also, I'm hoping he'll say "ha-ha, my name is…"

But he doesn't. He just smiles and says, "You have time. Once more?"

I hold the chair, close my eyes, and refocus. I'm not as nervous. My hyper need to please has calmed. I feel ready. I do it again. Repeating it this way feels as though I'm learning a piece of music, playing with the tempo and the volume and everything that changes the experience. This time, though, he doesn't laugh.

"What?" I ask, trying not to show my alarm.

"Just different," he says. "It was sad. What were your thoughts as you were running it?"

What were my thoughts?

"I was thinking, 'I'm just so stuck and hurt,'" I say. "Not me, I mean. As Tira. That was what I was feeling as Tira."

He nods.

"Thinking, 'I don't know what's wrong with me' and 'how come no matter what I try to be for men, they just don't see me. Why am I not a keeper?'"

470

"Yeah. It seemed like you weren't covering it as much that time," he says. "Take a breath."

I do, but my nerves are so on the surface that I almost cry, exhaling. I'm so scared this is going to go bad. That I can ruin it just by a different thought in my head. Coming into this understanding is new, maybe fragile.

"I was feeling, "if I am nothing to men, am I nothing?' Anyway, I'll cover it more. I'll do it again," I say, trying to put a period to this discussion and move on.

"It's actually better," he says. "Because it feels like you hit something deeper. Did you feel that?"

I don't actually know.

"You look worried. Don't worry. Now, draw out what you found. Then you can go back to covering it up, which is where the funny is, right?" he asks.

"Number twenty-five, twenty-six on deck," says the PA.

My heart flip-flops. I close my eyes; my hand goes to my throat. I almost cry, so I giggle.

"Oh, boy. I'm getting nervous to the max." I breathe deep and exhale, giggling. "I'd rather just go back to doing it the way I was," I say. "This is getting so heavy, it might be dragging me down."

"You're going to be fine," he reassures. "I never read the play," he says, "but it seems like all the men feel entitled to be pretty terrible," he says. "Narcissistic."

"But that's not the point," I say, not knowing what narcissistic means. "That doesn't matter to her. She just

471

wants them to love her. So, she's stuck." I feel as though I'm defending my best friend.

"I get it," he says.

My smile is forced and my eyes are blurry, so I look down at my hands. My fingertips dig into the top of the chair, my palms wet. I'm not sure what we're getting at here. I can't change her.

I wish we weren't doing this now. I look at him like, should I go? He shakes his head and pushes his hand down on the air as if he's telling me to chill out.

This is getting so confusing. I can't untangle this. I have no distance. Tira's problem is my problem. Get more perfect, don't bore people with your true self, be what people need, then you'll have value to them. Get over it.

"My dad once said, 'all men are wolves.'" I roll my eyes.

He raises his eyebrows.

"I don't think so, obviously," I say. "I think, Tira thinks, if she just was perfect, any guy would love her and keep her."

"Any guy? Even the wolves?" he asks.

"Yes!" I say, with a faux foot stomp, charmingly adamant. "Because, ok, if a loving person lives in a loving world and a hostile person lives in a hostile world, and everyone you meet is your mirror, then how could Tira not think there was something wrong with her. Men are her mirror."

"Is that from something? That mirror thing?" he asks.

"It's from this spiritual book, the *Handbook to Higher*

Consciousness," I say, thinking I could give him my copy that I carry in my purse.

"It's kinda a warped mirror," he says.

"What do you mean?" I ask. "Why can't she expect if she's kind she'll get kindness back? If she doesn't, she's doing something wrong. Everyone you meet is your mirror."

"Sure, sure. You give out positive vibes, maybe you'll get positive vibes. But Tira is seeking kindness from a wolf. The problem isn't Tira," he says. "The problem is the wolf."

That makes me gasp. I feel raw, scared. All my beliefs, everything that I had faith in that was true, is naked on a cutting board. I never stopped to think that, maybe, the problem wasn't me.

I sit in the chair and close my eyes. I let everything we just said hiss out of me like air from a tire. Empty now, I hold my breath. I let the pressure build in my throat. Pressure builds on my temples, throbbing behind my ears. I gasp for air and open my eyes. Surprise!

Startled, hot tears well behind my eyes. Stay in, stay in. Push them away. Go on the roll. I am no longer waterskiing over the real pain. The obvious pain. I sink, letting the feelings cut deep to my own very real pain. It wasn't all my fault. Somehow, that hurts more. I work harder to cover now what is even deeper pain so it's funnier. This time he laughs as he did before but at the end, it's he who has tears welling.

***

"Forty-four!"

He stands backstage, watching, and it makes me feel better that he's there. I walk onstage and smile my cheerleading smile. My waitress smile. My actress smile. *My* smile.

I introduce myself. I introduce my piece. I sit in the chair, close my eyes, let my shoulders relax, feel my head become helium and float up, feel my aloneness, take a deep inhale through my nose. Hold my breath.

My emotional neck snaps back, the ride begins, and I am fully in the moment.

"Oh! Hello. Tira. My name…"

Startled, too, they laugh.

Their laughter rises and rolls in all the places that I and he knew they would. I relax into the feelings under the words as each man is hope and each man is my mirror and, as they discard me, I feel the shredding of my heart flesh. Do I matter at all? Am I nothing? Of no value?

I cover it. Self-deprecating. Entertaining. They can't help but laugh. It's like a riddle, isn't it? If you think you have value but no one else thinks you do, do you have value? Ha-ha-ha.

Then the final man.

"I love you, please stay with me," I plead.

"I'll ask nothing of you," I plead.

"I'll give and give and ask nothing in return," I plead.

"No one with an ounce of self-respect would go near you," he says. He leaves.

We are crying now, Tira and me, in front of the audience. Just me and her.

Tears, really? Oh how silly, ridiculous, and I promised I wasn't going to do that. I'm sorry. Good grief.

I know!

"I'm going to commit suicide," I say.

That'll keep 'em in their seats.

"I'm going to commit suicide by holding my breath," I say. Ha-ha.

But not so ha-ha. Who knows? I might.

Don't worry. You'll still be entertained.

I hold my breath and squeeze my closed eyes together. Yellow and black spread out under my lids.

You're a slut, she's a slut.

I hold my breath.

Jett's light-blue Monte Carlo.

His dial tone after I tell him I'm pregnant.

I hold my breath.

Under my chin, pressure spreads into my throat.

Michael lifting my skirt. Joseph lifting my skirt. Rick in the pungent morning.

I hold my breath.

Breaker, breaker, this is Spice of Life. The white washrag, Chief Motel embroidered in red. Dennis's skeletal body on top of me.

I hold my breath.

Throb, throb, throb in my neck.

No, no, you're right. You need, you want. It's more important. I understand. I can be ok.

I hold my breath.

Don't make a fuss. Don't make people uncomfortable. I can get over it, I'm strong that way.

I hold my breath.

I will behave. Not get in the way. Not disturb the comfort. I know you're more tender. I can be ok.

I hold my breath.

I don't need to speak, to be heard, to have. Here. Take everything. Take it, take it. It's too exhausting trying to hold onto it.

I hold my breath.

I am ok, here, underneath you.

See, I am invisible.

Tears fall. I surrender to the burning hurt.

I exhale.

I take a breath, a vacuum of oxygen.

I'm dizzy.

I open my eyes into a white, floaty haze.

Drifty side to side steadying. My face is wet.

Euphoria.

I see them.

A laugh coughs out of me,

My suicide attempt has failed but.

The answer to the riddle, yes, even if no one thinks I have value, I do. Despite and no matter.

The audience is looking at me, expectant.

I wait until I feel it.

Then, seeping up inside me from the earth, rejuvenating strength, making me a willow. I am free.

"Oh well," I say.

There's no erasing what went before.

"At least that's one good thing about me," I say. "I'm consistent." I hold my look.

The audience holds their breath.

I smile a people-pleasing smile, crack the mirror, and claim myself.

They applaud. I surrender to the applause like I surrendered to the pain. Then I hop and skip off stage as if it's the end of a cheerleading tryout. He hugs me, the angel from the costume shop. Squeezing my arms, he whispers, "They clapped for you."

I nod.

"Directors don't applaud after an audition," he says.

A rush of warm and chill pours from my head down through my feet.

***

Now we wait. Lists will go up of the actors these theaters want to interview and possibly hire for their summer season.

Our teacher gathers our class. He stands next to me and looks me in the eye. For the first time. He smiles at me and puts his arm on my shoulders.

We go to the lists. Cosmo and I are together. Almost all the theaters are interested in interviewing me. There will be a lunch break, then we will go to the rooms to meet the Artistic Directors. Cosmo has a few less meetings, and I feel bad she'll have to wait until it gets dark for me to finish. That means we will have to drive home at night.

"It's cool," she says. "Do your thang."

During the break, I go to the costume room to see if he's there. He is.

I thank him. I thank him, thank him for his patience. For giving me the gift of his attention. For helping me work it out. For liking me.

"Can I have your address so I can send you a thank you?" I ask.

I want to but, also, I'm hoping he'll write his name.

"You don't have to send anything," he says. "I had a great time."

Am I never going to know his name? Will I never know what becomes of his directing career? Am I never going to see him again? I should just admit I don't know his name. He deserves so much more than this. But I don't. We hug.

"You're really good," he says.

My throat gets thick. I always imagined what it would feel like to hear that one day.

"It felt so easy," I say, giddy and astonished.

"If it was easy, we'd all do it," he says.

478

Over the speakers, they call us to the interviews. I hug him one last time, squeezing him hard.

"You'll get a ton," he says, meaning job offers.

I know I will never forget him. He taught me more that morning about rehearsing and auditioning than I learned in two years of undergrad school. He taught me more about what was within me. He showed me to me.

Sometimes, when someone sees the wonderfulness in you, you become the wonderfulness that they see. And more. So, when I stepped on stage, there it was, shining out for everyone to see.

So maybe, yes, sometimes someone you meet *is* your mirror.

Because Tira and I are kindred spirits, all I had to do was be comfortable being myself. Every line was just a tip of that iceberg. I didn't have to worry about the lines or how to be fascinating, or where to move or how to be. Just surrendering to what I, she, was feeling, every ugly, gawky, insecure, raw, vulnerable, sweet, hopeful, generous, insecure, oversensitive, people-pleasing, dramatic, embarrassing, mortifying part of myself, was all I needed to be.

I had just become an actress.

– 47 –
EPILOGUE

When I started writing this book, I was exploring why being a career Courtesan was what I became and why it seemed like a good match. Also, throughout that time, I would hear a lot of assumptions about why women like me might choose that path. Stereotypical reasons were "daddy issues," childhood abuse, greed, laziness, or a lack of morality. I didn't feel these fit me or most of the women I knew in that business. But maybe I wasn't really looking? If I did look back, what would I find? I thought there'd be a moment of "aha!" There were two.

Growing up middle-class, I had more opportunities than those poorer than I and less opportunity and privilege than those wealthier than I, yet, in writing about a girlhood in relation to men, it seemed many women (in America, anyway) could relate, no matter her background. We shared cultural messages that shaped us.

The spoken and unspoken rules we grew up with were very similar.

Finding who you were allowed to become, what you were allowed to hope for, how your sexuality was allowed to blossom, what agency you were allowed to have over your body and personhood, what you were allowed to voice, how much you were protected or not, how much you counted at all. Lots of girls had girlhoods like mine. Very few grew up to be escorts.

What did it mean to grow up female in America? Messages from the cultural system we grew up in told us what was valuable about ourselves and backed it up. Backed it with monetary rewards, opportunity rewards, or with punishment. Men held so much power. Please men and doors open. Don't please men and be prepared to take the long way home.

Things that happened to me didn't happen to everyone. But we were all affected, growing up under patriarchal training from an early age. I wrote a girlhood unique to me and was surprised at how universal it was. But should it be?

Women's voices, women's experiences aren't given a lot of room on the shelves, on the screen, in public discourse. There are many wonderful, noble, loving, kind, do-right, men in the world. They, too, are inundated with the same messages from the other side so the pattern continues.

I didn't know that's what was happening to me, so when the forces of debt, desire, and fear collided, I stepped into the space I knew would save me, the place I was valued.

Why did the business suit me? Although no one single moment led me on the path, my innate nature seemed to be seeking love and intimacy in the most unlikely places. My love of sensuality, my fascination with touch, and my desire as an actress to want to live truthfully in imaginary circumstances—these were the positives I would bring with me into the business. Then, once I became an escort and started to get paid, it felt like I was finally being paid for what was taken from me for free. Parts of me and my life I didn't mean to give away were taken as if we were at a free-for-all. When I was working, much of the actions were the same, but this time I got paid. It was so familiar. It was as if I trained for it my entire life.

And that's why the slipper fit. I'd already put in my ten thousand hours. I trained for this my entire girlhood.

Now, I was a professional.

THE END, FINI, KAPUT, FOR NOW...

A NOTE FROM THE AUTHOR

Thank you for sharing this story with me. Thank you for your open heart and the vulnerability it takes to allow the young me to tell you her story. I hope it resonated in some way.

The next book, we're back to Escort Adventures. Cock-Tales, an amuse-bouche of loose stories. Heehee and **You!** **I need you!**

My next book I'd like your help. When I started writing the stories about my escort days, it came from people asking me questions. And I would love to know what you're genuinely curious about. If you are, please hop over to my web blog and you can contact me with questions. And if you'd like, I'd be happy to thank you in my next book.

It's so much more fun with company.

Keep in touch at: www.sephehaven.com

There will be a free, exclusive story waiting there for you.

What's that saying?

Feed a cold, starve a fever? Noooooo.

Feed an Author, Leave a Review. That's it!

Reviews are important to us wee toiling little scribes.

If you were to take a moment to leave a rating and a review from wherever you purchased the book, it would mean so much.

See you in the next adventure!

Sephe Haven

Praise for My Whorizontal Life

MY WHORIZONTAL LIFE

The first book in the series, *My Whorizontal Life: An Escort's Tale*, is available on Amazon now! Follow Sephe Haven as she find love and intimacy in the most unlikely places. Based on a true story, this book details Sephe's life as she bounds from fantasy to reality, trying to make it as an actress.

"The author takes us on a journey from survival and despair to triumph and success. This is a human story of kindness, compassion, and making the world a better place."

"This book had me at the first page. It is so well-written, cinematic and funny."

"The author is both talented and gifted in her writing – I was immediately drawn into her point of view, I was able to begin to easily walk in her shoes and visualize her journey into the 'Underworld.'"

"I am inspired by the author's integrity and intention. Her writing style paints her world in boldness and subtlety and makes her experiences palpably one's own."

"It is a thrilling, effortless read that left me wanting more. This is a film that is demanding to be made."

"I could not stop reading!!! I LOVE THIS BOOK!"

To read more reviews from happy readers and buy the book on Amazon, follow the QR code below!

ACKNOWLEDGMENTS

HUGEST thank you to my readers who seem like kindred spirits, many who have their own secrets and feel the simpatico. Thank you for being brave enough to order a book with the words Escort or Courtesan on the cover, and read that book on a plane or train, in actual public. Thank you for your reviews of my first book. I didn't truly understand what I was writing about until I read your reviews and understood what part of what I was saying, touched your hearts. Thank you. You are giving me my voice.

To Aubyn Philabaum, my gorgeous, beyond talented, actor, writer, immensely generous friend, who read every rough over-written, over-wrought chapter and yet could still intuit the heart and beauty I was trying to say. I would have given up long ago if it weren't for you. Thank you for telling me this story was universal.

I owe brobdingnagian gratitude to David D. for admiring my ability to never run out of words even if I have to make up new ones. (Heehee. This is now sending him to the dictionary.) Thank you for enjoying my endless stories when everyone else would have long left the party.

Gratitude overflowing to my friend and incredible book coach Emily Tamayo Maher. Somehow, in a trash pile up of words, mountains of repetition and explaining the same point over and over, you calmly and very cheerfully (you are a miracle) highlight what works and always help me exhale. Without you, I don't think there would be a book one or book two. Let's have triplets! I love you.

Thank you thank you! to my Sunday night group of incomparable writers who listened to chapter after chapter and gave such good notes, I suddenly realized, in your care, I had built a book. Alex Stein, thank you for being the conduit and fearless leader of our scribe tribe: Martha Thompson, (my dear friend friend the Juilliard days), Art P, Suzanna Regos, Karen Golden, Vicki Kirschenbaum & Cara Lopez-Lee. Ready for the next? Oy vey!

Thank you to Jim Ballam for driving me around, not letting me burn down the house or throw away appliances when I say they're broken just because a, I forgot how to turn them on and or b. they're not plugged in. I would say your patience is epic, but, prunes and dates are not basically the same thing. Hehehe.

Of course to my extraordinary daughter who is struggling through these same teenage years, hopefully better than I. I know you won't read this until I'm dead, but know, I thought of you everyday I wrote this.

To my Kolya, maniac monster Baryshnikov Rambo doggie who forces me to take walks, play with squeaky toys and not be so boring.

Although they will not be, should not be ever reading this, oh Lordy lord, noooooo!, I owe an apology and deepest gratitude to my parents and my brothers Marc and Jeff for putting up with me during this most monsterous time of my teenage-ness. Yes, your therapy bills are my responsibility.

I am so fortunate to have so many talented actors and writers in my life who share their work and time and love and inspire me and advise me and I hope will like me outside our zoom squares. My dear sister-friend Rachel Parker. Thank you for believing in me and caring and loving me and sharing your life and beautiful work with me. And oh my god thank you for your precise eye for detail, especially by not letting my cover look like it had a pig's hoof on it. (Long story. But seriously. Thank god for Rachel!)

And JD Cullum. Watching you act, hearing your writing, you are the definition of brilliant. I learn from you every week and I am blessed to work with you on anything! Thank you for our Saturday writing group.

Thank you Steven Steifel, for being the first eyes, over a decade ago, to read a swath of these stories when they were babies, and then coming in at the end to take a peek.

Thank you to Carolyn Czajka Polos who, without knowing what exactly I was going to write, let me write her into this book and reminded me after decades, that my memory was sound and added a few juicy details I had forgotten. I'm so grateful we're still in each other's lives.

Thank you to Sara Stratton for helping me publish my tomes. Your knowledge, your patience, your grounded dependability and your easy going warmth are not only reassuring but make the final process such a pleasure. I feel so blessed to have you in my life.

In the end, I needed a wife but they're expensive and demanding, so I reached out and was pulled ashore by two calm, capable and very understanding guides/assistants. Thank you Karina Kantas for showing me what needed to be done after I typed The End, and being there these final steps.

And Maria Connor for making me aware there was such a thing as author assistants in the first place. (that freed me from having to get a wife.) Who knew?! Thank you for knowing everything and sharing your help and guidance with me.

Thank you to my editor Cheyenne Sampson. Not only was the editing process not painfully perfunctory, but somehow, through just Track Changes, you made me laugh, took away my fears and started a friendship. Thank you for knowing how to spell every German word and discussing how we should say the naughty bits....whose coming where? And thank you for understanding and letting me keep the bad grammar I insisted on/upon. I hope you'll let me torture you book after book.

Thank you to my friends who let me pop up like a groundhog in and out of your lives to share our travails and hearty laughs. I love you and would name you but I'm already at too many words and they're cutting me off.

PS: Thank you to the teachers who believed in me and who would believe in me. Mrs. Schwartz, my fourth grade teacher who told me I was a writer, (even though I preferred Sexpot), published all my childhood stories in the school book, and had such hopes for me I began to plagiarize to keep up to her expectations. Ok. Just once. The Crow poem in 4th grade. But oh my gosh, the pressure.

ABOUT THE AUTHOR

Sephe Haven is the author of the My Whorizontal Life series, a compelling memoir exploration of her journey from girlhood to contemporary Courtesan. Sephe moved from Chicago where she studied acting to New York City where she graduated The Juilliard School of Drama. Performing in Shakespeare & classical theater around the country for years she made the decision that ultimately changed her life. Decades later, as one of the top courtesans in the nation, Sephe went back to the Arts, performing stand up comedy and in storytelling shows. She has written a one-woman play/show based on her life as a courtesan (and book series) that she hopes to perform on 2022/2023 and is continuing the creation of the next books in the series. Sephe Haven writes under her pseudonym so she can talk about freely about the times she spent doing the work of love and pleasure.

Made in the USA
Las Vegas, NV
23 August 2022

53801667R00293